Philosophy of Science

The Delaware Seminar

Volume 1

Philosophy of Science

The Delaware Seminar

General Editor: William L. Reese
Chairman, Department of Philosophy
University of Delaware

Philosophy of Science

The Delaware Seminar

Volume 1   1961–1962

Edited by Bernard Baumrin

Department of Philosophy, University of Delaware

Interscience Publishers

a division of John Wiley & Sons, New York · London

Printed in the United States of America

Introduction to the Series

At its inception the purpose of the Delaware Seminar in the Philosophy of Science was declared to be one of bridging "the growing chasm between the two intellectual cultures of our time." The task of reconciling the scientific and humanistic communities is clearly an important one; and, indeed, may be the appropriate long-range goal of the seminar as it continues to develop through the years. In its present form, however, the seminar is addressed to the somewhat easier task of exploring differences of opinion among scientists interested in the philosophic implications of scientific subject matter; and differences of opinion among philosophers who have carefully considered various scientific subjects. Nor is this enterprise lacking in significance. At the very least, it represents what can now be done about the original, and more magnificent, declaration. The present volume of essays perpetuates the record of the seminar in its first year.

It is impossible for me to withhold the added comment that what can be done in these matters is most appropriately done in Delaware. The Seminar depends for its success upon the cooperation of the University of Delaware, the philosophers and scientists of our day who are concerned with problems in the philosophy of science, and the thousands of scientists and engineers with professional training in the sciences at work in Delaware. Through the fruitful interplay of these factors it will be possible, I am convinced, for the Delaware Seminar to contribute significantly to these purposes.

WILLIAM L. REESE

v

Preface to Volume I

PREFACE TO VOLUME I

Philosophy of Science was once a field that engaged few philosophers and few scientists. Occasionally a scientist turned his attention to making general statements about the nature of knowledge, scientific method, or the value of scientific research. Though philosophers, on the whole, considered it their duty to place "science" in philosophic perspective, there was a tendency, particularly in the last century, to "use" well-confirmed and ill-confirmed scientific theories as bases for philosophic systems. However, some philosophers of note devoted a good deal of their attention to the problems of human knowledge, and not disproportionately did they attend to that branch of it now called scientific knowledge. Thus, when one looks for the originative works in philosophy of science, from the background of the history of philosophy, Aristotle's *Posterior Analytics,* Descartes' *Rules for the Direction of the Mind,* Hume's *Treatise,* and Kant's *Critique of Pure Reason* stand out sharply. Yet it would not be an incorrect assessment of the development of modern philosophy to observe that philosophy of science as an independent discipline is a rather recent arrival among the traditional branches of philosophic research. Perhaps because it is of such recent interest it is now a very exciting field of inquiry.

The situation noted above, that generally characterized philosophic discussion of scientific knowledge in the nineteenth century, has changed considerably. Today many of the most respected scientists are active participants in philosophical research, and many competent philosophers devote most if not all of their energy to philosophy of science. A number of both of these groups is represented in this volume by new contributions to the literature of philosophy of science.

One mark of the vigor of philosophy of science today is the several continuing programs in the field. Besides the Delaware Seminar, there is the Program in Philosophy of Science at the University of Pittsburgh, the Boston Colloquium for the Philosophy of Science, and the Minnesota Center for Philosophy of Science. Each of these enterprises goes on throughout the academic year; they are not "conferences" that meet from time to time, but continuing exchanges that have as their purpose the continual advancement and dispersal of research in philosophy of science. Three volumes of the *Minnesota Studies in the Philosophy of Science* have already appeared and also the first volume of the *Pittsburgh Studies*. The Delaware Seminar volumes will reproduce papers and sometimes discussions of them. One special feature of the Delaware Seminar is the constant involvement of the participants. To this end each paper presented to the Delaware Seminar is distributed immediately to every participant in the program, present and past. An University course is connected to the Seminar also, providing a constant group of participants at hand for each public lecture. Each contributor can take into consideration the research and criticism of the other participants prior to publication. In this way the cohesiveness of the research and the direction of future investigation are joint projects. Thus, besides making available to the general reader an index of the scope and depth of philosophy of science today, we hope to help create a literature in philosophy of science which clarifies the issues, and shows the way for future research.

The present volume aims mainly to represent the scope of philosophy of science. Volume II will deal in detail with current philosophical developments pertaining to the physical sciences, and subsequent volumes will focus on the biological sciences, the social and behavioral sciences, and the formal disciplines of logic and mathematics. This volume, then, introduces these areas and also other more general topics.

Among the general topics are F. S. C. Northrop's analysis of *The Relation between the Natural and the Normative Sciences*, and N. R. Hanson's elucidation of the distinction between *Retroductive Inference* and hypothetico-deductive inference.

One of the main areas of research and controversy in philosophy of science in recent years has been the formulation of the proper description of scientific explanation and scientific prediction. S. Morgenbesser provides the introductory essay, followed by A. Grünbaum's expansion and defense of the Hempel-Oppenheim covering-law model of scientific explanation. M. Scriven, one of the most active opponents of this view replies, and finally C. G. Hempel clarifies and defends his covering-law theory against recent critics, particularly Scriven.

What are the objects that symbolic expressions represent? This question, which has a long philosophic history, has been a central concern of mathematicians and logicians since Frege. A. R. Anderson presents the Platonist view, i.e., that symbolic expressions do sometimes designate abstract entities, and R. Rudner, the nominalist view, i.e., that they cannot designate abstract entities since there are none. In the third essay in this section, J. Ullian deals directly with mathematical objects themselves, and presents a pragmatic view of their nature.

In the section on biology we are presented with two dissimilar, but not inconsistent, analyses of indeterminism in biology on the genetic level. T. Dobzhansky approaches the problem mainly from the viewpoint of biological populations and B. Glass from the direction of genes and mutations.

The several branches of the social sciences raise many philosophic questions, and three are here treated. A. Donagan argues for the existence of a distinction between nomothetic and idiographic sciences, arguing that history at the very least is an example of the latter. A. G. N. Flew reviews and clarifies the structure of Malthus' important theory of population. In the concluding essay of this section, A. Waterman, Director of the National Science Foundation, discusses the relation between the U. S. Government and the scientific community and the impact that each has made and is making on the other.

In the last section of this volume, Philosophical Aspects of Physics, we are presented with Professor Landé's sharp criticism of the dominant view today in quantum mechanics, the so-called Copenhagen interpretation. The other two papers on the philosophical aspects of physics that were presented at the Seminar are not yet in final form for publication and will appear in a future volume of the series.

Several discussions have been included. Their selection was based on two criteria. Thus, where the discussion further clarified the content of the essay or where the discussion indicated sharp disagreement with the view put forth by the speaker, we have reproduced the course of the argument engaged in by the Seminar participants.

Many have taken part in forwarding the success of The Delaware Seminar in the Philosophy of Science and the volume before you. Without the general support of the University of Delaware and in particular the assistance of Dr. William Reese, Chairman of the Philosophy Department, and Dean Gordon Godby, Director of the Division of University Extension, the project would not have been begun or carried through. Lacking Dean Godby's unfailing support, both personal and administrative, the Seminar would have many times foundered. Much of the technical assistance necessary to continuing programs was excellently provided by Mr. Robert Cunningham and Mr. Walter Balcavage. The bibliography was prepared by Mr. James Thomas. Others who performed important functions were Mr. Thomas Katen and Mr. Terrell Bynum. Finally, we thank Mrs. Caroline Mace, the product of whose unfailing work here lies before you.

BERNARD H. BAUMRIN

Contributors

ALAN ROSS ANDERSON; A.B. (Yale), M.Litt. (Cambridge), Ph.D. (Yale), Professor of Philosophy, Yale University, Formerly Director of the program of Directed Studies in the Humanities. Investigator for the Office of Naval Research, and for the National Security Agency; Fulbright Fellow; Morse Fellow.

BERNARD H. BAUMRIN; A.B. (Ohio State), Ph.D. (Johns Hopkins), Assistant Professor of Philosophy and Chairman of the Seminar, University of Delaware. He has taught also at Butler University and Antioch College.

THEODOSIUS DOBZHANSKY; Professor and Member, The Rockefeller Institute. Formerly Da Costa Professor of Zoology, Columbia University. He has also taught at the University of Leningrad and the California Institute of Technology. His books include *Genetics and Origin of Species* and *Evolution Genetics and Man.* He was a recipient of the Elliot Medal of the National Academy (1941) and the Kimber Award (1958).

ALAN H. DONAGAN; A.B., M.A. (Melbourne), Ph.D. (Oxford), Professor of Philosophy and Chairman of the Department, Indiana University. He has also taught at Minnesota and Cornell. His study, *The Later Philosophy of R. G. Collingwood* is now being published by the Oxford University Press.

ANTONY G. N. FLEW; B.A., M.A. (Oxford), Chairman, Department of Philosophy, University of Keele, Staffordshire, England. He has also taught at Oxford, Aberdeen, New York University, Swarthmore, and Minnesota. He is the author of *A New Approach to Physical Research* and *Hume's Philosophy of Belief,* and the Editor of the influential *Logic and Language* volumes.

H. BENTLEY GLASS; A.B., M.A. (Baylor), Ph.D. (Texas), Professor of Biology, Johns Hopkins University. He is on the editorial boards of the *Quarterly Review of Biology, Science, Scientific Monthly, Biological Abstracts,* and *The Survey of Biological Progress.* He is an advisor to the Atomic Energy Commission, a member of the National Academy of Science, and from 1958–1960 he was the President of the American Association of University Professors. Among his many publications is *Genes and the Man.*

ADOLF GRÜNBAUM; B.A. (Wesleyan), M.S. (Yale), Ph.D. (Yale), Andrew Mellon Professor of Philosophy and Chairman of The Program in Philosophy of Science at the University of Pittsburgh. He has also held the Selfridge Chair at Lehigh and was twice visiting Research Professor at the Minnesota Center for Philosophy of Science. He was an American Council of Learned Societies' Fellow, and a Ford Fellow. His papers have appeared in such journals as *Philosophy of Science, Analysis, American Scientist, British Journal for Philosophy of Science, Scripta Mathematica, The Review of Metaphysics, The Scientific Monthly, Archiv für Philosophie, The Journal of Philosophy, American Journal of Physics, The Philosophical Review, Nature,* and others. A volume to be published this year by A. Knopf is *Philosophical Problems of Space and Time.*

NORWOOD RUSSELL HANSON; A.B. (Chicago), B.Sc., A.M. (Columbia), B.Phil., D.Phil. (Oxford), A.M., Ph.D. (Cambridge). Professor of History and Logic of Science, Indiana University. He has been a Johnstone Scholar, a Fulbright Scholar, Fulbright Fellow, Ford Fellow, Rockefeller Fellow, and has been a Fellow at the Institute for Advanced Study (Princeton), the Minnesota Center for Philosophy of Science, and St. John's College (Cambridge). Among his publications are the books, *Patterns of Discovery* and *The Discovery of the Positron.*

CARL G. HEMPEL; Ph.D. (Berlin). Stuart Professor of Philosophy, Princeton University. He has also taught at Chicago, City College of New York, Queens College, Yale, and Harvard. He is a Fellow of the American Academy of Arts and Sciences and has been a Guggenheim Fellow, and a Senior Fulbright Fellow. Among his many influential publications are *Fundamentals of*

Concept-formation in Empirical Science (Chicago), and with Paul Oppenheim *Der Typusbegriff im Lichte der Neuen Logik* (Leiden), and the essay, *Studies in the Logic of Explanation.*

ALFRED LANDÉ; Ph.D. (Munich). Professor Emeritus of Physics, The Ohio State University. Before coming to Ohio State in 1931, he was Professor of Physics at Tubingen. His best known English volumes are *The Physics of Flight, Quantum Mechanics, Zeeman Effect, Principles of Quantum Mechanics,* and his recent volume, *From Dualism to Unity in Quantum Physics* (Cambridge, 1960).

SIDNEY MORGENBESSER; B.J.P. (Jewish Theological Seminary), B.S.S. (College of the City of New York), M.A., Ph.D. (Pennsylvania), Associate Professor of Philosophy, Columbia University. He has also taught at Swarthmore, Brandeis, and The New School for Social Research. He is a co-editor of two volumes of selected readings, *Philosophy of Science,* and *Free Will,* and the author of the forthcoming *Determinism in Human Action.*

FILMER S. C. NORTHROP; B.A. (Beloit), M.A. (Yale), M.A., Ph.D. (Harvard), Sterling Professor of Philosophy and Law, Yale University. He has been a visiting Professor at the Universities of Iowa, Michigan, Virginia, Hawaii, Mexico, Melbourne and Rollins College. He is also a Fellow of the American Academy of Arts and Sciences. Among his many books are *Science and First Principles* and *The Logic of the Sciences and the Humanities.*

RICHARD S. RUDNER; B.A. (Queens), M.A., Ph.D. (Pennsylvania), Professor of Philosophy and Chairman of the Department, Washington University. He has also taught at Cornell, Tufts, Swarthmore, and Michigan State University. He is currently doing research at Cambridge University, and is the Editor-in-Chief of the journal, *Philosophy of Science.*

MICHAEL J. SCRIVEN; B.A., M.A. (Melbourne), D.Phil. (Oxford), Professor of History and Logic of Science, Indiana University. He has taught at Melbourne, Minnesota, and Swarthmore. He was Research Associate at the Minnesota Center for Philosophy of Science, and author and co-editor of Volumes I and II of the *Minnesota Studies in the Philosophy of Science.*

JOSEPH ULLIAN; A.B., M.A., Ph.D. (Harvard), Visiting Assistant Professor of Philosophy, University of Chicago. He has taught at Stanford, Pennsylvania, Johns Hopkins, and California (Berkeley), and has been a Research Associate in the National Science Foundation Project in Transformations and Discourse Analysis at the University of Pennsylvania.

ALAN T. WATERMAN; A.B., Ph.D. (Princeton), Director of the National Science Foundation. He has taught at Cincinnati and Yale and did research at King's College (London) and the Massachusetts Institute of Technology. He is a recipient of the U. S. Medal for Merit and the Public Welfare Medal of the National Academy of Sciences.

Contents

PART I

Two Basic Distinctions

The Relation between the Natural and the Normative Sciences

F. S. C. Northrop, *Yale University*

In an important paper entitled "A Philosopher Looks at Political Science," Professor John G. Kemeny, the Chairman of the Department of Mathematics at Dartmouth College, has observed that human beings make three different kinds of judgments.[1] He calls them "logical judgments," "factual judgments," and "value," or what we shall call "evaluative," judgments. The character of a logical judgment is that, assuming certain premises, irrespective of their truth or falsity, the judgment when correct specifies what other propositions or theorems follow of formal necessity. The nature of a factual or descriptive judgment is that it concerns itself with the truth or falsity of propositions with respect to the facts to which they purport to refer. An evaluative judgment, on the other hand, is one that evaluates the facts after they have been correctly or incorrectly described.

Professor Kemeny goes on to observe that the sciences whose business it is to determine the criteria and methods for making correct logical judgments are formal logic and pure mathematics. The sciences which determine the criteria and method for making correct descriptive judgments are the empirical natural sciences and the social sciences in their purely descriptive function. Those subjects, on the other hand, whose task it is to provide the criteria and method for making correct evaluative judgments are personal ethics and the social sciences of law, politics, and even religion in their evaluative, as distinct from their descriptive, function.

Professor Kemeny adds that there seems to be a great deal

3

of confusion not merely among politicians, but also among political and social scientists with respect to the difference between descriptive and evaluative judgments and the methods that must be used in reaching trustworthy conclusions about each. By way of illustration, he states that, from the standpoint of a carefully trained philosopher of science, it is difficult to understand why politicians in the government, whose political questions are evaluative rather than merely descriptive in character, should put as much trust as they do in the advice of natural scientists or social scientists whose expertness is solely in the realm of descriptive judgments.

We will do well to take Professor Kemeny's observations seriously, since he brings expertness in all three types of judgments to his observations. Not only is he the very able Chairman of a department of mathematics, but he took his Ph.D. in philosophy at Princeton, where he had to learn to distinguish evaluative from descriptive judgments before he was allowed even to start his thesis in symbolic logic and the philosophy of science. Also while there he was an assistant to Einstein, so he knows what expertness is with respect to the theory and method for obtaining trustworthy descriptive judgments in the natural sciences. His paper shows that he learned the distinguishing mark of an evaluative judgment; for he states the fallacy, called by the English ethical philosopher G. E. Moore the "naturalistic fallacy," which occurs when anyone uses the method for answering a question of descriptive fact to answer a question concerning the evaluative judgment to be placed upon that correctly described fact. The philosopher David Hume described what G. E. Moore later called the naturalistic fallacy in the following manner in his *Treatise of Human Nature:*

> In every system of morality, which I have hitherto met with, I have always remark'd, that the author proceeds for some time in the ordinary way of reasoning, and . . . makes observations concerning human affairs; when of a sudden I am surpriz'd to find, that instead of the usual copulations of proposi-

tions, *is*, and *is not*, I meet with no proposition that is not connected with an *ought*, or an *ought not*. This change is imperceptible; but is, however, of the last consequence. For as this *ought*, or *ought not*, expresses some new relation or affirmation, 'tis necessary that it shou'd be observ'd and explain'd; at the same time that a reason should be given, for what seems altogether inconceivable, how this new relation can be a deduction from others, which are entirely different from it.[2]

A concrete case from any criminal law court will make clear the distinction between describing a given set of facts and evaluating those facts after they are once described. Precisely because of the necessity for this distinction, especially in criminal law cases, the experience of lawyers over the centuries has resulted in separating the question of fact from the question of how those facts are to be evaluated after they have been first correctly determined and described. In a jury trial, the question of fact is assigned solely to the jury, the question of evaluating the facts being left to the judge who appeals to the norms of the legal and political system in question as the criterion of his evaluative judgment of the described facts after the jury's specification of them. For example, the jury brings in its verdict, reporting that the defendant's observed behavior was such and such, after the manner in which Kepler brought in his descriptive verdict that the behavior of any planet is a motion in a mathematically describable orbit which is an ellipse. When, therefore, the judge or anyone of us in our evaluative judgments of the defendant's *de facto* behavior concludes that his behavior ought not to have been what it was and that, therefore, as measured by the evaluatively summated judgments of the community, the defendant is guilty of murder and should suffer imprisonment or death in the electric chair, it is as if, after Kepler had reported that the planet's behavior was motion in an orbit which is an ellipse, we then went on to affirm that the planet is guilty of a misdemeanor since it ought to have moved in an orbit which is rectangular, doing a "squads right" at each corner.

Clearly, a correct descriptive judgment of how the planets do in fact move or how the defendant in the criminal case did in fact behave, cannot be the basis for the evaluative judgment that the defendant is guilty of murder. To suppose, therefore, that the scientific method of the natural sciences, or of the descriptive social sciences, for making correct descriptive judgments about a particular person's or nation's behavior, can be the type of expertness that is required for making a correct evaluative judgment of what that person's or nation's correctly described behavior ought to have been, is what G. E. Moore meant by the "naturalistic fallacy." In other words, as Hume noted before Moore, it is to commit an error in one's logical judgment—the logical error of supposing that the "is" of a particular fact can imply the "ought" by which it is evaluated.

Recently, the writer [3] has expressed Hume's observation by describing the descriptive method for determining the norms of a particular culture, legal system, or nation and the quite different scientific method for evaluating them once they are correctly described. Most judicial decisions in a courtroom, votes of a citizen, and international foreign policy statements are the products of both a descriptive normative judgment and an evaluative normative judgment. Otherwise, for example, there would be no such thing as the Justices of the Supreme Court of the United States, in a particular case, agreeing on (1) the facts of the case as described by a court of lower jurisdiction and (2) the relevant normatively worded legislative statute or Bill of Rights article for measuring (1), and then (3) disagreeing in majority and dissenting opinions on their evaluative judgment of (2) as applied to (1). It is to be remembered that the correctly described normatively worded statutes of the legislature, which define what the normative words *murder* and *guilt* mean are but the deposit of evaluative judgments of the legislators and ordinary folk such as you and I.

There is a difference also between the scientific method for describing the facts in the natural sciences and the scientific method for describing the facts of cultural anthropology and comparative law, for example. This becomes evident when one notes that the descriptive sentences of natural science contain no normative words, such as *good, bad, obligated, murder, guilty,* or *innocent,* whereas those of cultural anthropology and law do. As the anthropologists Kroeber and Kluckhohn have emphasized, it is impossible to describe a culture without specifying its values—i.e., its particular evaluative ought-to-be for ordering the relations between its members. For examples, see Professor E. A. Hoebel's *The Law of Primitive Man* (Harvard Univ. Press, 1954). In this book Professor Hoebel is not evaluating the different norms of the seven different primitive societies he studies; instead, he is merely describing each. Nonetheless, the language he has to use contains normative words, quite unlike any description of the subject matter of the natural sciences. The writer's specification of the scientific method for describing the facts of the natural sciences is to be found in the early chapters of *The Logic of the Sciences and the Humanities* [4]; that for merely describing the facts of the cultural, legal, and political sciences in Chapters VII and VIII of *The Complexity of Legal and Ethical Experience* [5] and in Chapter 6 of *Philosophical Anthropology and Practical Politics.* [6]

To recall Hume's observation and understand Moore's naturalistic fallacy is to realize that the scientific method, *if there be one,* for evaluating, as distinct from describing, the norms of a culture, a legal system, or a particular nation must be different from both of the foregoing descriptive methods. I say "if there be one," for Professor Kemeny leaves this question open, maintaining that it is beyond the competence of the political scientist. The Anglo-American philosophers A. J. Ayer and Charles E. Stevenson, in their respective books *Language, Truth and Logic* and *Ethics and Language,* and the Danish lawyer Professor Alf Ross in his book *Towards a Realistic Jurisprudence,* each give reasons for believing the evaluative question to be scientifically meaningless. The writer gives reasons to the contrary in *The Complexity of Legal and Ethical Experience* and *Philosophical Anthropology and Practical Politics,* and also specifies the unique scientific method for evaluating, as distinct from merely describing, the norms of a particular culture, legal system, or nation.

In any event, Professor Kemeny's and Hume's distinction between a descriptive and an evaluative judgment is exceedingly important. Otherwise we as citizens in our daily political judgments, which usually combine evaluative *ought-to-be* conclusions with merely descriptive *is* statements, will fall into the prevalent facile and false notion of many research natural scientists and engineers, and even some philosophers of science who should know better, that the reason the Justices of the Supreme Court are divided frequently in their opinions and that our politicians fall on their face in Cuba or elsewhere is because they do not use the methods of natural science. This quite overlooks the fact that whereas the judgments of the natural sciences are merely descriptive, those of the cultural sciences including law and politics with their normative words are not merely (*a*) descriptively normative but also (*b*) evaluatively so. For a crystal clear statement of this distinction and its importance, see Professor Ayer's exposition of the difference between "descriptive ethics" and "evaluative ethics" in his aforementioned book.

To fail, therefore, to be continuously aware of this distinction, not merely in all one's daily evaluative judgments of one's neighbors and politicians, but also in one's comparative judgments of the differing legal and political norms of one's own and other nations, is to contribute to the present moral, legal, and political confusion, both domestic and international, which makes our lives today in this atomic age so emotionally disturbing and even suicidally precarious. The confusions and fears that cause us to hesitate to read the headlines of the morning newspaper result more from not knowing how to make correct evaluative decisions than from uncertainty about how to make trustworthy logical or descriptive judgments.

Furthermore, we are seeking a scapegoat from our own folly when we put the blame for our present evaluative confusion and demoralization on domestic or foreign politicians. This is the case because there are no politicians either at home or in the Soviet Union except as people, such as you and I, have put them there by either intercommunicating and agreeing upon and sharing our own individual, private evaluative judgments or by failing to agree and then allowing dictators of the German *volk*, the glorious Italian people, "the proletariat," or the Birch Society to make them for us.

Nevertheless, something constructive, and perhaps even reassuring and optimistic, can be said. First, every evaluative judgment is about facts which one knows only after someone has made a descriptive judgment of what they are. It follows that if the descriptive judgment is the result of the use of erroneous methods and criteria for determining the facts of the defendant's or another nation's behavior, the evaluative judgment is sure to be wrong also. This means that if one has an erroneous theory in one's descriptive philosophy of the natural sciences, one will have a faulty theory also of the meaning and correct method for making trustworthy evaluative judgments. More specifically, if one interprets erroneously the descriptive theories of the facts of human nature and nature generally, and this is precisely what happens when one has an erroneous philosophy of natural science, then one's value theory is certain to be in error also. This means that what follows in this volume is as important for your own personal, moral, legal, political, and even religious evaluative judgments as it is for your descriptive judgments of fact.

The implications of this conclusion have not received the attention they deserve. The first one is that the aforementioned naturalistic fallacy does not imply what many people have supposed. The usual inference has been that all evaluative subjects must be independent, autonomous subjects.

Kant drew this conclusion when he affirmed that the philosophy of mathematics and of natural science of his *Critique of Pure Reason* did not provide any meaning for the philosophy of morals and other evaluative subjects of his *Critique of Practical Reason,* his philosophy of religion, and his philosophy of law. The result was an unbridgable gulf between the *Naturwissenschaften* and the *Geisteswissenschaften* or humanities. G. E. Moore reached a similar conclusion when he sought the meaning for the word *good* and all other evaluative words in an immediately apprehended, non-empirical, and hence non-naturalistic ethical predicate. Another example is the prevalent statement by American humanists and humanistic philosophers to the effect that natural science and its methods are at best neutral, and at worst (and for humanists they are usually at their worst) a hindrance to correct evaluative judgments. The analysis above shows this prevalent notion to be false. An evaluative judgment is meaningless except as it is an evaluation of the naturalistically describable facts of a particular person or nation's behavior, as determined by a descriptive judgment. To affirm, therefore, that the humanities and evaluative judgments have no connection with the natural sciences and their descriptive judgments is to make evaluative judgments meaningless. Any case of an innocent defendant who is sent to jail for life because the jury made a false descriptive judgment of fact confirms this conclusion.

But, if there is no meaning to an evaluative judgment except as it refers to the product of an antecedently naturalistic descriptive judgment, and if descriptive judgments are certain to be in error when one's philosophy of the natural sciences is in error with respect to what the words "fact" and "correctly described facts" mean, then we already know one part of what the criterion is for making correct evaluative judgments. It is to evaluate the facts of a particular person's behavior as measured by a descriptively correct philosophy of natural science, including naturalistically described human beings, instead of an erroneous natural philosophy.

In short, the evaluatively good and just for one's personal conduct and communal law, politics, and the humanities generally is *in part* one's philosophy of the descriptively true in the natural sciences, including naturalistic psychology.

The italicized words "in part" are important. They remind us that the foregoing criterion is a necessary, but not a sufficient, condition for specifying the scientific method for evaluating the facts of a person's behavior or the norms of a particular legal system and nation once they have been correctly described. To find the additional sufficient conditions, two distinctions must be made. The first is factual or empirical, the second linguistic.

The empirical distinction was implicit in the difference noted above between the descriptive sentences of (*1*) the natural sciences and (*2*) the cultural sciences including comparative descriptive ethics and law. The former descriptive sentences do not contain normative words; the latter do. This difference is of prodigious significance. It means that the former facts are what they are *per se*, antecedent to any descriptive judgment of what they are, whereas the latter are the effects of human descriptive and evaluative judgments. An examination of what law students study makes this difference inescapable. They read casebooks composed of the descriptive and evaluative judgments of particular judges. It is necessary that these two quite different kinds of facts be not confused. To this end, in Chapter XIX of *The Complexity of Legal and Ethical Experience* the non-man-made facts of the natural sciences and of the non-man-made art of human nature, all of which exist antecedently to any human descriptive judgment, were called "first-order facts," whereas the cultural artifacts in the lawyers' casebooks and in anthropological treatises, which are the causal effect of descriptive beliefs about first-order facts, were called "second-order facts." With the latter, the descriptive beliefs about first-order facts come first and the second-order facts in the casebooks are the result. It is because the second-order facts of a culture are the causal effect of an evaluative judgment of a descriptive judgment of first-order facts that the descriptive language of cultural second-order facts is normatively worded, as the descriptive comparative anthropologists Kroeber and Kluckhohn have emphasized and the language of the cases in the law students' books demonstrates. Conversely, it is because first-order facts exist antecedent to any descriptive or evaluative judgment of them that the descriptive language of the first-order facts which make up the subject matter of the natural sciences contains no normative words.

First-order facts have one other characteristic. It is meaningless to say that they are in error. Only of entities capable of error is it meaningful to predicate normative words such as *good, bad, just, unjust, guilty,* or *innocent.* This is why it is nonsensical to call the behavior of a planet "naughty" or to say of a falling stone which kills someone that it is "guilty of murder."

Only with respect to second-order facts is error possible and even for them not *qua* fact but only derivatively, because they are the causal effect of self-assented-to beliefs and commitment upon the part of the person in question. The reason, as the writer noted in Chapter XX of *The Complexity,* is that facts *qua* facts merely *are;* they are neither true nor false; hence they are incapable of being in error; only propositions about facts can be in error.

But with respect to what facts can the propositional beliefs that are the cause of second-order facts be in error? Clearly not the second-order facts, since they are the effects of the beliefs. The only alternative is that they are in error with respect to first-order facts. This means that any second-order factual human behavior is capable of being in or not in error if and only if it is the causal effect of cognitively testable beliefs about first-order facts.

Practically, this means the following three things:

1. If the behavior of the person *p* is the causal effect of a descriptive belief about the first-order (i.e., non-man-made) facts of nature or human nature, that is in part or

whole false, this is what one means by saying that the behavior of p is in error, or, in other words, bad, unjust, or sinful.

2. If the descriptive belief which causes the second-order factual behavior of p is empirically in accord with the epistemological and ontological (if any) philosophy that philosophical analysis of the verified theories of natural science, including non-man-made human nature, makes explicit, then the behavior of p is not in error, i.e., good, just, or virtuous.

3. If the behavior of p is completely the causal effect of temporally antecedent factors having nothing to do with the cognitive beliefs of p or of anyone else concerning first-order factual nature and the non-man-made part of human nature, to that extent the behavior of p is evaluatively neither good nor bad, just nor unjust, virtuous nor vicious, since where error is nonexistent all such evaluative words are meaningless.

If the reader is inclined to think that the difference between behavior of species 3 and that of species 1 and 2 is unimportant, he has never been in a criminal trial where he is sentenced to jail for life because of behavior which was the effect of an injury, occurring at childbirth, in the motor area of his cortex. Reflection upon such occurrences will make the reader aware also that if he ever finds himself the defendant in a criminal trial on very scanty circumstantial evidence, he will want both an attorney and a judge who do not suppose that the second-order facts of the cultural sciences and the humanities, of which alone evaluative words are meaningfully predicable, are identical with the first-order facts of the natural sciences of which to predicate guilt due to willful first-degree murder is to utter nonsense.

The linguistic distinction referred to above is equally important if our scientific method for testing evaluative, as distinct from merely descriptive, ethical and legal judgments is to be understood. The method does not mean that the "ought" for evaluating the second-order factual behavior of a person p is that correctly described behavior itself. This would be to commit the naturalistic fallacy in a way that does not arise from drawing false inferences from the fallacy. Nor does our thesis mean that one can deduce what is good, just, and religiously virtuous from the substantive content of Einstein's general theory of relativity or quantum mechanics, even though this, as the writer shows in a forthcoming book entitled *Man, Nature and God*,[7] may be a necessary, though not a sufficient condition for the meaningfulness and empirically verifiable correctness of at least some evaluative judgments. Instead, our complete thesis is one which the following well-known linguistic distinctions should make clear.

Most students of ethics today distinguish between (*a*) ethical sentences and (*b*) metaethical sentences about the meaning of ethical sentences. Even those linguistic philosophers who use the words "metaphysical nonsense" profusely find no nonsense in talking about meta-ethics. In fact, they find such talk to be necessary, if one is not to fall into the error of confusing an ethical and legal sentence, such as "Pleasure is good" or "The defendant is guilty of murder," with the quite different sentences about these sentences which tell us what the words *good, guilty,* and *murder* mean. The metalegal sentence about the legal sentence is what one means, when one knows what one means, by a philosophy of law. Similarly, a metasentence about the sentences and methods of physicists is what one means, when one is linguistically clear, by the philosophy of physics. It is, therefore, no more nonsensical to use the word *metaphysical* as the equivalent of "the philosophy of physics" than it is to use the word *metaethical* or *metalegal* as the equivalent of the philosophy of ethics or the philosophy of law.

It is now possible to so state our proposed solution to the problem of correct evaluative judgments in less misleading terms: The epistemological metalinguistic theory of what evaluative words in morals, law, politics, religion, and the humanities generally mean is the epistemological metalinguistic theory of what descriptive words in the natural sciences mean. In short, although the sentences of descriptive subjects and evaluative subjects are quite different, the latter, as Hume noted, not being deducible from the former, the epistemological metalanguage of both is identical.

Since the epistemological metatheory of the language of the natural sciences is a cognitively determinable inquiry, it then follows that the epistemological standard for measuring evaluative judgments is also. Moreover, should the epistemology entailed by natural science make ontology meaningful, then the substantive content of scientific knowledge in the natural sciences, as well as the epistemological meaning of its language, gives additional content to the measuring rod for making evaluative judgments.

The degree, therefore, to which we can agree on our metalinguistic theory of natural science, i.e., on our philosophy of natural science, will specify agreement on the metaethical and metalegal criterion to use in making correct evaluative judgments. Also, to the extent that the traditional philosophy of natural science, i.e., traditional metaphysics, is erroneous, to that degree our philosophy of the criterion for making correct evaluative judgments must undergo a corresponding reconstruction.

Is such a reconstruction necessary? If so, what direction must it take?

To answer these two questions is too great an undertaking for the present occasion. In fact, one of the important contributions of what follows in this book will be to provide the kind of knowledge necessary to reach reasonable answers to these two questions.

Even so it seems wise, by way of giving a sense of proportion with respect to what will follow, as well as indicating the present writer's conclusions with respect to the foregoing questions, to sketch quickly, briefly and, of necessity, somewhat dogmatically, what seems to him to be the philosophy of natural science upon which more and more theoretical physicists and philosophical analysts of this difficult subject are coming to agree. This does not mean that there is complete unity about what follows. The reason, however, why one states it with some confidence is that expert philosophical analysts of the language and method of mathematical physics, men such as the earliest logical positivists who initially started out with a different theory, have gradually found themselves forced to this one. We shall call the theory (1) *nominalistic radical empiricism* in (2) *epistemic correlation* with (3) *logical realism.*

The *nominalistic radically empirical component* of this philosophy of science will be the concern of Professor Richard Rudner. The *logically realistic component* will be treated by Professor Alan Anderson. (1) is necessary because there can be no natural science without observation, observation is possible only with one's senses, and one's senses give only nominalistic, perishing particulars which are relative to the physical frame of reference upon which one stands; to different observers, even when they stand on the same frame of reference; and to different sense organs of the same observer. Being thus relative to the perceiver, the rods and cones in his eyeballs, and his frame of reference, such nominalistic, directly sensed particulars are not objective facts in the sense of being objects that are the same for all observers.

The *logical realism* (3) is essential because in mathematical physics, as in common sense, we do know speculatively discovered, imageless mathematically described objects, events, and their laws which remain invariant for any transformation of coordinates, i.e., no matter where one stands or when one is observing, or what are the differences in the observer's eyeballs and other sense organs.

The adjective "logical" is required to distinguish this realism from *naive realism.* The latter is the thesis that objective, invariant, scientific objects, events, and their laws are not merely directly observed by the senses but are completely definable in terms of imageful sensed properties that are also directly observed. Aristotle's physics and metaphysics was what it was precisely because of this naive realistic notion. For example, in his physics there were but four elementary scientific objects, all being supposedly directly sensed, at least in the aggregate. These four elements were air, fire, water, and earth. Also, these four scientific atoms or their aggregates were defined in terms of the objects of the sense of touch. Even Aristotle realized that objects of the other senses are not objectively the same for all observers. But touch, he believed, gave objectivity. The consequence was that he defined his elementary scientific particles in terms of the direct tactual sense objects: hotness, coldness, wetness, and dryness.

Modern mathematical physics and its quite different scientific method of knowing began when Galilei rejected this Aristotelian tactile naive realism by returning Western mathematical physics to the *logical realism* of the Democritean, Platonic, and Stoic Greek mathematical physicists and Roman lawyers. This is why Professor Anderson, if I anticipate correctly the significance of the title of his lecture, is quite correct when he realizes that Western mathematics and mathematical physics require the kind of imageless, logically and mathematically constructed ideas which Plato described. In short, they require *logically realistic* ideas.

In this, however, Plato and his Platonic pupil, the greatest of Greek mathematical physicists, Eudoxus, were not unique. Democritus and the Stoics agreed with Plato also, as did the Stoic lawyers who created Western legal science with its imageless, logically realistic legal constructs. The only difference between the Democriteans, the Platonists, and the Stoics was with respect to the content of the logically realistic scientific symbols and ideas. In other words, all these ancient physicists, like their modern successors, differed from one another exactly as the content of Einstein's logically realistic mathematical physics differs from that of Newton, the latter being a special case of the former.

This is part of what Newton means when he tells us that he "stood on the shoulders of the Ancients." It is also what Einstein means when he suggests that the person who has not been thrilled by Euclid does not understand contemporary mathematical physics and adds that natural science rests on the belief in an external world, and we know such a world only by speculative means. In short, we do not get objective knowledge by direct observation which is naive realistically.

The *epistemic correlations* (2), which some philosophers of science call "rules of correspondence" or "coordination-definitions," are necessary because otherwise one's speculatively discovered, logically realistic, mathematically described physical theory could not be related to the directly observable, nominalistically describable, radically empirical data, to be thereby tested experimentally with respect to whether it is confirmed or disconfirmed. The reason why the writer prefers the expression "epistemic correlations" to the aforementioned alternative names of these relations should now be evident. Because (i) *nominalistic radical empiricism* is an epistemological theory of how we gain correct knowledge and make correct descriptive judgments and *logical realism* is a different, but quite compatible, theory of knowledge and how we make correct descriptive judgments, and (ii) Democritean, Platonic, Stoic, and modern mathematical physics combine both these ways of knowing, it follows that the "rules of correspondence" or the "coordination-definitions," by means of which the combination is made specific and effective, are epistemological relations. The adjective "epistemic" prevents them also from being confused with other kinds of definitions and correspondences.

In *The Complexity of Legal and Ethical Experience* and *Philosophical Anthropology and Practical Politics* the writer has given reasons for believing that precisely this same metalanguage of nominalistic radical empiricism in epistemic correlation with logical realism is required to make the procedures and discourse of our law courts and, *ipso facto,* our own legal and political institutions, both meaningful and effective. If this be the case, then we have an independent confirmation of the thesis that one's metaethical and metalegal theory of the good and the just with respect to evaluative judgments is one's metaphysical theory of the descriptively true in the natural sciences, the metalanguage of both evaluative language and descriptive language being identical.

References

1. J. G. Kemeny, in *Conflict Resolution*, Vol. IV, No. 3, Sept. 1960, p. 292.
2. David Hume, in *A Treatise of Human Nature*, T. H. Greene and T. H. Grose, Eds., Longmans, Green & Co., London, 1886, Vol. II, pp. 245–246.
3. F. S. C. Northrop, *Philosophical Anthropology and Practical Politics*, Chapters 6 and 7.
4. F. S. C. Northrop, *The Logic of the Sciences and the Humanities*, Macmillan, New York, 1947.
5. F. S. C. Northrop, *The Complexity of Legal and Ethical Experience*, Little Brown, Boston, 1959.
6. F. S. C. Northrop, *Philosophical Anthropology and Practical Politics*, Macmillan, New York, 1960.
7. F. S. C. Northrop, *Man, Nature and God*, Simon and Schuster, New York, 1962.

Retroductive Inference

Norwood Russell Hanson, *Indiana University*

The history of philosophy has in part been a history of attempts to describe scientific argument. In the *Posterior Analytics*, Aristotle writes of how naturalists argue from finite observations to general laws. Critics, like Sextus Empiricus, challenged Aristotle's account as unsound. A spectrum of views concerning scientific reasoning gradually proliferated. From Bacon through Reichenbach it was urged that all scientific argument reduces to induction by simple enumeration. From Mill through Braithwaite, scientists were seen to proceed by the hypothetico-deductive method (henceforth "HD"). Still others have espoused something called "retroduction" (RD) as the analysis of how scientists reason. Peirce, and Aristotle himself, opted for this view.

One objective of this paper will be to demonstrate that the differences between these philosophical accounts are not "merely psychological," but genuinely conceptual. Perhaps neither the HD nor the RD account has any application for the analysis of scientific argumentation. Or maybe both apply, but never at once. However this may be, it is not the case that the HD and the RD accounts constitute conceptually *equivalent* characterizations of any one scientific argument.

Our second objective is to distinguish yet again how people *do* argue from abstract questions about the form of argument. The delineation of the moves through which scientists reason while problem solving is as much the business of philosophy of science as is the *post factum* formal reconstruction of that argument for abstract logical purposes.

If these two objectives can be achieved, an historical point may then be made. The distinction drawn by 19th century astronomers between the Orthodox Problem of Perturbations and the Inverse Problem of Perturbations exemplifies the contrast we shall draw between the HD and RD accounts. Part of the conceptual excitement of the 19th century may be lost to logicians and historians who remain insensitive to this distinction.

I. Hypothetico-Deductive Inference

The insight of the HD analysis consists in distinguishing the rational activity of the natural scientist from that of the mathematician, a distinction which Popper, Reichenbach, Braithwaite, Bergmann, and Carnap draw better and more finely than earlier inductive logicians like Hume, Mill, Jevons, Venn, and Johnson. The mathematician argues "typically" when he entertains certain premises solely to "unpack" them. His concern is neither with their contingent truth nor falsity, nor with that of the conclusions unpackable therefrom. It is the *unpacking relationship* which alone interests the formal scientist. The natural scientist, however, cares not only about consistency within a universe of discourse; he is concerned also with the contingent truth of claims about the universe in which we live. That a statement follows from *some* premise cluster may be a necessary condition for its descriptive utility. But it is not sufficient. False conclusions can follow validly from contingently false premises, or from logically false ones.

If each premise is contingently true, and if the deduction is valid, the conclusion will have "about" the same probability as has the premise cluster. There is thus a formal connection between a conclusion's probability and the joint probability of its premises. But problems seldom come to the scientist thus. Rarely is he given a list of claims and charged to draw up another list of their consequences. Usually he encounters some anomaly, and desires an explanation. It cannot follow from any *obvious* premise cluster, else it would not be anomalous. So, one proceeds to cluster *some* established truths with hypotheses to see whether they may not jointly entail the anomaly. But now estimate the probability: the anomaly's description is assumed correct. The available premises obtain. From the joint probability of the anomaly plus these obvious premises one now estimates the probability of an hypothesis which, when conjoined with the premises, entails the anomaly.

The HD account is concerned not only with *conclusion deducing*, but with *hypothesis testing*. Hypotheses are tested by linking them with already confirmed statements to form a premise cluster. From this cluster, observational consequences are generated. If these are confirmed, the hypothesis is to that extent confirmed. But if further consequences turn out false, the probability of the hypothesis diminishes.

Much scientific reasoning and argumentation displays this HD pattern. Whenever the extension of a partially confirmed theory is in question, one generates further observational consequences of the theory and checks them against the facts. Indeed, detecting flaws in apparatus, and deviations in measuring instruments—as well as the theoretical discovery of "unexpected" phenomena—consists largely in deductively decomposing the premise clusters of theoretical science. This sets out the "logical expectations" of a given theory, and hence highlights any deviation from these expectations. The very identification of an event as "anomalous" depends on this HD elaboration of familiar premise clusters.*

II. Retroductive Inference

The HD theorist attends thus to the scientist's inferences from contingent premise clusters to observationally vulnerable conclusions. The RD account focuses rather on the explanation of anomalies. RD enthusiasts think scientific argu-

* There are other "less active" interpretations of the HD account. No matter. Even if every HD theorist were perfectly clear in setting out his views as *ex post facto* abstract logical analyses of scientific argumentation (which is not the case), this paper would still be making a distinction of import.

mentation to consist first in the recognition of anomalies, and then in the hunt for some premise cluster which, if confirmed, would explain the anomaly. This premise cluster will contain initial conditions and an hypothesis, the form of which "reveals itself" by its initial absence from the cluster. Thus, that the law of Universal Gravitation had an inverse square *form* seemed clear to the young Newton from the logical gap left in the cluster of known mechanical laws when he assumed that such laws were sufficient to explain *all* mechanical phenomena—the tides, hydrodynamics, ballistics, celestial motions, etc. A further hypothesis was needed. But although it was not discovered until 1687, Newton perceived its form "lurking" in the very statement of his problem in 1665. So while the HD account pictures the scientist with a ready-made theory and a store of initial conditions in hand, generating from these testable observation statements, the RD account pictures him as possessing only the initial conditions and an upsetting anomaly, by reflections upon which he seeks an hypothesis to explain the anomaly and to found a new theory. Again, the HD account focuses on *hypothesis testing;* the RD account is concerned with *anomaly explaining.*

Some signal events in history have involved reasoning of this RD kind. The discovery of Neptune, and of the neutrino, are characterizable thus. Just as the discovery of Pluto, and of the antiproton, seem better described in HD terms. Here one runs out the consequences of an accepted theory and tests them. In the RD case, some facts surprisingly fail to confirm the consequences of an accepted theory; one then argues from these to some new hypothesis which may resolve the anomaly.

III. That the HD and RD Accounts Are but *Psychologically* Different

HD and RD enthusiasts both recognize that their formal criteria for success in argument are *precisely the same.* Thus, imagine that one scientist argues from premises *A, B, C* and hypothesis *H*, to conclusion *D* (which, although originally unexpected, ultimately is confirmed in fact). Another encounters the anomalous fact that *D*, and conjoins this with *A*, *B*, and *C* so as to "corner" an hypothesis *H* which, when bracketed with *A*, *B*, and *C*, will "explain" *D*. Both scientists have been arguing; both have been using their heads. Differently. But the criterion for their having succeeded with their different tasks will be simply this: that *D* follows from *A*, *B*, *C*, and *H*. If either the first or the second scientist was mistaken in thinking *D* to be entailed by *A*, *B*, *C*, and *H*, then his reasoning fails.

But if the *logical* criteria for success or failure of reasoning in either case are the *same*, then whatever distinguishes these two scientific arguments must be nonlogical, and therefore (so the position develops) *merely psychological*. This is the strong form of the thesis that, though the aspects of scientific thinking distinguished by the HD and RD accounts may be interesting to psychologists, they contain nothing of importance for philosophers and logicians. My first objective is to attack that conclusion.

IV. The "Direction" of Arguments

Consider a logic teacher presenting a problem to his class. One orthodox assignment might be this: "Here are three premises, *A*, *B*, and *C*. From these alone generate the theorem, *D*." The teacher is here charging his students to find what follows from premises written "at the top of the page." This is related to the traveler's puzzlement when he asks, "here I am, river to the left, mountains to the right, canyon ahead; *where do I go from here?*"

Contrast with this the different assignment a logic teacher might give: "Here is a theorem *D*. Find any three premises *A*, *B*, and *C* from which *D* is generable." Here, he gives his students *D* written, as it were, "at the bottom of a page." He asks them to work back from this to three premises which, if written at the top of the page, will be that from which *D* follows. Analogously, the traveler's question would be *"would I be able to return here from over there?* or there? or there?"

These two queries of the traveler will be answered, and appraised, by the same geographical criterion; "is there a geographical route connecting point A with point B?" Whether one is at A asking if he can get from there to B, or asking while at B whether he could return from some other point A *back* to B—the ultimate geographical issue is only whether some traversable route connects A and B.

Similarly, the criteria for assessing the logic students' answers are the same whether the teacher asks his question in terms of premise unpacking, or in terms of premise hunting. "Is there a logical route connecting A, B, C with D?" Whether one is at D and looking for some A, B, C, H from which he could get back to D, or whether one begins at A, B, C, H and asks whether he can make it to D—that these are different is not relevant in strict logic. The question of the existence of a route, logical or geographical, is independent of whether the route is traversed from one end to the other, or from the other end to the one: from A, B, C, H, to D or from D to A, B, C, H.

V. The Form of an Argument vs. Arguing According to Form

It is often supposed that when considering the *form* of an argument one should consider it as if it were *mathematical*. It is imagined that the ways logicians and mathematicians argue illuminates the issue of logical form. This is false. Mathematicians no less than other reasonable men argue sometimes from premises to conclusions, and sometimes from an anomaly to its explanation independently of any *general* metamathematical question of whether some logical route connects the beginning point of the argument with its terminus. The actual arguments of mathematicians are just like ours. They have an arrow built into them; they progress from a starting point to a finish line.

The *logical form* of an argument, however, does not progress at all. It is static, time-independent, problem-neutral—above the battles of natural science and formal science alike. Hence, if deducing is what logicians and mathematicians *do* when arguing from premises to conclusions, then "deductive" cannot distinguish the formal characteristics of one kind of argument as against others, i.e., probabilistic, analogical, etc. If deduction is what someone does during the *de facto* business of reasoning, then alternative ways of proceeding with one's reasoning might be different and might have different names, e.g., "hypothetico-deduction," "retroduction," etc. This may be so even though from a *strictly* formal standpoint nothing may distinguish such procedures.

VI. More on the Direction of a Scientific Argument

Just as arguing from premises at the top of a page down to a conclusion differs from working from a conclusion "up" to premises at the top, even when the logical form of each will be identical to that of the other—so also, arguing from initial conditions plus hypothesis, A, B, C, H, down to an observation statement D is different from working "up" from an anomaly D to some H which, when conjoined with initial conditions A, B, C will entail, and hence explain, the anomaly. This, although the logical structure of each procedure is the same as that of the other. The only question here is "does some logical route connect A, B, C, and H with D?"

VII. The HD Procedure Consists in Arguing from the Top of a Page Down

The HD account centers on hypothesis testing. It stresses the generating of observation statements D from premises A, B, C, and H. When the D's square with the facts, H is, insofar, confirmed. The typical description gives A, B, C as known, H as conjectured, while D_1, D_2, D_3, . . . have yet to be "unpacked" from this premise cluster. The analogy between what the mathematician does during some of his problem solving and what the scientist is taken to do by the HD philosopher, is instructive. The natural scientist does not know in advance *what* observation statements D_1, D_2, D_3 may be generable from A, B, C, and H. This is what makes this HD procedure an indirect test of H (*after* it has been formulated and conjoined with A, B, and C). In both mathematics and natural science, arguments often exfoliate deductively; they proceed from the "top of the page" down to the D-statements. This does not identify the two procedures, however. The formal scientist is not concerned with the empirical truth of A, B, C, or H or of the conclusions drawn therefrom. That a conclusion D is validly generable from premises A, B, C, H, contingent truth or falsity aside, will be his one concern. A natural scientist proceeding in the HD manner, however, will begin with initial conditions A, B, and C established as true. The status of H remains unknown. After D is deduced from this set and discovered to describe the facts, H may be said to have become "probabilified." The natural scientist's concern is to determine whether a given H can thus be raised to the same degree of acceptability as the initial conditions A, B, and C. This he settles by enlarging and diversifying the set of observation statements D_1, D_2, D_3, . . . the regular confirmation of which will systematically raise H's probability. This distinguishes the epistemic context within which the mathematician and natural scientist work. Still, vis-à-vis the *direction* of argument, the mathematician and the natural scientist will both on occasion argue from the top of the page down, and this is traditionally described as "deducing."

VIII. The RD Procedure Consists in Arguing from the Bottom of a Page Up

When wearing his RD cap, the natural scientist begins his inquiry in puzzlement. After unpacking a well-established theory, replete with hypothesis H, into the expected observation statements D, he discovers that nature is not described by some of these latter. His normal expectations (and those of the theory) are thus thwarted. He has no reason to doubt initial conditions A, B, and C; their independent verification is what made them initial conditions. But he is astonished to note that the *orthodox* hypothesis H does not, when conjoined with A, B, C, generate descriptions of the facts. Thus the question: "Given the anomaly D, and initial conditions A, B, C—from the hypothesis H' * does D follow when H' is bracketed with A, B, and C?"

IX. Again, the Formal Criteria Are Identical

Consider these two schemata:

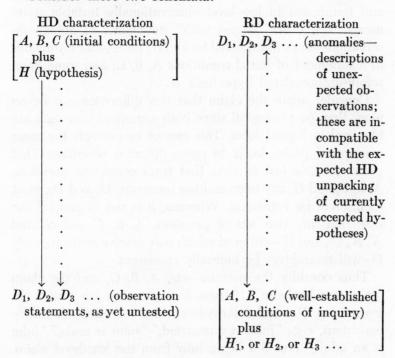

Notice that the solid arrows represent the *actual* order of the scientist's argument. The "beginning" in the one case is H plus A, B, C, which set is then unpacked into the heretofore-unformulated D_1, D_2, D_3. In the other case, the occasion for the inquiry is the anomaly D: the rational moves from that point are towards a premise cluster A, B, C, H

---

* *I.e.*, any hypothesis other than H.

which can "explain" the anomaly. The dotted arrow, however, represents the *logical* order of the progressions. It points the same way in both cases—towards D_1, D_2, D_3; hence the logical criteria for appraising the validity of arguments of either form above are identical. Here then are two argument-schemata which, vis-à-vis logical structure, are the *same* argument, but, vis-à-vis their *de facto* development within the problem-solving context, are clearly different. The HD "starts from" initial conditions and an hypothesis and terminates in low-level observationally testable statements. The other "begins with" statements of actual observations—ones unexpected on an HD basis—and terminates in a statement of initial conditions A, B, C, and some heretofore-unformulated hypothesis H.

Consider again the claim that this difference can be no more than psychological since both argument schemata are identical in logical form. This cannot be correct: the same conceptual probe leads to quite different reactions. That probe consists just in this: that from consistent premises, A, B, C, and H, any two resulting theorems, D_1 and D_2, must themselves be consistent. Whereas, it is not in general the ease that any two sets of premises, A, B, C and H, and A', B', C', and H'—either of which may resolve some anomaly D—will themselves be mutually consistent.

Thus consider the premise sets, A, B, C, *and* the claim "John is a bachelor." If these four premises are consistent, everything, D, which follows from them will also be mutually consistent, e.g., "John is unmarried," "John is male," "John is an adult," etc. But begin now from the low-level claim, D: "John is male." This *can* be shown to follow from A, B, C *and* "John is a bachelor." But it also follows from A, B, C, *and* "John is a married uncle." These two premise sets, however, are not consistent with each other. Since conceptually different answers result from this probe, the two characterizations must therefore be conceptually different and not merely psychologically so.

Here it might be objected, "Yes, 'John is a bachelor' and

'John is a married uncle' *are* inconsistent, and any premise sets in which they are imbedded will also be inconsistent. But these two premise sets are not inconsistent with respect to what is required in order to generate the single conclusion 'John is male.' Indeed, they could not be so, by the principle that if p entails q (and q is not necessary) then $\sim p$ cannot also entail q. The only analysis is this: that when $(r \cdot p)$ obtains and $p \to q$, then q will follow—and it will follow also from $(\sim r \cdot p)$ and $p \to q$. Hence a single anomaly D (i.e., q) can follow from two mutually incompatible premise sets only when the incompatibility plays no immediate role in the deduction."

This is an extremely potent objection. But it leaves the conceptual issue unscathed. It remains that A, B, C, H and R, if consistent, will entail only compatible conclusions D_1, D_2, D_3 . . . , etc. But an anomaly, D_3, might be explained not only by *different* premise sets—A B C H R and M N L O P—but also by *incompatible* premise sets—A B C H R and A B C H $\sim R$—where R and $\sim R$ are admittedly redundant to the derivation. Redundant or not, the conceptual distinction persists and rules out the "mere psychology" interpretation.

Moreover, in distinguishing premise sets *as embedded in scientific theories,* no premises are wholly redundant in the degenerate logical sense. For, although R and $\sim R$ may be redundant for this *one* accounting of D_3, they will not be redundant in general (as would a tautology) in the business of distinguishing the whole theories in which these arguments occur. Thus, in the wave theory of light, R may signify that a light ray *decelerates* on entering a denser medium, whereas in the particulate theory $\sim R$ will signify that the light *accelerates* on entering a denser medium. But neither R nor $\sim R$ will be needed immediately in the deduction of D—e.g., the proposition that the sines of the angles of incidence and refraction stand in ratio to each other. Nonetheless, *explaining* this latter phenomenon will involve reference ultimately not just to the premise set A,

B, *C*, and *H* (which may be identical in both the wave theory and the particle theory): the explanations will sooner or later involve *A*, *B*, *C*, *H*, and *R*, on the one hand and *A*, *B*, *C*, *H*, and ~*R*, on the other. So the conceptual difference remains, and is not trivialized by the redundancy move just noted.

X. Some Illustrations from the History of Science

Suppose someone urged that, so far as conceptual differences go, nothing distinguishes the "Classical Problem of Perturbations" and the "Inverse Problem of Perturbations." Such a person would not be taken seriously either by astronomers or by historians. I wish to describe these different approaches to perturbation theory, and to mark the analogies between them and the contrasts already drawn.

The Classical Problem of Perturbations may be characterized thus: Suppose we know the dynamical elements of some planet *A* (e.g., its mass, mean angular velocity, mean period of revolution, mean distance from the sun, orbital eccentricity, perihelial precession, etc.). And suppose also that we know the dynamical elements of some other planet *B*. Assuming the truth of the law of universal gravitation (*H* in this case), we can easily calculate the perturbation on *B* caused by *A* and *vice versa*. These calculations readily convert into predictions of the future positions of both planets. These are confirmed or disconfirmed by future observations. Should the observations confirm the predictions, they will indirectly reconfirm the law of gravitation, and reassure us also that the dynamical elements of both *A* and *B* have been properly described.

The Classical Problem of Perturbations thus reads remarkably like an HD reconstruction. So, knowing, as we do, the dynamical elements of the earth and Mars, we can predict the future positions of both by adding correction terms in the form of perturbation readjustments to the appropriate celestial theory. Indeed, by the systematic use of the HD method the discrepancies in unadjusted theories are regularly discovered, and the need for correction terms at the observational level clearly perceived. Nor is this HD technique *merely* a way of generating the detailed consequences of specific hypotheses. Nor is it merely ancillary to scientific theorizing; it is probably the only way of coming to perceive the need for further correction terms. The HD description is more accurate than any other in characterizing advances like the discovery of Halley's comet, of Pluto, of the antiproton and the antineutron. So, nothing in this paper is calculated to minimize the services rendered by cerebrations of the HD variety.

XI. The Inverse Problem of Perturbations

Other discoveries—of the planet Neptune, the neutrino, and the positive electron—are different from what has been discussed. The Inverse Problem of Perturbations is a case in point; it may be characterized thus: Suppose we know the dynamical elements of some planet B, and that we know from "unadjusted" celestial dynamics that the observed positions of B do not correspond to those predicted. B is perturbed from its expected path. The problem is now one of reasoning from this anomaly, these perturbations, to an hypothesis about some as-yet-undetected planet A whose specially designed dynamical elements would explain the observed perturbations. Explanation will have been achieved if B's observed perturbations logically follow from the hypothesis that A, with its tailor-made properties, exists. [This is precisely the argument which prepared us for the neutrino. Anomaly: Unlike the α particles ejected from a spontaneously decaying radioactive source, the β particles display ranges, and hence energies covering a wide spectrum. But this conflicts with the accepted principle of the conservation of energy, since if the radioactive source is homogeneous, and all β particles have the same properties, then that some should have more energy than others suggests that in these "others" energy is not being conserved. Hypothesis: if β particles were always ejected *along with* some other as-yet-undetected particle (neutral charge, no rest mass, etc.) then each emitted particle-pair (*β and* neutrino) would have an aggregate energy equal to that of every other particle-pair. Emitted *β* particles do not leave a "star" of tracks, as do *α* particles, because these "neutrinos" are consuming different amounts of energy in each pair-emission: a fact which cannot show up in a Wilson chamber. *Therefore* neutrinos exist!] The existence of planet *A* will explain *B*'s perturbations, if from this "existence hypothesis" *B*'s perturbations can be shown to follow. And then we should be able to predict *B*'s *future* perturbations on the basis of this same hypothesis. The HD procedure and the RD procedure are therefore indissolubly linked. They are even, indeed, conceptually linked. They are two stages of a three-stage rational process consisting in (*1*) unpacking the perhaps heretofore unformulated observational consequences of a given theory, or of a typical premise set within that theory, and (*2*) noting that one of these observational consequences, anomalously, does not square with the facts. The hunt is then on for some new hypothesis which, when conjoined with the orthodox premises *will* entail the anomaly, (*3*) unpacking in orthodox HD fashion this new premise set (containing the new hypothesis) into *other* as yet unformulated observational consequences: this is a further indirect test of the new anomaly explainer.

One of the great misunderstandings within the history of 19th century astronomy arose from this failure to distinguish arguing of the RD type from that of the HD type. My example is concerned with an exchange of letters between John Couch Adams and Professor George Airy, the distinguished Astronomer Royal.

Without engaging the vexed question of assigning ultimate priority, there can be little doubt that Adams' calculations in 1845 were sufficient for detecting the then-unknown planet which was perturbing Uranus. Adams' work was unknown to Leverrier when he took up this problem. But it is significant that both these astronomers, independently, concerned themselves with the Inverse Problem of Perturbations. Both of them recognized that they were departing from the usual perturbational problems of theoretical celestial mechanics.

As early as 1841 Adams formulated the problem of Uranus' orbit as follows: Given the anomalous motions of Uranus, from assuming the existence of what kind of planet, having what elements, could Uranus' observed positions be reconciled with orthodox Newtonian theory? *From* the anomaly, in other words, Adams envisages a rational process proceeding through the laws of celestial mechanics to some additional existence hypothesis which, if confirmed, would "explain" the Uranus' observed positions—rendering them thereby non-anomalous. Adams explicitly distinguishes this formulation of his problem from quite another one, namely the *arbitrary* assumption of some planets' existence—some planet having properties conjured up *de novo*. From this hypothesis of such a planet (plus associated initial conditions) to reason one's way in accordance with unadjusted Newtonian theory to observation statements—this is not Adams' idea of his own procedure. For even if this arbitrary hypothesis does explain the observed positions, it remains a different undertaking. Again, from the point of view of logical form, no distinction can be drawn between these two procedures: The inverse problem of perturbations and the orthodox problem of perturbations are thus indistinguishable in strict logic. But Adams sharply distinguishes the two as being different in *kind*. And no contemporary astronomer would be satisfied with being told by a philosopher that only a psychological difference demarcates the inverse from the orthodox problem of perturbations.

In one of his haughty letters to Adams, the Astronomer Royal thanks him for his detailed calculations and for having deduced the consequences of his *hypothesis* of a trans-Uranic premise. This convinced Adams that Airy had not really understood his work. For Adams did not arbitrarily select some hypothesis out of the air and unpack it into observation statements (some of which "accidentally" fit the facts). He began rather with incontrovertible observational facts (however "anomalous" in terms of the accepted theory) and slowly reasoned his way from these *back* to an hypothesis *H* which, almost as soon as it was formulated was seen *not* to be arbitrary in that it easily generated the anomaly.

Leverrier also sharply distinguishes the inverse from the orthodox problem of perturbations and definitely identifies his undertaking as being of the former variety. (Cf. Hanson, "Leverrier: The Zenith and Nadir of Newtonian Mechanics," in *Isis*, Vol. 53, Part 3, No. 173, Sept. 1962, pp. 359–378.)

Now this is a moment in the history of 19th century science which, I submit, could be misunderstood by one who minimized the *conceptual* differences between the HD description of scientific discoveries and the RD descriptions. These are not all-or-nothing exclusive accounts. You cannot recognize anomalies without the HD unpacking of accepted hypotheses. And you can't get new hypotheses for future HD unpacking without an RD type hunt for new hypotheses. Some HD theorists, by focusing only on logical form, which move has the consequence of conflating the HD and RD accounts, take all significant scientific *reasoning* in fact to be of the HD variety. A rationale of quite a different kind is often in evidence in the head work leading to discoveries such as that of the positive electron, the neutrino, and Neptune. To set out the conceptual structure of all of these examples as if they were instances of the same thing—and this the proponents of the HD analysis sometimes certainly do—would be to afford but a very incomplete understanding of the place of reason in the world of scientific discovery.

Long before this moment the following counter-claim will have been formulated: The HD philosopher had never purported to *describe* the process of scientific thinking. Since his interests are fundamentally *logical*, his concern is only to distinguish—in an *ex post facto* logical manner—arguments within formal science from arguments within natural science.

Since the distinction between statements which are, within a given language, certifiably true or false, and hypotheses which are at most *probably* true or false, is a *logical* distinction—and since the HD theorist is concerned *only* with this distinction—his is not a descriptive undertaking, but a logical one.

This is unobjectionable. But many HD philosophers have gone further. They have characterized the HD account not simply in *ex post facto* terms, but as somehow relevant to the way in which scientists *actually proceed*, and the way in which science *actually develops*. Insofar as this is done it is an incomplete account; two stages of a irreducible trinity of processes. Moreover, *whether or not* HD theorists are concerned with the distinction we have drawn here, whether or not my exegesis of their views is correct, there *is* such a distinction to be drawn. And insofar as HD philosophers have denied that such a distinction can be drawn on anything but psychological grounds, it has been my objective here to deny precisely that.

Scientific Explanation
and Prediction

PART II

Scientific Explanation

and Prediction

The Explanatory—Predictive Approach to Science

S. Morgenbesser, *Columbia University*

The once popular thesis that science describes but does not explain has few adherents today. This is also true for the extreme pragmatic thesis that science, or, at any rate, physics, is a collection of theories which are not true or false statements or bodies of statements, but instruments for the solution of problems, intellectual and otherwise.

With the demise of these and other theories, e.g., that science is distinguished by its method and not by its content, an abhorred vacuum was created. To fill it many philosophers of science adopted the view that *science is explanatory and predictive*, or its kin that *science aims at explanation and prediction*. Neither of these two related theses are novel, though neither have, I think, ever been as popular nor as well supported as they have been recently. I shall here be concerned with the limitations of these approaches to science; I assume their history and their defenses are either well known or readily available.

The thesis that *science aims at explanation and prediction*, and its cousin that *science is explanatory and predictive* may both be taken as *descriptive* theses. But taken in that way they are either dull and nondisconfirmable or general and false. The former characterization applies, I think, to those versions of the thesis which assert that scientists attempt to explain and predict, or that some scientists believe that it is the ultimate aim of science to explain and predict, or that it is the function of some scientific theories to explain and predict. The latter description, that of being false, applies to the generalized applications of the theses. It is not

41

the case that all scientists attempt to explain and predict, nor that all agree that explanation and prediction is the ultimate aim of science, nor is it true that all scientific theories are used for explanatory and predictive purposes.

Of course, in all these cases we may save the generalized thesis by definition. We may, for example, insist that theories that are not employable for predictive and explanatory purposes, e.g., a theory about the age of the earth, are not really empirical scientific theories, but either mere descriptive statements or theory sketches or normative theories. Analogously, we may argue that Botanists, Papyrologists, Sociologists, etc., who do not attempt to explain and predict are data collectors, classifiers, or mere model builders. However, this method of saving the thesis is reminiscent of the behavior of some theologians as described by Russell. He writes that they first describe certain things as impossible and then denounce them as such if they are proven actual.

Other descriptive interpretations of the thesis under consideration might be presented, but they would not, I fear, survive after analysis as interesting or true hypotheses. A new tack is needed and the suggestion that the thesis that science is explanatory and predictive should be construed as a proposal or as a *normative* thesis, leaps up for consideration. Here, too, a number of alternative formulations may be suggested, but we will review only the *normative* thesis that *science, as a collective whole, ought to have explanation and prediction as its ultimate aim*. The relevant difficulties, if any, that this normative version would experience would be shared by other versions of the thesis, not only in their difficulties but also in their advantages. Being a thesis about the long-range aims of science, it could not be objected to on the grounds that it is advice addressed to scientists, informing them from the philosophical heights as to what to do from day to day. Moreover, a normative thesis would escape the criticisms we have hurled at the descriptive versions of the thesis with which we began. But both of these advantages are short lived. Since it is not addressed to any given scientist it may be objected to as useless advice, for it is addressed to no one. Secondly, the thesis, not being descriptive, is not at variance with the other approaches to science it ostensibly challenges and replaces. Those who subscribe to the descriptive and pragmatic approaches would insist that they are elucidating the nature and structure of scientific theories, not specifying goals for science. Moreover, they would add that one cannot escape criticism by changing the topic, one thereby incurs it.

The dialectic must, however, be continued. Defenders of the normative thesis would insist that they are not merely specifying goals for science, or at any rate not merely expressing a personal taste; they would also object to the sharp distinction between the normative and descriptive, or at least point to the factual and conceptual backing that their thesis has—backing which they would aver counts against some formulations of the nature and aims of science that we have mentioned. Against the descriptive thesis they would note that scientists are not interested merely in discovering what there is, but also in explaining the findings; and against the pragmatic theory they would insist that no good reason has been given for thinking that scientific objects, e.g., electrons, do not exist. They would further add that those who insist they do not exist usually contradict themselves when they interpret the results of specific experiments. Finally, against those who object to their persuasive use of "theory," they would rest their case with the trite observation that scientists do attempt to replace theories like gestalt, functionalism, etc., with well-formed statements or bodies of statements that do function predictively and are used for explanatory purposes. Hence, they would conclude that they are specifying a thesis which is one that would be made by science about itself if it were self-conscious of its goal.

Notice, however, that the normative thesis has been transformed to a higher-order, Hegelian-like, and descriptive one. And though a consideration of the descriptive aspects of the original thesis may by now be tiresome, the three arguments, bearing as they do upon one topic, need review and deserve criticism; for despite their popularity they are debatable or at any rate not conclusive. The first incorrectly assumes that scientists simply agree upon that which is in need of explanation, that given any descriptive finding they immediately ask How come or Why. But such is not the case. That which Eddington thought worthy of or in need of explanation was considered by his fellow scientists simply another interesting addition to knowledge; and Einstein's request for an explanation of certain asymmetries in classical electrical theory was considered almost idiosyncratic.

Therefore, the first argument is to be challenged, for it falsely assumes that scientific requests for explanation are, as it were, triggered off by any finding. The second, too, cannot be accepted. It misleadingly assumes that there is a sharp distinction between the *realistic* position on the existence of theoretical entities and at least a modified *pragmatic* interpretation of the role of theories which countenance such entities. But there is no such sharp distinction. One may agree that electrons or molecules exist and nevertheless insist that many models and theories of their behavior contain sentences and expressions which are of use only because they facilitate computation, e.g., the computation of dissociation energies. Finally, as against the third argument, it should be remembered that at least some scientists disagree that their long-run descendents should expect to discover theories which contain only true and lawful statements. Duhem noted that physical laws of his and most likely of future days are not laws (not true), but nevertheless useful approximations. And a sizeable number of economists argue, partly on the authority of Marshall, that economic theory must always remain a body of semi-lawlike statements with a specification of the type of factors that might play a role in various circumstances, a specification that resembles a list more than it does a set of well-formulated laws.

In light of these counter-arguments we need not conclude that only those deaf to the message of science would dissent from the thesis that it is the ultimate aim of science to explain and predict. Moreover, even if scientists did speak with one voice on these issues, I doubt that we would be in the clear. Though "explain" and "predict" appear to be clear terms, "ultimate aim" and "science as a whole" appear as dark ones. But here I shall not be guided by appearance but shall allow the latter terms and challenge, or at least concern myself with, the former; for scientists who do insist that it is the ultimate aim of science to explain and predict use "explain" and "predict" in a number of ways and, hence, actually specify a number of alternative formulations or goals. And, of course, it is not enough simply to say that science ought to predict and explain and why. And here, too, diversity is introduced, for scientists and philosophers of science disagree as to what scientists should be expected to predict and why, and hence offer us many goals and many defenses for consideration. A review of all these goals would here be a luxury, and I shall, therefore, consider only some well-known version of the thesis that science ought to be explanatory and predictive. To aid in the understanding of these goals, I shall begin with a review of some uses of "predict."

When scientists evaluate theories on the basis of their predictive powers, or insist that they are seeking theories that predict, they are not, I think, using "to predict" and its offspring in a standard manner. Standardly, "to predict" is used interchangeably with "to forecast"; standardly, "to predict" is to act. Hence, to say that a theory predicts is to use "predicts" in one of the nonstandard ways, of which three—the semantic, the epistemological, and the evidentially relevant—may be noted. In the semantic use, a theory T can be said to predict S if "S" is deducible from T alone, or T conjoined with suitable admissible additional hypotheses; in the epistemological use, a theory T predicts S if S is predicted semantically from T and "S" is conceptually novel. A theory T can be said to predict E in the evidentially relevant sense of "predict" if T semantically predicts S and if our knowledge of the truth of "S" would enable us to decide between the acceptance of T and alternative scientific theories which compete with T for acceptance.

Given these four uses we may specify at least four different goals for science, but here we may avoid difficulties if all the goals are co-achievable; if, for example, a scientist can predict with warrant, if and only if his theories are predictive. Unfortunately, such is not the case. A doctor may predict with warrant that a patient will recover, but few medical predictions are deduced from medical theories. Conversely, not every scientific predictive theory allows the scientist to predict anything. Among other things, a scientific theory may predict a regularity, and it makes little sense to say that scientists predicted a regularity.

Again, a scientist may have confirmed an epistemologically predictive theory and not have added to his predictive power at all, for a theory which may have epistemologically novel results may be a theory about the past and hence not enable the scientist to forecast anything. Of course, when the scientist first introduces this theory he may predict that his theory will be confirmed, but this prediction is a personal forecast, and though it may be justified, it is not deduced from a theory and hence not predicted (in the semantic sense). Finally, a scientist who introduces a theory about the past may, when contrasting his theory with another available one, insist that his theory predicts L while the other does not. It is, I think, clear that "predicts" is here used in the evidentially relevant sense. Hence, we can conclude that if a theory T which either epistemologically predicts L, or is one for which L is evidentially relevant, then T need not add to the predictive power of the scientist.

Though only some interconnections between the uses of "predict" have been noted, the moral is clear. Rather than consider the co-achievability of a variety of goals, we should review a number of them singly. In each, of course, the term "predict" will be used in one way only.

Theories which have novel conceptual results are, of course, of great interest to science, but it is, I think, only the disguised romantic who would prize theories which are epistemologically novel for their own sake, and insist that science ought to be predictive in the sense of seeking such theories. An epistemologically novel theory is of interest if current ones are false, or if our current conceptual scheme is defective. To prize the production of epistemologically novel theories without end is to prize having false theories available for disconfirmation and replacement. And such a state of affairs is, I presume, desirable only as a way of keeping scientific enterprise alive. If we ask why the enterprise should be kept alive and are told that it should because it produces predictive theories, then we are back to where we began.

Not quite. We might mean that science is of value because it furnishes us with theories which are predictive, not epistemologically but semantically. Note, however, that short of reviewing issues about completeness and decidability, we cannot specify a sense for "predictive theory," nor even conclusively decide whether it is desirable to have such theories. But assuming that the phrase "predictive theory" is clear, we may agree that only logicians gone mad would love well-formed systems for their own sake. It is not enough to suggest that science ought to seek predictive and true theories, for such theories may be conceptually poor and just plain dull. Still it might be argued that predictive theories are valuable because they can be easily tested, but then the view that science aims at prediction reduces itself to the methodological triviality that science ought to seek testable theories.

Much the same results are reached if we demand that science have predictive theories in the evidentially relevant sense of that term. Once again we can translate that demand into a methodological one, directing scientists to set up tests and experiments which will enable them to decide between alternative theories. But to go even further and insist that science adopt the maxim that theories which have the same testable consequences should be equated, is to forget that other factors—simplicity, naturalness, standardability, etc.— have always entered, and, indeed, must enter when we want to judge the scientific worth of theories.

The last trip remains one upon which we attempt to decide whether scientists ought to attempt to predict or forecast events or sequences of events. Here, many would insist that this trip is not necessary, that scientists *qua* scientists ought not to be interested in predicting specific events, but only in confirming theories; that only applied scientists predict specific events while pure scientists make only conditional predictions, asserting not that E will occur but only that E will occur if K will occur. These arguments, though grist for our mill, will here not be accepted, for they are based on a dubious distinction between pure and applied science and on the dubious lemma that "E if K" type of statements are always more easily confirmable than statements of the form "E will occur."

Nevertheless, since it is reasonable to expect unconditional scientific predictions only under certain conditions (e.g., when we are dealing with closed systems), it is unreasonable to expect scientists to predict everything. The thesis that scientists ought to be predictors totters close to being identified with the triviality that scientists ought to aim to predict those events which they can predict with warrant. Yet even this triviality is questionable.

Unless a scientist wants to be given good grades simply for forecasting, he will concern himself only with forecasting those events which at least some men want to know about on independent grounds. There is little point scientifically forecasting the number of people who will touch their eyebrows within a given year, if no use can be made of the information. Moreover, it is important to remember that we do not simply predict events, but predict events under certain descriptions of them. A man might be able to predict correctly that a pitcher will throw to his catcher, but he might not be able to predict whether the pitcher will throw a curve or fast ball. Therefore, we have to be careful and assign utilities not only to the desirability of knowing whether certain events will occur, but to the desirability of knowing whether they will occur under certain descriptions of them as well. Hence, the scientist may be able to make more refined predictions than can be made simply on the basis of common sense knowledge, but it does not follow that he is doing anything socially worthwhile. And if we add that his theories are, at any rate, predictive, and that he ought to aim at such theories, we are thrown back to reviewing the issues we have already considered.

Most of the issues we have raised when considering the thesis that science is or ought to be predictive have their counterpart when we turn and attend to the view that science is or ought to be explanatory. But here they can be dealt with with greater dispatch. Thus we may assume that the act of explaining has direct utility, that there is one use of "explain" that is here relevant, and that it has at least been partially explicated by defenders of the deductive and nomological model.* These assumptions are, of course, subject to dispute, but they are not ludicrous.

On all accounts, these assumptions are, I think, made by those who inform us that science should attempt to explain nature, or explain all there is, or explain everything. The latter formulas are welcome, for it is patently not enough to assert that it is the aim of science to explain. But though they are welcome, they cannot be used interchangeably or simply adopted as they stand.

A scientist may insist that it is the aim of science to explain nature but think it silly to expect science to explain everything or all there is. Science, he will inform us, does not intend to explain the existence of classes and properties,

* [*Editor's note.* Cf. the articles in this volume by C. G. Hempel (p. 107) and A. Grünbaum (p. 57).]

and he may add that it is senseless to demand an explanation of chairs. Thinking that we understand him, we may expect him to suggest that it is the aim of science to explain all events and not to explain entities, abstract or concrete ones. But here we would be mistaken, for most scientists and philosophers of science argue that it is the intent of science to explain all events and regularities. To those who find this formulation unclear, we may propose that the intent behind it is that science aims to explain all events and laws. But this proposal is counter-intuitive. Science, it will most likely be claimed, is concerned not with the explanation of the laws, but that which (in one appropriate sense of "about") they are about. Hence, though with misgivings, we accept and do not challenge the hybrid formula that it is the aim of science to explain all events and regularities as the reconstruction of the thesis that it is the aim of science to explain nature.

But our acceptance is only temporary, for we must remind ourselves, as we did when we considered prediction, that we do not simply explain events but explain them under certain descriptions. The same event can be explained under one description and not under another one, not merely when these descriptions are logically unrelated, but also when one is, for example, a refinement of the other. Trying to mirror the importance of explaining events under descriptions, we may finally suggest that those who insist that science ought to explain nature mean that science ought to explain all events under all descriptions or under any description of them. Here it must be assumed that to explain an event is to find a suitable explanation containing a law. Further, it must be taken for granted that it is the aim of science not simply to explain but also to know that the explanation is warranted as a result of a certain kind of inductive inquiry. Further, we must remember that the assumption involved does not commit science to reductionistic determinism or to the finding of one theory by reference to which all events and occurrences will be explained. And, finally, we must add that science aims not merely to explain all events but also all regularities.

Those who insist that science ought to explain all events obviously mean that scientists ought to attempt to explain all events under all or any description of them. They do not necessarily mean that science or scientists will succeed. Nevertheless, they, I assume, would add that the progress of science is some evidence for the hope that scientists, given luck, time, and proper social standing, will come closer and closer to accomplishing this aim.

But here they would be challenged by some philosophers who would insist that this entire approach is based upon a misunderstanding of the history of science and supported by a misinterpretation of the nature of scientific explanation. For they would claim that this approach suggests that first we describe an event and then we seek a suitable explanans * by reference to which we can explain that event under that description. However, such is not the case. We cannot simply explain an event under any description but only under those which will enable us to refer to the event in the language or the vocabulary of a given theory which we will employ when we want to explain that event. Theories do not merely guide us in the discovery of interesting or new descriptions of events; without theories we will not know how to describe the event, at least how to describe it for explanatory purposes.

There is much substance to this criticism, especially if it is taken as a correction of an ostensibly genetic account of explanation. Indeed, one can go further and admit with these critics that frequently we do not know whether a given description is true unless we accept a given theory. And we may go further still and agree that often we cannot know, short of accepting a theory, whether we can ever decide whether a description of an event is meaningful, in the sense of being testable. But though all these points may

* Cf. C. G. Hempel, this volume, p. 108, for a precise formulation of the technical use of this term.

be granted, the main contention of these critics is not, I think, correct.

It is, of course, first to be noted that not all scientific explanations appeal to theories. But even when they do, it is not the case that we explain an event under a given description T only if T contains terms of the theory; for that description may be extensionally equivalent to some description L which does not contain terms of the theory, and by making use of that knowledge we may explain the event even under description T. A simple illustration will suffice.

If someone asks why Johnny caught a cold on his birthday, we may dismiss the question as a silly one. But if we do, we do so because we believe that there is no law connecting catching colds with birthdays, and that the person who raised that question was a fool who did not even know that elementary fact of life. However, here we may be hasty or at any rate forget that we can give an obviously appropriate and possibly true explanation of why Johnny caught a cold on his birthday. "It was cold and rainy and Johnny took a walk without a hat, etc.," may suffice. Obviously more abstruse considerations enter when we appeal to more complicated theories, but the over-all procedure remains the same. We can explain an event under one description even if the laws in the explanans do not essentially contain the terms of the original description. And we may note that this fact has been overlooked by many recent British philosophers who insist that we cannot give neurological explanations of psychological events, since the language of neurology and the language of psychology differ. I presume that they mean that neurological and psychological descriptions are not synonymous, a true but here irrelevant consideration.

We must therefore differ from those critics who insist that the thesis we are discussing has been conceived in confusion. Yet with them we may try to investigate that thesis by reference to the theories that do play a role in science. And so, granting the thesis is meaningful, we may then try to show that scientific results may lead us to believe that the aim of explaining all events under all descriptions and all regularities is not an acceptable one. And, indeed, such may be the case.

Scientists may give us some good reasons for believing that they have discovered some ultimate laws; they may also give us some good reasons for believing that they have discovered a nonreducible statistical law or theory. In the first case we may then say that we are unable to explain the regularities which are described by the ultimate laws; in the second, that we are unable to explain some events under some descriptions. Note that the latter point does not require that we abandon the notion of a statistical explanation of an event. We may allow such explanations and agree that we have explained the occurrence of an event of type K under conditions L if a theory predicts that events of type K occur under type L conditions with 0.95 probability and the theory is well confirmed. But if H type events occur under conditions L and the theory predicts that an H-type event will occur under L only with 0.02 probability, we cannot appeal to the theory for explanation of the occurrence of an H event.

We have tried to specify two conditions under which we might say, with some good reason, that science cannot explain everything. Other conditions might be given, but they would not introduce new relevant features, though they would, I hope, strengthen our case. But here many critics would demur and insist that no point at all has been made and that our discussion of these two cases has been singularly defective. Thus some critics might contend that our discussion has overlooked the fact that no scientist would ever agree that a law is ultimate and hence that our first case cannot arise in practice; others might contend that our discussion has not paid sufficient heed to the principle of sufficient reason. But both of these contentions are not crushing. Despite the current emphasis upon the eternal open frontier of science, it is not true that scientists never claim that they have discovered ultimate laws. Scientists in the nineteenth century claimed that they did; and many scientists today, especially those who work in elementary particle theory, are at least seeking ultimate laws. Neither is it the case that our remarks are at variance with the principle of sufficient reason; for even if we grant that principle, we might argue that that which science cannot explain can be explained metaphysically or religiously. We are not discussing whether every event can be explained in some way, but whether it can be explained scientifically.

But since we are discussing scientific explanations, we must, it will be insisted, be more careful than we have been in our discussion of the second case. Some philosophers of science would claim that the second case should lead us to say and to say only that a certain kind of event cannot be explained by a given theory, not that a certain kind of event simply cannot be explained. But I have assumed that we are dealing with a theory which resembles contemporary quantum mechanics and which claims that the statistical laws cannot be explained away or replaced by causal ones, and further assumes that we have good reason for accepting such a theory. And if we are told that never have there been any good reasons for accepting such a theory, we may, I think, answer that we may have as good a reason for accepting this sort of theory as any other. And if we are told that we may have a good reason for accepting this theory only for the purposes of calculation but not as a true and possibly explanatory one, our answer is similar to the one we have given to the preceding argument. Moreover, such an answer is not open to those who claim that science is explanatory, and it is their views that we are reviewing.

Of course, in all this discussion I have not assumed that we can prove that we have discovered ultimate laws or nonreducible statistical ones, and hence I have not proved that science cannot explain everything. But here it is not a question of proof, but only of giving some reasons for abandoning the hope that science will explain everything. Given this outcome, we might conclude that science has been shown to be incapable of accomplishing its ends. But this conclusion can only be reached by those who begin with the assumption that science aims to explain everything. Moreover, this conclusion is somewhat puzzling on independent grounds. A discovery of and confirmation of ultimate laws, construction of and confirmation of certain types of statistical theories should *prima facie* be evidence for the strength of science and not its bankruptcy.

And to allow us to conclude thusly, we should begin not with the assumption that it is or ought to be the aim of science to explain everything, but with the one that it is the aim of science to discover true theories as a result of which we will know what is capable of explanation and what is not. This discussion obviously bears upon topics in philosophical psychology and especially upon the topic of freedom of the will, but I will here not draw the obvious implications. This discussion assumes that we can discover the truth. And if our tormenter asks us what is truth, we need not ask him to walk away; we may send him to Tarski.

Temporally Asymmetric Principles, Parity between Explanation and Prediction, and Mechanism versus Teleology*

Adolf Grünbaum, *University of Pittsburgh*

1. Introduction

In order to consider the role of temporal asymmetries in scientific induction, I wish to deal with three major questions. These are:

1. What are the principles governing those conditions under which there is the following kind of temporal asymmetry of inferability: It is possible to infer from the state of a system at some particular time t_0 one or more states at times t *prior* to t_0—this inference being called a "retrodiction"—but the same information pertaining to the time t_0 does not permit the corresponding predictive inference concerning the times $t > t_0$?

2. What is the bearing of the existence of the asymmetry between retrodiction and prediction on the following quite distinct question: Is there symmetry between the *explanation* of an event E on the basis of one or more *antecedents* of E, when E belongs to the *past* of the explaining scientist, on the one hand, and, on the other hand, the *prediction* of the same (kind of) E by reference to the same (kind of) *ante-*

* Professor Grünbaum's paper is substantially similar in content to his chapter in *Induction: Some Current Issues*, published by the Wesleyan University Press. It is here published by arrangement with Wesleyan University Press.

cedent(*s*) of *E*, when *E* belongs to the *future* of the scientist making the prediction?

3. What is the import of our findings in regard to the two preceding issues for the controversy between mechanism and teleology?

2. Conditions of Asymmetry between Retrodictions and Predictions *

Our concern in this section is with the kind of asymmetry in which retrodiction is possible while the corresponding prediction is impossible.† To deal with it, we must first give an account of certain features of the physical world having the character of initial or boundary conditions within the framework of the theory of statistical mechanics. The sought-after basis of the asymmetry will then emerge from principles of statistical mechanics relevant to these *de facto* conditions.

The universe around us exhibits striking disequilibria of temperature and other inhomogeneities. In fact, we live by virtue of the nuclear conversion of the sun's reserves of hydrogen into helium, which issues in our reception of solar radiation. As the sun dissipates its reserves of hydrogen via the emission of solar radiation, it may heat a terrestrial rock embedded in snow during the daytime. At night, the rock is

* I am indebted to Professor Allen I. Janis for helpful discussions of aspects of statistical mechanics relevant to this section. The treatment of the barometer as an advance indicator benefited from a criticism which Nicholas LaPara made of an earlier formulation.

† For a discussion of the conditions under which the *inverse* asymmetry obtains, see A. Grünbaum, "Das Zeitproblem," *Archiv fur Philosophie*, Vol. 7, 1957, pp. 184–185. Cf. also M. S. Watanabe, "Symmetry of Physical Laws. Part III. Prediction and Retrodiction," *Reviews of Modern Physics*, 27, 179–186 (1955). A simple illustration of the *inverse* temporal asymmetry obtaining in equilibrating processes is given by the case of a ball rolling down on the inside wall of a round bowl subject to friction: If the ball is found to be at rest at the bottom of the bowl, we *cannot retrodict* its particular motion prior to coming to rest; but if the ball is released at the inside wall near the top, we *can predict* its subsequent coming to rest at the bottom.

no longer exposed to the sun but is left with a considerably higher temperature than the snow surrounding it. Hence, at night, the *warm* rock and the *cold* snow form a quasi-isolated subsystem of either our galactic or solar system. And the relatively low entropy of that subsystem was purchased at the expense of the dissipation of the sun's reserves of hydrogen. Hence, *if* there is some quasi-closed system comprising the sun and the earth, the branching off of our subsystem from this wider system in a state of low entropy at sunset involved an entropy increase in the wider system. During the night, the heat of the rock melts the snow, and thus the entropy of the rock–snow system increases. The next morning at sunrise, the rock–snow subsystem merges again with the wider solar system. Thus, there are subsystems which branch off from the wider solar or galactic system, remain quasi-closed for a limited period of time, and then merge again with the wider system from which they had been separated. Following Reichenbach,[1] we shall use the term "branch system" to designate this kind of subsystem.

Branch systems are formed not only in the natural course of things, but also through human intervention: When an ice cube is placed into a glass of warm ginger ale by a waiter and then covered for hygienic purposes, a subsystem has been formed. The prior freezing of the ice cube had involved an entropy increase through the dissipation of electrical energy in some larger quasi-closed system of which the electrically run refrigerator is a part. While the ice cube melts in the covered glass subsystem, that quasi-closed system increases its entropy. But it merges again with another system when the then chilled ginger ale is consumed by a person. Similarly for a cold room that is closed off and then heated by burning logs.

Thus, our environment abounds in branch systems whose initial relatively low entropies are the products of their earlier coupling or interaction with outside agencies of one kind or another. This rather constant and ubiquitous formation of a branch system in a relatively low entropy state resulting from interaction often proceeds at the expense of an entropy increase in some wider quasi-closed system from which it originated. And the *de facto,* nomologically contingent occurrence of these branch systems has the following *fundamental consequence,* at least for our region of the universe and during the current epoch: Among the quasi-closed systems whose entropy is relatively low and which behave as if they might remain isolated, the vast majority have not been and will not remain permanently closed systems, being branch systems instead.

Hence, upon encountering a quasi-closed system in a state of fairly *low* entropy, we know the following to be overwhelmingly probable: The system has *not* been isolated for millions and millions of years and does *not* just *happen* to be in one of the infrequent but ever-recurring low-entropy states exhibited by a permanently isolated system. Instead, our system was formed not too long ago by branching off after an interaction with an outside agency. For example, suppose that an American geologist is wandering in an isolated portion of the Sahara desert in search of an oasis and encounters a portion of the sand in the shape of "Coca-Cola." He would then infer that, with overwhelming probability, a kindred person had interacted with the sand in the recent past by tracing "Coca-Cola" in it. The geologist would not suppose that he was in the presence of one of those relatively low entropy configurations which are assumed by the sand particles spontaneously but very rarely, if beaten about by winds for millions upon millions of years in a state of effective isolation from the remainder of the world.

There is a further *de facto* property of branch systems that concerns us. For it will turn out to enter into the temporally asymmetrical statistical regularities which we shall find to be exhibited in the entropic behavior of these systems. This property consists in the following *randomness* obtaining *as a matter of nomologically contingent fact* in the distribution of the W_1 micro states belonging to the initial macro states of a *space* ensemble of branch systems, each of which has the same initial entropy $S_1 = k \log W_1$: For each class of *like* branch systems having the *same* initial entropy value S_1, the micro states constituting the identical initial macro states of entropy S_1 are *random samples* of the set of all W_1 micro states yielding a macro state of entropy S_1.[2] This attribute of randomness of micro states on the part of the initial states of the members of the *space* ensemble will be recognized as the counterpart of the following attribute of the micro states of one single, permanently closed system: There is equiprobability of occurrence among the W_1 micro states belonging to the *time* ensemble of states of equal entropy $S_1 = k \log W_1$ exhibited by one single, permanently closed system.

We can now state the statistical regularities which obtain as a consequence of the *de facto* properties of branch systems just set forth, when coupled with the principles of statistical mechanics. These regularities, which will be seen to yield a temporally asymmetric behavior of the entropy of *branch* systems, fall into two main groups as follows.

Group 1. In most space ensembles of quasi-closed branch systems each of which is initially in a state of non-equilibrium or relatively *low* entropy, the majority of branch systems in the ensemble will have *higher* entropies *after* a given time t (ref. 3, pp. 270, 192–193). But these branch systems simply did not exist as quasi-closed, distinct systems at a time t *prior to* the occurrence of their initial, branching-off states. Hence, not existing then as such, the branch systems did in fact *not* also exhibit the same higher entropy states at the *earlier* times t, which they would indeed have done then had they existed as closed systems all along.

The increase after a time t in the entropy of the over-whelming majority of branch systems of initially low entropy —as confirmed abundantly by observation—can be made fully intelligible. To do so, we note the following property of the *time* ensemble of entropy values belonging to a single, permanently closed system and then affirm that property of the space ensembles of branch systems: Since *large* entropic downgrades or decreases are *far less* probable (frequent) than moderate ones, the *vast majority* of *non*-equilibrium entropy states of a permanently closed system are located either at or in the immediate temporal vicinity of the *bottom* of a *dip* of the one-system entropy curve. In short, the vast majority of the *sub*maximum entropy states are on or temporally very near the *upgrades* of the one-system curve. The application of this result to the space ensemble of branch systems whose initial states exhibit the aforementioned *de facto* property of randomness then yields the following: Among the initial low-entropy states of these systems, the vast majority lie at or in the immediate temporal vicinity of the bottoms of the one-system entropy curve at which an upgrade begins.

Group 2. A decisive *temporal asymmetry* in the statistics of the temporal evolution of branch systems arises from the further result that in most space ensembles of branch systems each of whose members is initially in a state of *equilibrium* or very *high* entropy, the vast majority of these systems in the ensemble will *not* have *lower* entropies *after* a finite time *t*, but will still be in equilibrium.[3] For the aforementioned randomness property assures that the vast majority of those branch systems whose initial states are equilibrium states have maximum entropy values lying somewhere *well within* the plateau of the one-system entropy curve, rather than at the extremity of the plateau at which an entropy *decrease* is initiated.[*]

* Although the decisive asymmetry just noted was admitted by H. Mehlberg (ref. 4, p. 129), he dismisses it as expressing "merely the factual difference between the two relevant values of probability." But an asymmetry is no less an asymmetry for depending on *de facto*, nomologically contingent boundary conditions rather than being assured by a *law* alone. Since our verification of laws generally has the same partial and indirect character as that of our confirmation of the existence of certain complicated *de facto* boundary conditions, the assertion of an asymmetry depending on *de facto* conditions is generally no less reliable than one wholly grounded on a law. Hence, when Mehlberg [*op. cit.*, p. 117, n. 30] urges against Schrödinger's

We see therefore that in the vast majority of branch systems, either one end of their finite entropy curves is a point of low entropy and the other a point of high entropy, or they are in equilibrium states at both ends as well as during the intervening interval. And it is likewise apparent that the statistical distribution of these entropy values on the time axis is such that the vast majority of branch systems have the *same direction of entropy increase* and hence also the same opposite direction of entropy decrease. Thus, the statistics of entropy increase among branch systems assure that in most space ensembles the vast majority of branch systems will increase their entropy in *one* of the two opposite time directions and decrease it in the other. In this way the entropic behavior of branch systems confers the same statistical anisotropy on the vast majority of all those epochs of time during which the universe exhibits the requisite disequilibrium and contains branch systems satisfying initial conditions of "randomness." *

Let us now call the direction of entropy increase of a *typical representative* of these epochs the direction of "later," as indeed we have done from the outset by the mere assignment of higher time numbers in that direction but *without* prejudice to our findings concerning the issue of the anisotropy of time. Then our results pertaining to the entropic

___

claim of asymmetry that for every pair of branch systems which change their entropy in one direction, "there is nothing to prevent" another pair of closed subsystems from changing their entropy in the opposite direction, the reply is: Mehlberg's criticism can be upheld only by gratuitously neglecting the statistical asymmetry admitted but then dismissed by him as "merely" factual. For a more detailed criticism of Mehlberg's denial of temporal anisotropy, see A. Grünbaum, reference 5.

* Readers familiar with Reichenbach's "hypothesis of the branch structure" as set forth in his *The Direction of Time* (p. 136) will note that though heavily indebted to Reichenbach, my treatment of the assumptions regarding branch systems departs from Reichenbach's in several *essential* respects. A statement and justification of these departures is given in reference 6, footnote 97.

behavior of branch systems show that the directions of "earlier than" and "later than" are not merely opposite directions bearing decreasing and increasing time coordinates, respectively, but are statistically *anisotropic* in an objective physical sense.*

We are now prepared to elucidate the bearing of this conclusion on the conditions under which there is asymmetry between retrodiction and prediction.

Suppose we encounter a beach whose sand forms a smooth surface except for one place where it is in the shape of a human footprint. We know from our previous considerations with high probability that instead of having evolved *isolatedly* from a prior state of uniform smoothness into its present uneven configuration according to the statistical entropy principle for a permanently closed system, the beach was an *open* system in *interaction* with a stroller. And we are aware furthermore that if there is some quasi-closed wider system containing the beach and the stroller, as there often is, the beach achieved its ordered low-entropy state of bearing the imprint or interaction-indicator at the expense of at least compensatory entropy increase in that wider system comprising the stroller: The stroller increased the entropy of the wider system by scattering his energy reserves in making the footprint.

We see that the sandy footprint shape is a genuine indicator and not a randomly achieved form resulting from the unperturbed chance concatenations of the grains of sand. The imprint thus contains information in the sense of being a veridical indicator of an interaction. Now, in all probability the entropy of the imprint-bearing beach system in-

---

* This is *not* to say that entropic changes are the *sole* source of the anisotropy of time. But processes which are *de facto* irreversible though not involving any entropy increase [cf., K. R. Popper, "The Arrow of Time," *Nature*, 177, 538 and 178, 382 (1956); A. Grünbaum, ref. 7] are *not* of importance for the asymmetry between retrodiction and prediction, which is our guiding concern in this section.

creases after the interaction with the stroller through the smoothing action of the wind. And this entropy increase is parallel, in all probability, to the direction of entropy increase of the majority of branch systems. Moreover, we saw that the production of the indicator by the interaction is likely to have involved an entropy increase in some wider system of which the indicator is a part. Hence, *in all probability the states of the interacting systems which do contain the indicators of the interaction are the relatively higher entropy states of the majority of branch systems, as compared to the interaction state. Hence the indicator states are the relatively later states as compared to the states of interaction which they attest.* And by being both *later* and indicators, these states have *retrodictive* significance, thereby being traces, records, or memories. And due to the high degree of retrodictive univocity of the low-entropy states constituting the indicators, the latter are veridical to a high degree of *specificity.*

Confining our attention for the present to indicators whose production requires only the occurrence of the interaction which they attest, we therefore obtain the following conclusion. Apart from two classes of *advance* indicators requiring very special conditions for their production and constituting *exceptions,* it is the case that *with overwhelming probability, low-entropy indicator states can exist in systems whose interactions they attest only after and not before these interactions.** If this conclusion is true (assuming that there are either no cases or not enough cases of *bona fide* precognition to disconfirm it), then, of course, it is not an *a*

---

* The two exceptions, which we shall discuss in some detail below, are constituted by the following two classes of advance indicators: (i) veridical predictions made and stored (recorded) by human (or other sentient, theory-using) beings, and physically registered, *bona fide* advance indicators produced by computers, and (ii) advance indicators (e.g., sudden barometric drops) which are produced by the very cause (pressure change) that also produces the future interaction (storm) indicated by them.

priori truth. And it would be very shallow indeed to seek to construe it as a trivial *a priori* truth in the following way: calling the indicator states "traces," "records," or "memories" and noting that it then becomes tautological to assert that traces and the like have only retrodictive and no predictive significance. But this transparent verbal gambit cannot make it true *a priori* that—apart from the exceptions to be dealt with below—interacting systems bear indicators attesting veridically only their *earlier* and *not* their later interactions with outside agencies.

Hence, the two exceptions apart, we arrive at the fundamental asymmetry of recordability: *Reliable indicators in interacting systems permit only retrodictive inferences concerning the interactions for which they vouch but no predictive inferences pertaining to corresponding later interactions.*

And the logical schema of these inductive inferences is roughly as follows: The premises assert (i) the presence of a certain relatively low entropy state in the system, and (ii) a quasi-universal statistical law stating that most low-entropy states are interaction indicators *and* were *preceded* by the interactions for which they vouch. The conclusion from these premises is then the inductive retrodictive one that there was an earlier interaction of a certain kind.

As already mentioned, our affirmation of the temporal asymmetry of recordability of interactions must be qualified by dealing with two exceptional cases, the first of which is the prerecordability of those interactions which are veridically predicted by human beings (or computers). For any event which could be predicted by a scientist could also be "prerecorded" by that scientist in various forms such as a written entry on paper asserting its occurrence at a certain later time, an advance drawing, or even an advance photograph based on the predrawing. By the same token, artifacts like computers can prerecord events which they can predict. A comparison between the written, drawn, or photographic prerecord (i.e., recorded prediction) of, say, the crash of a plane into a house and its postrecord in the form of a caved-in house, and a like comparison of the corresponding pre- and postrecords of the interaction of a foot with a beach will now enable us to formulate the essential differences in the conditions requisite to the respective production of pre-records and postrecords as well as the usual differences in make-up between them.

The production of at least one retrodictive indicator or postrecord of an interaction such as the plane's crash into the house requires only the occurrence of that interaction (as well as a moderate degree of durability of the record). The retrodictive indicator states in the system which inter-acted with an outside agency must, of course, be distin-guished from the *epistemic use* which human beings may make of these physical indicator states. And our assertion of the sufficiency of the interaction for the production of a postrecord allows, of course, that the *interpretation* of actual postrecords by humans as *bona fide* documents of the past requires their use of theory and not just the occurrence of the interaction. In contrast to the sufficiency of an inter-action itself for its (at least short-lived) postrecordability, no such sufficiency obtains in the case of the prerecordability of an interaction: Save for an overwhelmingly improbable freak occurrence, the production of even a single prerecord of the coupling of a system with an agency external to it requires, as a necessary condition, *either* (*a*) the use of an appropriate theory by symbol-using entities (humans, com-puters) having suitable information, *or* (*b*) the prerecord's being a partial effect of a cause that also produces the pre-recorded interaction, as in the barometric case to be dealt with below. And in contexts in which (*a*) is a necessary condition, we find the following: Since prerecords are, by definition, veridical, this necessary condition cannot *gen-erally* also be sufficient, unless the predictive theory em-ployed is deterministic *and* the information available to the theory-using organism pertains to a closed system.

In addition to differing in regard to the conditions of their production, prerecords generally differ from postrecords in the following further respect: Unless the prerecord prepared by a human being (or computer) *happens* to be part of the interacting system to which it pertains, the prerecord will not be contained in states of the interacting system which it concerns but will be in some other system. Thus, a prerecord of the crash of a plane into a house in a heavy fog would generally *not* be a part of either the house or the plane, although it can happen to be. But in the case of *post*recording, there will always be at least one postrecord, however short-lived, in the interacting system itself to which that postrecord pertains.

Our earlier example of the footprint on the beach will serve to illustrate more fully the asymmetry between the requirements for the production of a prerecord and of a postrecord. The prerecording of a *later* incursion of the beach by a stroller would require extensive information about the motivations and habits of people not now at the beach and also knowledge of the accessibility of the beach to prospective strollers. This is tantamount to knowledge of a large system which is *closed,* so that all relevant agencies can safely be presumed to have been included in it. For otherwise, we would be unable to guarantee, for example, that the *future* stroller will *not* be stopped enroute to the beach by some agency not included in the system, an eventuality whose occurrence would deprive our prerecord of its referent, thereby destroying its status as a veridical indicator. In short, in the case of the footprint, which is a postrecord and *not* a prerecord of the interaction of a human foot with the beach, the interaction itself is *sufficient* for its postrecording (though not for the extended *durability* of the record once it exists) but *not* for its prerecording and prediction. Since a future interaction of a potentially open system like the beach is *not* itself sufficient for its prerecordability, open systems like beaches therefore do not themselves exhibit prerecords of their own future interactions. Instead—apart from the second species of prerecordability to be considered presently—prerecordability of interactions of potentially open systems requires the mediation of symbol and theory-using organisms or the operation of appropriate artifacts like computers. And such prerecordability can obtain successfully only if the theory available to the prerecording organism is deterministic and sufficiently comprehensive to include all the relevant laws and boundary conditions governing the pertinent closed systems.

The second species of exceptions to the asymmetry of recordability is exemplified by the fact that a sudden drop in the pressure reading of a barometer can be an advance indicator or "prerecord" of a subsequent storm. To be sure, it is the immediately *prior* pressure change in the spatial vicinity of the barometer and only that particular prior change (i.e., the *past* interaction through pressure) which is recorded numerically by a given drop in the barometric reading, and *not* the pressure change that *will* exist at that same place at a *later* time: To make the predictions required for a *pre*recording of the pressure changes which will exist at a given space point at later times (i.e., of the corresponding future interactions), comprehensive meteorological data pertaining to a large region would be essential. *But* it *is* possible in this case to base a rather reliable prediction of a future storm on the present sudden barometric drop. The latter drop, however, is, in fact, a *bona fide* advance indicator *only because* it is a partial effect of the very comprehensive cause which also produces (assures) the storm. Thus, it is the fulfillment of the *necessary condition* of having a causal ancestry that overlaps with that of the storm which is needed to confer the status of an advance indicator on the barometric drop. In contrast to the situation prevailing in the case of *post*recordability, the existence of this necessary condition makes for the fact that the future occurrence of a storm is *not sufficient* for the existence of an advance indicator of that storm in the form of a sudden barometric drop at an earlier time.

An analogous account can be given of the following

cases, which Mr. F. Brian Skyrms has suggested to me for consideration—situations in which *human intentions* are highly reliable advance indicators of the events envisaged by these intentions. Thus, the desire for a glass of beer, coupled with the supposed presence of the conditions under which beer and a glass are obtainable produces as a partial effect the intent to get it. And, *if* external conditions permit (the beer is available and accessible), and, furthermore, if the required internal conditions materialize (the person desiring the beer remains able to go and get it), then the intent will issue in the obtaining and drinking of the beer. But in contrast to the situation prevailing in the case of retrodictive indicators (postrecords), the future consumption of the beer is *not* a *sufficient condition* for the existence of its probabilistic advance indicator in the form of an intention.

The consideration of some alleged counterexamples will serve to complete our statement of the temporal asymmetry of the recordability of interactions. These purported counterexamples are to the effect that there are prerecords *not* depending for their production on the use of predictive theory by symbol-using organisms, or on the prerecord's being a partial effect of a cause that also produces the prerecorded interaction.

In the first place, it might be argued that there are spontaneous prerecords as exemplified in the following two kinds of scientific contexts:

1. In any essentially closed dynamical system such as the solar system, a dynamical state later than one occurring at a time t_0 is a *sufficient condition* for the occurrence of the state at time t_0, no less than is a state prior to t_0; hence the state at time t_0 can be regarded as a *pre*record of the later state no less than it can be deemed a postrecord of the earlier one.

2. A certain kind of death—say, the kind of death ensuing from leukemia—may be a sufficient condition for the existence of a prerecord of it in the form of the onset of active leukemia. But these examples violate the conditions on which our denial of spontaneous prerecordability is predicated in the following essential respect: They involve later states which are *not* states of *interaction* with outside agencies entered into by an otherwise closed system, in the manner of our example of the beach.

In the second place, since the thesis of the temporal asymmetry of spontaneous recordability makes cases of *bona fide* precognition overwhelmingly improbable, it might be said that this thesis and the entropic considerations undergirding it are vulnerable to the discovery of a reasonable number of cases of genuine precognition, a discovery which is claimed by some to have already been made. To this I retort that if the purported occurrence of precognition turns out to become well authenticated, then I am, of course, prepared to envision such alterations in the body of current orthodox scientific theory as may be required.

3. The Bearing of the Retrodiction–Prediction Asymmetry on the Issue of Symmetry between Explanation and Prediction

In Sec. 1, we gave a preliminary demarcation of the retrodiction–prediction antithesis from the explanation–prediction distinction as understood by writers such as Hempel.* We shall now complete that demarcation and will then represent the results on a diagram.

For Hempel, the particular conditions C_i ($i = 1, 2, \cdots n$) which, in conjunction with the relevant laws, account for the *explanandum* event E may be *earlier* than E in *both* explanation *and* prediction or the C_i may be *later* than E in *both* explanation and prediction. Thus, a case of *prediction* in which the C_i would be *later* than E would be one in astronomy, for example, in which a future E is accounted

* I refer here to the original paper of C. G. Hempel and P. Oppenheim: "Studies in the Logic of Explanation," *Philosophy of Science*, 15, 135 (1948). For Hempel's most recent statement of his account of scientific explanation, see reference 9.

for by reference to C_i that are still further in the future than E. These assertions hold, since Hempel's criterion for an explanation as opposed to a prediction is that E belong to the scientist's *past* when he offers his account of it, and his criterion for a corresponding prediction is that E belong to the scientist's *future* when it is made.

On the other hand, in the retrodiction–prediction antithesis, a *retrodiction* is characterized by the fact that the C_i are *later* than E, while the C_i are *earlier* than E in the kind of *prediction* which is antithetical to retrodiction but *not* identical with Hempelian prediction.

In the accompanying diagram, the i, k, l, m may each range over the values $1, 2, \cdots n$.

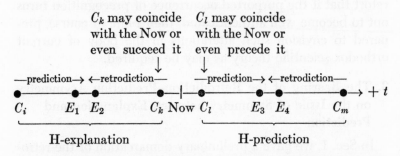

If we use the prefix "H" as an abbreviation for "Hempelian," then two consequences are apparent. First, a retrodiction as well as a prediction can be an H-prediction, and a prediction as well as a retrodiction can be an H-explanation. Second, being an H-prediction rather than an H-explanation, or conversely, depends on the transient homocentric "now," but there is no such "now"-dependence in the case of being a retrodiction instead of a prediction, or conversely.

The passage in the Hempel-Oppenheim essay setting forth the symmetry thesis espoused by K. R. Popper and these authors reads as follows: *

> the same formal analysis, including the four necessary conditions, applies to scientific prediction as well as to explanation.

* See reference 8, Sec. 3.

The difference between the two is of a pragmatic character. If E is given, i.e., if we know that the phenomenon described by E has occurred, and a suitable set of statements $C_1, C_2, \cdots, C_k, L_1, L_2, \cdots, L_r$ is provided afterwards, we speak of an explanation of the phenomenon in question. If the latter statements are given and E is derived prior to the occurrence of the phenomenon it describes, we speak of a prediction. It may be said, therefore, that an explanation is not fully adequate unless its explanans, if taken account of in time, could have served as a basis for predicting the phenomenon under consideration.*—Consequently, whatever will be said in this article concerning the logical characteristics of explanation or prediction will be applicable to either, even if only one of them should be mentioned.

Hempel's thesis of symmetry or structural equality between H-explanation and H-prediction can therefore now be formulated in the following way: Any *prediction* which qualifies logically *and* methodologically as an H-explanation also qualifies as an H-prediction, provided that the scientist is in possession of the information concerning the C_i prior to the occurrence of E, and conversely. And any *retrodiction* which qualifies logically *and* methodologically as an H-explanation also qualifies as an H-prediction, provided that the information concerning the relevant C_i is available at an appropriate time, and conversely.

Before examining critically the diverse objections which have been leveled against Hempel's thesis of symmetry in the recent literature by Rescher,[10] Barker,[11] Hanson,[12] and Scriven,[13,14] I wish to make a few remarks concerning my construal of both that thesis and of the philosophical task to whose fulfillment it pertains.

I take Hempel's affirmation of symmetry to pertain *not* to

* "The logical similarity of explanation and prediction, and the fact that one is directed towards past occurrences, the other towards future ones, is well expressed in the terms 'postdictability' and 'predictability' used by Reichenbach in [Quantum Mechanics], p. 13." [H. Reichenbach, *Philosophic Foundations of Quantum Mechanics*, University of California Press, Berkeley, 1948.]

the *assertibility per se* of the *explanandum* but to the either deductive or inductive *inferability* of the *explanandum* from the *explanans*. Popper and Hempel say: To the extent that there is ever explanatory *inferability*, there is also predictive inferability and conversely. They do *not* claim that every time you are entitled to *assert, on some grounds or other*, that a certain kind of event *did* occur in the past, you are *also* entitled to say that the same kind of event *will* occur in the future. Being concerned with *scientific understanding*, Popper and Hempel said that there is temporal symmetry *not* of assertibility *per se* but of assertibility *on the strength of the explanans*. The *scientific* relevance of dealing with predictive *arguments* rather than mere predictive assertions can hardly be contested by claiming with Scriven (ref. 14, Sec. 3.4) that in this context "the crucial point is that, however achieved, a prediction is what it is simply because it is produced in advance of the event it predicts; it is *intrinsically* nothing but a bare description of that event." For surely a soothsayer's unsupported prophecy that there will not be a third world war is not of scientific significance and ought not to command any scientific interest precisely because of the unreasoned manner of its achievement. Hence a scientifically warranted prediction of an event must be more than a mere pre-assertion of the event. And in any context which is to be scientifically relevant, the following two components can be distinguished in the meaning of the term "H-predict" no less than in the meaning of "H-explain" (or "post-explain"), and similarly for the corresponding nouns:

(i) the mere *assertion* of the *explanandum*, which *may* be based on grounds other than its scientific *explanans*, and

(ii) the logical *derivation* (deductive or inductive) of the *explanandum* from an *explanans*, the character of the content of the *explanans* remaining unspecified until later on in this essay.

My attachment of the prefix "H" to the word "explain" (and to "explanation") and my use of "post-explain" as a synonym of "H-explain" will serve to remind us for the sake of clarity that this usage of "explain" results from a restriction to the past of *one* well-established usage which is *temporally neutral,* viz., "explain" in the sense of providing scientific understanding (or a scientific accounting) of why something did *or* will occur. But, to my mind, the philosophical task before us is *not* the ascertainment of how the *words* "explain" and "predict" are used, even assuming that there is enough consistency and precision in their usage to make this lexicographic task feasible. And hence the verdict on the correctness of Hempel's symmetry thesis cannot be made to depend on whether it holds for what is taken to be the actual or ordinary usage of these terms. Instead, in this context I conceive the philosophical task to be both the elucidation and examination of the provision of scientific understanding of an *explanandum* by an *explanans* as encountered in actual scientific theory. Accordingly, Hempel's symmetry thesis, which concerns the inferability of the *explananda* from a given kind of *explanans* and *not* their assertibility, must be assessed on the basis of a comparison of H-predictive with H-explanatory *arguments* with respect to the measure of scientific understanding afforded by them. Thus, the issue of the adequacy of the symmetry thesis will revolve around whether there is temporal symmetry in regard to the degree of entailment, as it were, characterizing the logical link between the *explanans* and the *explanandum.* Specifically, we shall need to answer both of the following questions:

1. Would the type of *argument* which yields a prediction of a future *explanandum* event not furnish precisely the same amount of scientific understanding of a corresponding past event?

2. Does an *explanans* explain an *explanandum* referring to a past event any more conclusively than this same kind of *explanans* predictively implies the *explanandum* pertaining to the corresponding future event?

We are now ready to turn to the appraisal of the criticisms of Hempel's symmetry thesis offered by Rescher,

Barker, Hanson, and Scriven. In the light of my formulation of Hempel's thesis, it becomes clear that it does *not* assert, as Rescher supposes, that any set of C_i which permit a *predictive* inference also qualify for a corresponding *retrodictive* one, or that the converse is true. As Rescher notes correctly but irrelevantly, whether or not symmetry obtains between prediction and retrodiction in any given domain of empirical science is indeed *not* a purely logical question but depends on the content of the laws pertaining to the domain in question. We see, therefore, that Hempel was justified in claiming (ref. 9, Sec. 6) that Rescher has confused H-explanation with retrodiction. And this confusion is also facilitated by one of Scriven's statements of the symmetry thesis (ref. 13, p. 479), which reads: "To predict, we need a correlation between present events and future ones—to explain, between present ones and past ones."

In agreement with Sheffler,[15] Rescher offers a further criticism of the Hempelian assertion of symmetry: "It is inconsistent with scientific custom and usage regarding the concepts of explanation and prediction," for, among other things, "Only true statements are proper objects for explanation, but clearly not so with prediction."[10] And in support of the latter claim of an *"epistemological asymmetry,"* Rescher points to a large number of cases in which we have "virtually certain knowledge of the past on the basis of traces found in the present" but "merely probable knowledge of the future on the basis of knowledge of the present and/or the past."[10]

The question raised by Rescher's further objection is whether this *epistemological* asymmetry can be held to impugn the Hempelian thesis of symmetry. To deal with this question, it is fundamental to distinguish—as Rescher, Barker, Hanson, and Scriven unfortunately *failed* to do, much to the detriment of their theses—between the following two sets of ideas: (*1*) an asymmetry between H-explanation and H-prediction both in regard to the *grounds* on which we claim to know *that* the *explanandum* is *true* and correlatively in regard to the *degree* of our *confidence* in the supposed truth of the *explanandum,* and (2) an asymmetry, *if any,* between H-explanation and H-prediction with respect to the *logical relation* obtaining between the *explanans* and the *explanandum.* For the sake of brevity, we shall refer to the *first* asymmetry as pertaining to the *"assertibility"* of the *explanandum* while speaking of the second as an asymmetry in the *"inferability"* or *"why"* of the *explanandum.* In the light of this distinction, we shall be able to show that the existence of an epistemological asymmetry in regard to the assertibility of the *explanandum cannot* serve to impugn the Hempelian thesis of symmetry, which pertains to only the *why* of the *explanandum.*

If understood as pertaining to the *assertibility* of the *explanandum,* Rescher's contention of the existence of an epistemological asymmetry is indeed correct. For we saw in our Sec. 2 that there are *highly reliable* records of past interactions but no spontaneously produced records of corresponding future interactions. And this fact has the important consequence that while we can certify the *assertibility* or truth of an *explanandum* referring to a *past* interaction on the basis of a record *without* invoking the supposed truth of any (usual) *explanans* thereof, generally no pre-indicator but only the supposed truth of an appropriate *explanans* can be invoked to vouch for the assertibility or truth of the *explanandum* pertaining to a *future* interaction. And since the theory underlying our interpretations of records is confirmed better than are many of the theories used in an *explanans,* there is a very large class of cases in which an epistemological asymmetry does obtain with respect to the assertibility of the *explanandum.* But this asymmetry of *assertibility* cannot detract from the following *symmetry* affirmed by Popper and Hempel: To the same extent to which an *explanandum* referring to the past can be post-asserted *on the strength of its explanans* in an H-explanation, a corresponding *explanandum* referring to the future can be preasserted on the strength of the *same explanans* in an

H-prediction. In other words, you can post-assert an *explanandum on the strength of its explanans* no better than you can preassert it.

The entire substance of both Barker's objection to Hempelian symmetry and of Hanson's (1959) critique of it is vitiated by the following fact: These authors adduced what they failed to recognize as a temporal asymmetry in the mere assertibility of the *explanandum* to claim against Hempel that there is a temporal asymmetry in the *why*. And they did so by citing cases in which they invoke a spurious contrast between the *non-assertibility* of an *explanandum* referring to the future and the *inductive inferability* of the corresponding *explanandum* pertaining to the past. Thus we find that Barker writes (ref. 11, p. 271):

> It can be correct to speak of explanation in many cases where specific prediction is not possible. Thus, for instance, if the patient shows all the symptoms of pneumonia, sickens and dies, I can then explain his death—I know what killed him— but I could not have definitely predicted in advance that he was going to die; for usually pneumonia fails to be fatal.

But all that Barker is entitled to here is the following claim, which is wholly compatible with Hempel's symmetry thesis: in many cases such as the pneumonia one, there obtains postassertibility of the *explanandum* but no corresponding preassertibility because of the asymmetry of spontaneous recordability. But this does *not*, of course, justify the contention that a past death, which did materialize and is reliably known from a record, can be *explained* by reference to earlier pneumonia any more conclusively than a future death can be *inferred predictively* on the basis of a present state of pneumonia. For the logical link between the *explanans* affirming a *past* state of pneumonia and the *explanandum* stating the recorded (known) death of a pneumonia patient is precisely the *same* inductive one as in the case of the corresponding avowedly probabilistic *predictive* inference (H-prediction) of death on the basis of an *explanans* asserting a patient's *present* affliction with pneumonia.

It would seem that the commission of Barker's error of affirming an asymmetry in the why is facilitated by the following question-begging difference between the *explanans* used in his H-explanation of a death from pneumonia and the one used by him in the purportedly corresponding prediction: Barker's H-explanation of the past death employs an *explanans* asserting the onset of pneumonia at a past time as well as the *sickening* at a later past time, but the further condition of sickening is omitted from the antecedents of his corresponding H-prediction. Hence the spurious asymmetry of conclusiveness between the two cases.

It is now apparent that the valid core of Barker's statement is the commonplace that in the pneumonia case, as in others, postassertibility of the *explanandum* does obtain even though preassertibility does not. And once it is recognized that the only relevant asymmetry which does obtain in cases of the pneumonia type is one of assertibility, the philosophical challenge of this asymmetry is to specify the complex *reasons* for it, as I have endeavored to do in Sec. 2. But no philosophical challenge is posed for Hempel's symmetry thesis.

An analogous confusion between the assertibility asymmetry and one in the *why* invalidates the paper by Hanson which Barker cites in support of his views. Suppose that a certain kind of past measurement yielded a particular ψ-function which is then used in Schrödinger's equation for the H-explanation of a later past occurrence. And suppose also that the same kind of present measurement again yields the same ψ-function for a like system and that this function is then used for the H-prediction of a correspondingly later future occurrence, which is of the same type as the past occurrence. It is patent that in quantum mechanics the *logical relation* between *explanans* (the function ψ_1 and the associated set s_1 of probability distributions at the time t_1) and *explanandum* (the description of a *particular* micro event falling within the range of one of the s_1 probability distributions) is no less statistical (inductive) in the case of H-explanation than in the case of H-prediction. And this *symmetry* in the *statistical why* is wholly compatible with the following asymmetry: The reliability of our knowledge *that* a specific kind of micro event belonging to the range of one of the s_1 probability distributions *has* occurred in the past has no counterpart in our knowledge of the *future* occurrence of such an event, because only the results of *past* measurements (interactions) are available in records. Hence it was wholly amiss for Hanson to have used the latter asymmetry of recordability as a basis for drawing a pseudo contrast between the quantum-mechanical *inferability* of a *past* micro event—this inferability being logically identical with that of a future one—and the lack of *preassertibility* of the future occurrence of the micro event. Says he: [12]

> Any single quantum phenomenon P $\cdots$ can be completely explained *ex post facto;* one can *understand* fully just what kind of event occurred, in terms of the well-established laws of the . . . quantum theory. . . . But it is, of course, the most fundamental feature of these laws that the *prediction* of such a phenomenon P is, as a matter of theoretical principle, quite impossible.

Hanson overlooks that the asymmetry between preassertibility and postassertibility obtaining in quantum mechanics in no way makes for an asymmetry between H-explanation and H-prediction with respect to the relation of the *explanandum* to its quantum-mechanical *explanans*. And the statistical character of quantum mechanics enters only in the following sense: When coupled with the recordability asymmetry of classical physics, it makes for a temporal asymmetry in the assertibility of the *explanandum*.

We see that the statistical character of the quantum-mechanical account of microphenomena is no less compatible with the symmetry between H-explanation and H-prediction than is the *deterministic* character of Newton's mechanics. And this result renders untenable what Hanson regards as the upshot of his 1959 paper on the symmetry issue,* viz., "that there is a most intimate connection between Hempel's account of the symmetry between explanation and prediction and the logic of Newton's *Principia*."

It remains to deal in some detail with Scriven's extensive critique of Hempel's thesis. Scriven argues that (1) evolutionary explanations and explanations like that of the past occurrence of paresis due to syphilis fail to meet the symmetry requirement by not allowing corresponding predictions; (2) predictions based on mere *indicators* (rather than causes), such as the prediction of a storm from a sudden barometric drop, are not matched by corresponding explanations, since *indicators* are not explanatory, though they may serve to predict or, in other cases, to retrodict. And these indicator-based predictions show that the mere inferability of an *explanandum* does *not* guarantee scientific understanding of it, so that symmetry of inferability does not assure symmetry of scientific understanding between explanation and prediction.

I shall now examine several of the paradigm cases adduced by Scriven in support of these contentions.

1. Evolutionary Theory

Scriven [13] cites evolutionary theory with the aim of showing that "Satisfactory explanation of the past is possible even when prediction of the future is impossible."

Evolutionary theory does indeed afford valid examples of the epistemological asymmetry of assertibility. And this for the following two reasons growing out of our Sec. 2: (1) The ubiquitous role of interactions in evolution brings the recordability asymmetry into play. That asymmetry enters not only into the assertibility of the *explanandum*, for in cases of an H-prediction based on an *explanans* containing an *antecedent* referring to a *future* interaction, there is also an asymmetry of assertibility between H-prediction and H-explanation in regard to the *explanans* and (2) the existence

* See reference 12, p. 357.

of biological properties which are *emergent,* in the sense that even if all the laws were strictly *deterministic,* the occurrence of these properties could *not* have been *predicted* on the basis of any and all laws which could possibly have been discovered by humans in advance of the first known occurrence of the respective properties in question. Thus, evolutionary theory makes us familiar with past biological changes which were induced by prior *past* interactions, the latter being postassertible on the basis of present records. And these past interactions can serve to explain the evolutionary changes in question. But the logical relation between *explanans* and *explanandum* furnishing this explanation is completely *time symmetric.* Hence this situation makes for asymmetry only in the following innocuous sense: since corresponding future interactions cannot be rationally pre-asserted—there being no advance records of them—there is no corresponding preassertibility of those future evolutionary changes that will be effected by future interactions.

In an endeavor to establish the existence of an asymmetry damaging to Hempel's thesis on the basis of the account of a case of nonsurvival given in evolutionary theory, Scriven * writes:

> there are . . . good grounds [of inherent unpredictability] for saying that even in principle explanation and prediction do *not* have the same form. Finally, it is not in general possible to list all the exceptions to a claim about, for example, the fatal effects of a lava flow, so we have to leave it in probability form; this has the result of eliminating the very degree of certainty from the prediction that the explanation has, when we find the fossils in the lava.

But all that the lava case entitles Scriven to conclude is that the merely *probabilistic* connection between the occurrence of a lava flow and the extinction of certain organisms has the result of depriving pre*assertibility* of the very degree of certainty possessed by postassertions here. Scriven is not

* Reference 13, p. 480.

at all justified in supposing that *predictive inferability* in this case lacks even an iota of the certainty that can be ascribed to the corresponding postexplanatory inferability. For wherein does the greater degree of certainty of the postexplanation reside? I answer: Only in the assertibility of the *explanandum, not* in the character of the logical relation between the *explanans* (the lava flow) and the *explanandum* (fatalities on the part of certain organisms). What then must the verdict on Scriven's contention of an asymmetry in the *certainty* of prediction and postexplanation be in this context? We see now that this contention is vitiated by a confusion between the following two radically *distinct* kinds of asymmetry: (i) a difference in the degree of certainty (categoricity) of our knowledge of the truth of the *explanandum* and of the claim of environmental unfitness made by the *explanans,* and (ii) a difference in the "degree of entailment," as it were, linking the *explanandum* to the *explanans.*

Very similar difficulties beset Scriven's analysis of a case of biological survival which is accounted for on the basis of environmental fitness. He says:

It is fairly obvious that no characteristics can be identified as contributing to "fitness" in all environments. . . . we cannot predict which organisms will survive except in so far as we can predict the environmental changes. But we are very poorly equipped to do this with much precision * . . . However, these difficulties of prediction do not mean that the idea of fitness as a factor in survival loses all of its *explanatory* power. . . . animals which happen to be able to swim are better fitted for surviving a sudden and unprecedented inundation of their arid habitat, and in some such cases it is just this factor which explains their survival. Naturally we could have said in advance that *if* a flood occurred, they would be likely to survive;

* The environmental changes which Scriven goes on to cite are all of the nature of *interactions* of a potentially open system. And it is this common property of theirs which makes for their role in precluding the predictability of survival.

let us call this a hypothetical probability prediction. But hypothetical predictions do not have any value for actual predictions except in so far as the conditions mentioned in the hypothesis are predictable . . . : hence there will be cases where we can *explain why* certain animals and plants survived even when we could not have *predicted that* they would.*

There would, of course, be complete agreement with Scriven, if he had been content to point out in this context, as he does, that there are cases in which we can "explain why" but not "predict that." But he combines this correct formulation with the incorrect supposition that cases of post-explaining survival on the basis of fitness constitute grounds for an indictment of Hempel's thesis of symmetry. Let me therefore state the points of agreement and disagreement in regard to this case as follows. Once we recognize the ubiquitous role of *interactions*, we can formulate the valid upshot of Scriven's observations by saying: Insofar as future fitness and survival depend on future interactions which cannot be predicted from given information, whereas past fitness and survival depended on past interactions which *can* be retrodicted from that same information, there is an epistemological asymmetry between H-explanation and H-prediction in regard to the assertibility both of the antecedent fitness affirmed in the *explanans* and of the *explanandum* claiming survival.

This having been granted as both true and illuminating, we must go on to say at once that the following considerations—which Scriven can grant only on pain of inconsist-

* Reference 13, p. 478. In a recent paper "Cause and Effect in Biology" [*Science*, 134, 1504 (1961)], the zoologist E. Mayr overlooks the fallacy in Scriven's statement which we are about to point out and credits Scriven with having "emphasized quite correctly that one of the most important contributions to philosophy made by the evolutionary theory is that it has demonstrated the independence of explanation from prediction." And Mayr rests this conclusion among other things on the contention that "The theory of natural selection can describe and explain phenomena with considerable precision, but it cannot make reliable predictions."

ency with his account of asymmetry in the lava case—are no less true: The scientific inferability from a cause, and hence our understanding of the *why* of survival furnished by an *explanans* which *does* contain the antecedent condition that the given animals are able to swim during a sudden, unprecedented inundation of their arid habitat, is *not* one iota more probabilistic (i.e., less conclusive) in the case of a *future* inundation and survival than in the case of a *past* one. For if the logical nerve of intelligibility linking the *explanans* (fitness under specified kinds of inundational conditions) with the *explanandum* (survival) is only probabilistic in the *future* case, how could it possibly be any less probabilistic in the past case? It is evident that postexplanatory inductive inferability is entirely on a par here with predictive inferability from fitness as a cause. Why then does Scriven feel entitled to speak of "probability prediction" of *future* survival *without also* speaking of "probability explanation" of past survival? It would seem that his reason is none other than the pseudo contrast between the *lack* of preassertibility of the *explanandum* (which is conveyed by the term "probability" in "probability prediction") with the obtaining of postexplanatory inductive inferability of the *explanandum*. And this pseudo contrast derives its plausibility from the tacit appeal to the *bona fide* asymmetry between the preassertibility and postassertibility of the *explanandum*, an asymmetry which cannot score against Hempel's thesis.

2. The Paresis Case

In a further endeavor to justify his repudiation of Hempel's thesis, Scriven [13] says:

we can explain but not predict whenever we have a proposition of the form "The only cause of X is A" (I)—for example, "The only cause of paresis is syphilis." Notice that this is perfectly compatible with the statement that A is often not followed by X—in fact, very few syphilitics develop paresis (II). Hence, when A is observed, we can predict that X is *more* likely to occur than without A, but still extremely unlikely. So, we must, on the evidence, still predict that it will *not* occur. But if it does, we can appeal to (I) to provide and guarantee our explanation. . . . Hence an event which cannot be predicted from a certain set of well-confirmed propositions can, if it occurs, be explained by appeal to them.

In short, Scriven's argument is that although a past case of paresis can be explained by noting that syphilis was its cause, one cannot predict the future occurrence of paresis from syphilis as the cause. And he adds to this the following oral comment:

Suppose for the moment we include the justification of an explanation or a prediction in the explanation or prediction, as Hempel does. From a general law and antecedent conditions we are then entitled to deduce that a certain event will occur in the future. This is the deduction of a prediction. From one of the propositions of the form the only possible cause of y is x and a statement that y has occurred we are able to deduce, not only that x must have occurred, but also the proposition the cause of y in this instance was x. I take this to be a perfectly sound example of deducing and explanation. Notice however, that what we have deduced is not at all a description of the event to be explained, that is we have not got an *explanandum* of the kind that Hempel and Oppenheim envisage. On the contrary, we have a specific causal claim. This is a neat way of making clear one of the differences between an explanation and a prediction; by showing the different kinds of proposition that they often are. When explaining Y, we do not have to be able to deduce that Y occurs, for we typically know this already. What we have to be able to deduce (if deduction is in any way appropriate) is that Y occurred *as a result of* a certain X, and of course this needs a very different kind of general law from the sort of general law that is required for prediction.

I shall now show that Scriven's treatment of such cases as postexplaining paresis on the basis of syphilis suffers from the same defect as his analysis of the evolutionary cases: *Insofar as there is an asymmetry, Scriven has failed to dis-*

cern its precise locus, and having thus failed, he is led to
suppose erroneously that Hempel's thesis is invalidated by
such asymmetry as does obtain.

Given a particular case of paresis as well as the proposition that the only cause of paresis is syphilis—where a
"cause" is understood here with Scriven as a "contingently
necessary condition"—what can be inferred? Scriven maintains correctly that what follows is that both the paretic
concerned had syphilis and that in his particular case,
syphilis was the cause in the specified sense of "cause." And
then Scriven goes on to maintain that his case against
Hempel is established by the fact that we are able to assert
that syphilis *did cause* paresis while *not* also being entitled
to say that syphilis *will cause* paresis. But Scriven seems to
have completely overlooked that our not being able to make
both of these assertions does *not* at all suffice to discredit
Hempel's thesis, which concerns the time symmetry of the
inferability of the *explanandum* from the *explanans*. The in-
adequacy of Scriven's argument becomes evident the moment one becomes aware of the *reason* for not being entitled
to say that syphilis "will cause" paresis though being warranted in saying that it "did cause" paresis.

The sentences containing "did cause" and "will cause,"
respectively, *each* make *two* affirmations as follows: (i) the
assertion of the *explanandum* (paresis) *per se*, and (ii) the
affirmation of the obtaining of a causal *relation* (in the sense
of being a contingently necessary condition) between the
explanans (syphilis) and the *explanandum* (paresis). Thus,
for our purposes, the statement "Syphilis *will cause* person Z
to have paresis" should be made in the form "Person Z will
have paresis *and* it will have been caused by syphilis," and
the statement "Syphilis *did cause* person K to have paresis"
becomes "Person K has (or had) paresis *and* it was caused
by syphilis." And the decisive point is that insofar as a *past*
occurrence of paresis can be inductively *inferred from* prior
syphilis, so also a future occurrence of paresis can be. For
the causal relation or connection between syphilis and

paresis is incontestably time symmetric: Precisely in the way and to the extent that syphilis *was* a necessary condition for paresis, it also *will* be! Hence the only *bona fide* asymmetry here is the record-based but innocuous one in the *assertibility* of the *explanandum per se,* but there is no asymmetry of *inferability* of paresis from syphilis. The former innocuous asymmetry is the one that interdicts our making the predictive assertion "will cause" while allowing us to make the corresponding postexplanatory assertion "did cause." And it is this fact which destroys the basis of Scriven's indictment of Hempel's thesis. For Hempel and Oppenheim did *not* maintain that an *explanandum* which can be postasserted can *always* also be preasserted; what they did maintain was only that the *explanans* never postexplains any better or more conclusively than it implies predictively, there being complete symmetry between postexplanatory *inferability* and predictive *inferability* from a given *explanans.* They and Popper were therefore fully justified in testing the adequacy of a proffered *explanans* in the social sciences on the basis of whether the postexplanatory inferability of the *explanandum* which was claimed for it was matched by a corresponding predictive inferability, either inductive or deductive, as the case may be.

What is the force of the following comment by Scriven: In the postexplanation of paresis we do not need to infer the *explanandum* from the *explanans* à la Hempel and Oppenheim, because we know this already from prior records (observations) of one kind or another; what we do need to infer instead is that the *explanandum* event occurred *as a result of* the cause (necessary condition) given by the *explanans,* an inference which does *not* allow us to *predict* (i.e., preassert) the *explanandum* event? This comment of Scriven's proves only that here there is record-based post-assertibility of paresis but no corresponding preassertibility.

In short, Scriven's invocation of the paresis case, just like his citation of the cases from evolutionary theory, founders on the fact that he has confused an *epistemological* asymmetry with a *logical* one. To this charge, Scriven has replied irrelevantly that he has been at great pains in his writings— as, for example, in his discussion of the barometer case which I shall discuss below—to distinguish valid arguments based on true premises which do qualify as scientific explanations from those which do not so qualify. This reply is irrelevant, since Scriven's *caveat* against identifying (confusing) arguments based on true premises which are both valid and explanatory with those which are valid without being explanatory does not at all show that he made the following crucial distinction here at issue—the distinction between (1) a difference (asymmetry) in the assertibility of either a conclusion (*explanandum*) or a premise (*explanans*), and (2) a difference (asymmetry) in the inferability of the *explanandum* from its *explanans*. Although the distinction which Scriven does make cannot serve to mitigate the confusion with which I have charged him, his distinction merits examination in its own right.

To deal with it, I shall first consider examples given by him which involve *non*predictive valid deductive arguments to which he denies the status of being explanatory arguments. And I shall then conclude my refutation of Scriven's critique of Hempel's thesis by discussing the following paradigm case of his: the deductively valid *predictive* inference of a storm from a sudden barometric drop, which he adduces in an endeavor to show that such a valid deductive inference could not possibly qualify as a post*explanation* of a storm.

It would be agreed on all sides, I take it, that no *scientific understanding* is afforded by the deduction of an *explanandum* from itself even though such a deduction is a species of valid inference. Hence it can surely be granted that the class of valid deductive arguments whose conclusion is an *explanandum* referring to some event or other is wider than the class of valid deductive arguments affording scientific understanding of the *explanandum* event. But it is a quite different matter to claim, as Scriven does, that no *scientific* *understanding* is provided by those valid deductive arguments which ordinary usage would not allow us to call "explanations." For example, Scriven cites the following case suggested by Bromberger and discussed by Hempel: [*] The height of a flagpole is deducible from the length of its shadow and a measurement of the angle of the sun taken in conjunction with the principles of geometrical optics, but the height of the flagpole could not thereby be said to have been "explained." Or take the case of a rectilinear triangle in physical space for which Euclidean geometry is presumed to hold, and let it be given that two of the angles are 37° and 59°, respectively. Then it can be deductively inferred that the third angle is one of 84°, but according to Scriven, this would not constitute an explanation of the magnitude of the third angle.

Exactly what is shown by the flagpole and angle cases concerning the relation between valid deductive arguments which furnish scientific understanding and those which, according to ordinary usage, would qualify as "explanations"? I maintain that while differing in one respect from what are usually called "explanations," the aforementioned valid deductive arguments yielding the height of the flagpole and the magnitude of the third angle provide scientific understanding no less than "explanations" do. And my reasons for this contention are the following.

In the flagpole case, for example, the *explanandum* (stating the height of the flagpole) can be deduced from two different kinds of premises: (i) an *explanans* of the type familiar from geometrical optics and involving laws of co-existence rather than laws of succession, antecedent events playing no role in the *explanans*, and (ii) an *explanans* involving causally antecedent events and laws of succession and referring to the temporal genesis of the flagpole as an artifact. But is this difference between the kinds of premises from which the *explanandum* is deducible a basis for claim-

[*] Reference 9, Sec. 4.

ing that the coexistence-law type of *explanans* provides less *scientific understanding* than does the law-of-succession type of *explanans*? I reply: Certainly not. And I hasten to point out that the difference between *preaxiomatized* and axiomatized geometry conveys the measure of the scientific understanding provided by the *geometrical* account given in the flagpole and angle cases on the basis of laws of coexistence. But is it not true, after all, that ordinary usage countenances the use of the term "explanation" only in cases employing causal antecedents and laws of succession in the *explanans*? To this I say: This *terminological* fact is as unavailing here as it is philosophically unedifying.

Finally, we turn to Scriven's citation of cases of deductively valid predictive inferences which, in his view, invalidate Hempel's thesis because they could not possibly also qualify as postexplanations.

3. *The Barometer Case*

Scriven writes: [13]

What we are trying to provide when making a prediction is simply a claim that, at a certain time, an event or state of affairs will occur. In explanation we are looking for a cause, an event that not only occurred earlier but stands in a special relation to the other event. Roughly speaking, the prediction requires only a correlation, the explanation more. This difference has as one consequence the possibility of making predictions from indicators other than causes—for example, predicting a storm from a sudden drop in the barometric pressure. Clearly we could not say that the drop in pressure in our house caused the storm: it merely presaged it. So we can sometimes predict what we cannot explain.

Other cases of the barometer type are cases such as the presaging of mumps by its symptoms and the presaging of a weather change by rheumatic pains.

When we make a predictive inference of a storm from a sudden barometric drop, we are inferring an effect of a particular cause from another (earlier) effect of that same cause. Hence the inference to the storm is *not* from a *cause* of the storm but only from an *indicator* of it. And the law connecting sudden barometric drops to storms is therefore a law affirming only an indicator type of connection rather than a causal connection.

The crux of the issue here is whether we have no scientific understanding of phenomena on the strength of their deductive inferability from indicator laws (in conjunction with a suitable antecedent condition), scientific understanding allegedly being provided only by an *explanans* making reference to one or more causes. If that were so, then Scriven could claim that although the mere *inferability* of particular storms from specific sudden barometric drops is admittedly time-symmetric, there is *no* time symmetry in *positive* scientific understanding. It is clear from the discussion of the flagpole case that the *terminological* practice of restricting the term "explanation" though *not* the term "prediction" to cases in which the *explanans* makes reference to a partial or total cause rather than to a mere indicator cannot settle the questions at issue, which are: Would the type of argument which yields a *prediction* of a future *explanandum* event (storm) from an indicator type of premise furnish any scientific understanding, and, if so, does this type of argument provide the same positive amount of scientific understanding of a corresponding *past* event (storm)?

These questions are, of course, *not* answered in the negative by pointing out correctly that the law connecting the cause of the storm with the storm can serve as a *reason* for the weaker indicator law. For this fact shows only that the causal law can account for both the storm and the indicator law, but it does not show that the indicator law cannot provide any scientific understanding of the occurrence of particular storms. To get at the heart of the matter, we must ask what distinguishes a causal law from an indicator law such that one might be led to claim, as Scriven does, that subsumption under indicator laws provides no scientific understanding at all, whereas subsumption under causal laws does.

Let it be noted that a causal law which is used in an *explanans* and is not itself derived from some wider causal law is fully as *logically contingent* as a mere indicator law which is likewise not derived from a causal law but is used as a premise for the deduction of an *explanandum* (either predictively or postdictively, i.e., H-explanatorily). Why then prefer (predictive or postdictive) subsumption of an *explanandum* under a causal law to subsumption under a mere indicator law? The justification for this preference would seem to lie not merely in the greater generality of the causal law; it also rests on the much larger variety of empirical contingencies which must be ruled out in the *ceteris paribus* clause specifying the relevant conditions under which the indicator law holds, as compared to the variety of such contingencies pertaining to the corresponding causal law. But this difference both in generality and in the variety of contingencies does not show that the indicator law provides no scientific understanding of particular phenomena subsumable under it; it shows only, so far as I can see, that one might significantly speak of *degrees* of scientific understanding. And this conclusion is entirely compatible with the contention required by the symmetry thesis that the barometric indicator law furnishes the same positive amount of scientific understanding of a past storm as of a future one predicted by it.

I believe to have shown, therefore, that with respect to the symmetry thesis, *Hempel ab omni naevo vindicatus.**

4. The Controversy between Mechanism and Teleology

The results of our discussion of the temporal asymmetry of recordability have a decisive bearing on the controversy between mechanism and teleology.

* Believing (incorrectly) to have cleansed Euclid of all blemish, G. Saccheri (1667–1733) published a book (Milan, 1733) under the title *Euclides ab omni naevo vindicatus.*

By mechanism we understand the philosophical thesis that all explanation must be *only a tergo,* i.e., that occurrences at a time *t* can be explained *only* by reference to *earlier* occurrences and *not also* by reference to later ones. By teleology we understand a thesis which is the contrary rather than the contradictory of mechanism: All phenomena occurring at a time *t* (or, more narrowly, all phenomena belonging to a certain domain and occurring at a time *t*) are to be understood by reference to *later* occurrences only. We note that, thus understood, mechanism and teleology can *both* be false.

During our post-Newtonian epoch there is a misleading incongruity in using the term "mechanism" for the thesis of the monopoly of *a tergo* explanations. For in the context of the *time-symmetric* laws of Newton's mechanics, the given state of a closed mechanical system at a time *t* can be inferred from a state *later* than *t* (i.e., retrodicted) no less than the given state can be inferred from a state *earlier* than *t* (i.e., predicted). Instead of furnishing the prototype for mechanistic explanation in the philosophical sense, the phenomena described by the time-symmetric laws of Newton's mechanics constitute a domain with respect to which both mechanism and teleology are false, thereby making the controversy between them a *pseudo issue.* More generally, that controversy is a pseudo issue with respect to any domain of phenomena constituted by the evolution of closed systems obeying *time-symmetric* laws, be they deterministic or statistical.

But there is indeed a wide class of phenomena with respect to which mechanism is true. And one may presume that tacit reference to this particular class of phenomena has conferred plausibility on the thesis of the *unrestricted* validity of mechanism: Traces or marks of interaction existing in a system which is essentially closed at a time *t* are accounted for scientifically by *earlier interactions* or *perturbations* of that system—which are called "causes"—and *not* by later interactions of the system.

In view of the demonstrated restricted validity of mechanism, we must therefore deem the following statement * by Reichenbach as too strong: "We conclude: If we define the direction of time in the usual sense, there is no finality, and only causality is accepted as constituting explanation."

References

1. H. Reichenbach, *The Direction of Time*, University of California Press, Berkeley, 1956.
2. R. C. Tolman, *The Principles of Statistical Mechanics*, Oxford University Press, Oxford, 1938, p. 149.
3. R. Fürth, "Prinzipien der Statistik," in S. Flügge, Ed., *Handbuch der Physik*, Vol. 4, Springer-Verlag, Berlin, 1929.
4. H. Mehlberg, "Physical Laws and Time's Arrow," in H. Feigl and G. Maxwell, Eds., *Current Issues in the Philosophy of Science*, Holt, Rinehart and Winston, New York, 1961.
5. A. Grünbaum, *Philosophical Problems of Space and Time*, Alfred A. Knopf, New York, to be published.
6. A. Grünbaum, "Carnap's Views on the Foundations of Geometry," in P. A. Schilpp, Ed., *The Philosophy of Rudolf Carnap*, Open Court Publishing Co., LaSalle, Ill., 1962.
7. A. Grünbaum, "Popper on Irreversibility," in M. Bunge, Ed., *The Critical Approach, Essays in Honor of Karl Popper*, The Free Press, Glencoe, Ill., to be published.
8. C. G. Hempel and P. Oppenheim, "Studies in the Logic of Explanation," *Philosophy of Science*, 15, 135 (1948).
9. C. G. Hempel, "Deductive Nomological vs. Statistical Explanation," in H. Feigl and G. Maxwell, Eds., *Minnesota Studies in the Philosophy of Science*, Vol. III, University of Minnesota Press, Minneapolis, 1962.
10. N. Rescher, "On Prediction and Explanation," *British Journal for the Philosophy of Science*, 8, 281 (1958).
11. S. F. Barker, "The Role of Simplicity in Explanation," in H. Feigl and G. Maxwell, Eds., *Current Issues in the Philosophy of Science*, Holt, Rinehart and Winston, New York, 1961, pp. 265–286 and the comments on this paper by Salmon, Feyerabend, and Rudner with Barker's rejoinders.
12. N. R. Hanson, "On the Symmetry between Explanation and Prediction," *The Philosophical Review*, 68, 349 (1959).
13. M. Scriven, "Explanation and Prediction in Evolutionary Theory," *Science*, 130, 477 (1959).

* Reference 1, p. 154.

14. M. Scriven, "Explanations, Predictions and Laws," in H. Feigl and G. Maxwell, Eds., *Minnesota Studies in the Philosophy of Science*, Vol. III, University of Minnesota Press, Minneapolis, 1962.

15. I. Sheffler, "Explanation, Prediction and Abstraction," *British Journal for the Philosophy of Science*, **7**, 293 (1957).

The Temporal Asymmetry of Explanations and Predictions

Michael Scriven, *Indiana University*

Introduction

In my address at the University of Delaware, owing to my early place on the program, I found myself in the delightful situation of presenting my opponents' position as well as criticizing it. In these ideal circumstances, one can prune out any irrelevant details of their position, such as those not completely devastated by one's criticism. Unhappily, the printed volume destroys this advantage, and I must allow them to speak for themselves. My detailed criticisms of Hempel's original position and his extension of it to "statistical" explanations, as given at Delaware, will be found in my papers in *Theories of History*, edited by P. L. Gardiner, and Volume III of *Minnesota Studies in the Philosophy of Science*, edited by H. Feigl and G. Maxwell. I understand that some reactions to these will be found in his paper in this volume.

Rather than repeat these remarks here, I am taking the discussion a stage further by examining some attempts to defend a Hempelian position by another protagonist. Although I express these in a way which requires no reading beyond this volume, the following notes from a war-correspondent's scratch pad explain the background of this skirmish.

Professor Grünbaum has taken up the cudgels for Professor Hempel, and a paper by him in this vein, with my comments on an earlier version of it, will be found in *Philosophy of Science*, April, 1962. The first draft of that paper was criticized by me, at Professor Grünbaum's request, and substantial changes made before it was read at a symposium at Wesleyan in 1961. My comments in *Philosophy of Science* apply to the paper read, and published in the proceedings of that conference. Prior to publication in *Philosophy of Science*, he incorporated still further changes which he felt (quite rightly) bring us nearer together, and I am here commenting on this third version of his paper, in the hope of further clarifying the remaining important issues between us. The next rematch is to occur, I believe, at the Western Division meetings of the American Philosophical Association in May, 1962. Proceeds from the gate and television rights go to the Socrates-Schlick fund for the orphans of philosophers killed in the line of duty.

1. Types of Possible Inferential Asymmetry

Professor Grünbaum begins by rightly stressing the difference between two kinds of temporal asymmetry:

I. It might be possible to infer from the evidence available at time t_0 to the *prior* existence of certain states (retrodiction), although one cannot, at t_0, make the corresponding inference about *future* states (prediction). (Or the converse might hold: I'.)

II. It might be possible to explain an event E occurring at t_0 in terms of certain prior states, although one could not have predicted E at the time of and given knowledge of the occurrence of these earlier states. (Or the converse: II'.)

2. Actual Asymmetries

Professor Grünbaum, I think, regards only type I as respectable. It is my view that situations of all four kinds exist; examples follow, his being used to illustrate type I.

I: Robinson Crusoe finds a naked footprint on the beach; he infers with virtual certainty that someone besides himself has passed that way. He cannot properly infer that someone will do so again: It is *possible*, but not even *likely* in the absence of further evidence.

I': When cows lie down in the Scottish fields in the morning, we can infer with considerable reliability that it will rain by sunset. But we cannot retrodict anything about rain in some similar interval of the past.

II: Suppose we know that primary syphilis only leads to the tertiary condition, paresis, once in 5000 cases, but also know that paresis, when it does occur, can only be due to the spread of a prior syphilitic infection. Then we can give a causal explanation of the occurrence of paresis (E) in a particular patient as being due to his earlier condition of syphilis, although at the time of that earlier condition we would not be able to predict E—indeed, we would confidently and rationally predict that E would not occur. (Evolutionary biology and history afford other examples.)

II': The barometer falls sharply in the tropics after holding high: We can predict a storm (E), but when the storm has come, we cannot explain its occurrence in terms of the barometer's behavior—we need a great deal more knowledge about the nature and genesis of storms. (I' can also serve as an example of case II'.)

3. The Prediction–Retrodiction Asymmetries

It is Professor Grünbaum's contention, if I understand him rightly, that only types I and I' exist and that type I' is "an exception." He gives a very abstract account of the conditions which make these asymmetries possible in terms of entropy. I do not agree with all of it, and am unclear how much of it (if any) illuminates the logical issue. To avoid excessive diversion, I only comment that I think the matter rather simpler than he does. If we have laws of the form:

$$E\text{'s are always preceded by } P\text{'s} \qquad (A)$$

connecting variables for which a law of the form

$$E\text{'s are always succeeded by } P\text{'s} \qquad (B)$$

does not hold, then retrodiction will be possible when prediction is not: case I. The converse gives case I'. Since there are many conditions which are necessary conditions for something which is not a sufficient condition for them, and conversely, such cases are common. I am certain reference to statistical thermodynamics is not necessary to accommodate such possibilities and hence I am unclear of the value of bringing it in. Moreover, I must confess that I find his argument for regarding cases of the type I′ as "exceptional" entirely unconvincing. In his account, predictions by humans —whether reasoned or intuitive—are also said to be exceptions to his general condition that asymmetries of type I, but not of type I′, are normal. I find the argument there no more convincing, but bypass detailed comment as irrelevant to the main purpose of this paper, for Professor Grünbaum does not now deny that cases like I′ *exist* even if he feels they are atypical. In this respect, we are certainly closer than at Wesleyan, and I take this to be the first gain in the battle for the three asymmetries (out of four) that he originally regarded as illegitimate.

4. The Explanation–Prediction Asymmetries

In Hempel's account of prediction, some retrodictions are predictions. I take this to be one strike against the account. Professor Grünbaum takes it to be grounds for introducing the term "Hempelian prediction" and saying that Hempel's claim was that some retrodictions are H-predictions, not predictions. So they are, but if, whenever Jones makes an error in analyzing kerfloodles we introduce the term J-kerfloodle and say he was really and correctly talking about them, we abandon the criterion of truth. Jones was talking about kerfloodles, and he got them wrong; i.e., J-kerfloodles aren't the original article and should be returned to the store. Of course, some replacements are better value than the original, but I haven't seen anyone producing the performance figures to prove that point here.

I am *not* arguing that every little verbal distinction is sacred. Suppose H-predictions did not include retrodictions, but they did include what I shall now call "postdictions," then I would raise virtually no serious objections. A postdiction, in my sense, is an inference from the data of t_0 to a later occurrence at t_1, *made at* t_2 $(t_2 > t_1)$. E.g., we now infer that an eclipse occurred in B.C. 307 from Babylonian data of an earlier period. This is not prediction, but it does appear to be identical in every respect that is relevant to a discussion of inference. No such claim can be made about retrodiction because *the laws used there are, of necessity, temporally reversed* compared to those used in prediction. That is obviously a relevant and serious difference if we are talking about temporal symmetries.

The attacks in the literature on "the symmetry thesis" as I have called it, are *not* attacks on the symmetry of H-predictions (which include retrodictions) and H-explanations (which include completely non-explanatory inferences and exclude most scientific explanations). This symmetry may well exist. They have been attacks on the Hempel-Popper claim that sound predictions and sound explanations, in science particularly, are temporally symmetrical, i.e., "an explanation is not fully adequate unless . . . if taken account of in time, [it] could have served as a basis for predicting the phenomenon in question" and vice versa. And they have consisted in giving examples or predictions which do not meet this condition. It is clear these examples cannot be dismissed by showing they are not examples of H-explanations or H-predictions *since that only shows the weakness of the H-analysis of explanations.* But Professor Grünbaum frequently attempts to refute these counterexamples in this way and for the reasons given I think no purpose is served by examining these comments. However, he sometimes makes comments of a relatively independent kind which we can benefit from discussing.

The most striking example of the first procedure involves the suggestion that Hempel's thesis was not about explanations but about "the inferability of the *explananda* from a given kind of *explanans*." * Of course, deduction is deduction and it is *certainly* true that Hempelian explanations and predictions are both deductive arguments, i.e., symmetrical with respect to inferability!

A. Non-Inferential Predictions

"A soothsayer's unsupported prophecy that there will not be a third world war is not of scientific significance . . ."; * hence we should concern ourselves with predictive *arguments* (of which the H-prediction is supposed to be a paradigm) rather than predictions *simpliciter*.

What does "unsupported" mean here? If it means "non-inferential," the predictions may still be of the greatest scientific importance, as we often have good grounds for thinking that someone else's judgments are sound even when their judgments are not arrived at as the conclusion of an inference whose details they have unveiled. Our grounds in such cases are evidence for the *reliability of the judge,* rather than evidence for the *inferability of the judgment.* If "unsupported" excludes both these kinds of evidence, the prediction will indeed be scientifically insignificant, but then it will not be typical of the class of non-inferential predictions which Professor Grünbaum wishes to exclude. We may indeed have scientifically good reason for *believing* what we say even when we lack scientific reasons for *saying* what we say. Now Professor Grünbaum's interest in excluding non-inferential predictions arises from his desire to demonstrate a formal similarity between predictions and explanations. If he could show that scientific predictions typically consist of premises and conclusions, and are not just statements in the future tense, this would, he feels, make them more like scientific explanations. Now I think scientific— or any other—predictions, *are* just statements about the future, and are scientific or not, depending on (*a*) their subject matter and (*b*) the degree to which they are confirmed.

* Cf. Grünbaum, this volume, p. 74.

Incidentally, since I think *explanations* are also often simple statements, not argument forms, the possibility of symmetry remains. The idea that predictions or explanations must or should be complex, stems, in my view, from a simple confusion between predictions or explanations and the many possible kinds of grounds we may have for them.

B. *Explanation and Understanding*

In the present (third) version of Professor Grünbaum's paper, we have for the first time a confrontation of the connection between explanation and understanding. It was previously assumed that H-explanations would automatically provide understanding, i.e., it was assumed they were in this crucial respect an accurate analysis of what we usually call explanations. This is no longer *assumed;* it is now *stated* (though the second formulation of it in the preceding sentence is mistakenly rejected), but unfortunately not *established.*

For it is clear that Professor Grünbaum identifies understanding with inferability: ". . . the scientific inferability from a cause and hence our understanding of the *why* . . ." * Alas, understanding is both more and less than this. In particular, the kind of understanding I get from a causal account is not proportional to the extent to which the statement of the cause implies the statement of the effect. As long as (a) I am justifiably certain the cause mentioned *was* the cause, and (b) I am only looking for the cause, I understand *why* the effect occurred. And I can get a from the fact that no other potential cause was present, by no means requiring (as Professor Grünbaum assumes) that the occurrence of the cause makes the occurrence of the effect likely.

Given two angles of a Euclidean triangle, we can deduce the third. I would say this was not an explanation and that it does not provide scientific understanding of the magnitude of the third angle. Professor Grünbaum maintains "that

* This volume, p. 85.

while differing in one respect from what are usually called 'explanations,' the aforementioned valid deductive arguments . . . provide scientific understanding no less than explanations do." * His grounds are straightforward: Some valid deductions not involving coexistence laws provide understanding; this is a valid deduction involving coexistence laws; coexistence laws have no special deficiency with respect to the provision of understanding; hence, this argument provides understanding. As a proof this suffers from the falsehood of the missing premise; viz., the crucial feature of the triangle example is the presence of a coexistence law. I have nothing at all against such laws, which I fully agree can convey understanding. The weakness here is much simpler: Typically, there isn't anything to be explained, there isn't something which we do *not* understand. Hence, the little deduction does not explain or provide understanding. It simply leads us to a piece of *information* we lacked. I may tell you the date of my birthday or let you read letters from which it can be inferred: This is not, usually, explaining something to you or leading you into understanding.

Given the drop of a barometer we can predict a storm; given the storm we cannot explain it by reference to the barometer's drop (case II').

Professor Grünbaum feels this is a dull remark about the common usage of "explain." We do at least, he thinks, obtain *some* degree of scientific understanding from an indicator law of this kind. His argument for this is analogous to the one considered above; but even if it were valid, he appears to be conceding a difference in degree of understanding which is certainly an asymmetry. He argues that indicator laws are empirical laws just as are causal laws, though it is true they are, in two senses, not as general; hence, they provide scientific understanding, though perhaps to a lesser degree. The missing premise is apparently that the crucial factor for conveying scientific understand-

* This volume, p. 90.

ing is providing an empirical connection. About this, all I can say is that such a premise *ought* to be missing. The barometer's drop does not explain the storm for the same reason that the spots do not explain measles; one cannot answer a request for the cause of E by producing a second effect of this cause, E'.

5. Mechanism and Teleology

The symmetry thesis settles this ancient dispute if one assumes (*a*) that mechanism is the claim that explanations are always in terms of past conditions, and teleology the claim that only future conditions are explanatory (of a certain class of events), and (*b*) that explanations are simply inferences from laws and particular conditions. It then follows that (i) both theses are false with respect to the phenomena of Newtonian mechanics, where inferences can be made in both time directions, and (ii) mechanism alone is true with respect to many trace phenomena. This is Professor Grünbaum's argument. I think *a* a sufficiently serious oversimplification to invalidate the two conclusions, even assuming *b*; and I have endeavored to show that *b* is false, here and elsewhere.

The conclusion (ii) is true, but on other grounds, and it is not incompatible with the same claim, also true, for teleology. Teleological explanations can be and often are perfectly good explanations without any reference to alleged mechanistic reductions of them. But support for that claim would take us far from the symmetry thesis.

Explanation and Prediction by Covering Laws

Carl G. Hempel, *Princeton University*

1. The Two Covering-Law Models of Scientific Explanation

In this paper, I propose to present two models of scientific explanation; to comment on the range of their applicability and, briefly, on their qualifications as models of scientific prediction; and to examine some of the criticisms directed against these models and some alternatives to them that have been put forward in the recent literature. I will refer to the models in question as the deductive-nomological, or briefly the deductive, model, and the inductive-probabilistic, or briefly the probabilistic, model. Both have been described in considerable detail in earlier publications,* and I will therefore be brief in outlining their main characteristics here; but I will add some new amplificatory observations.

The two models are intended to exhibit the logical structure of two basic types of scientific explanation, of two ways in which empirical science answers the question as to the Why? of empirical phenomena. The two modes of explanation schematized by our models have one important feature in common: Both account for a given phenomenon—for example, a particular event—by showing that it came about in accordance with certain general laws or theoretical principles—say, $L_1, L_2, \ldots, L_m$—in the sense that its occurrence

---

* For a presentation of the deductive model, with references to earlier proponents of the basic conception, see Hempel and Oppenheim [17]; a shorter statement of the deductive model and a reply to some criticisms of it, as well as a detailed account of the probabilistic model are included in reference 14; brief characterizations of both models are also given in references 12 and 13.

can be inferred from those laws taken in conjunction with a set of statements—say, C_1, C_2, . . . , C_n—which describe certain particular empirical circumstances. Thus, the two modes of explanation agree in accounting for a given phenomenon by reference to what, following Dray's example, I will call *covering laws;* I will accordingly refer to both of the corresponding models as *covering-law models* of scientific explanation.*

The difference between the two types of explanation represented by those models lies in the character of the laws invoked and, as a consequence, in the logical character of the inference that links the statement of the phenomenon in question to the explanatory information. A deductive-nomological explanation is based on laws which express unexceptional uniformities; such laws are of strictly universal form, of which the following is a simple example: 'In every case x, without exception, when the (more or less complex) conditions A are satisfied, an event or state of affairs of kind B comes about,' or, symbolically, '$(x)(Ax \supset Bx)$.' Schematically speaking, a law of this kind might then serve to explain the occurrence of B in a particular case i by reference to the information that i satisfies conditions A. Generally, the deductive-nomological model construes an explanation by means of strictly universal laws as a deductive argument of the form

$$L_1, L_2, \ldots, L_m$$
$$\frac{C_1, C_2, \ldots, C_n}{E} \tag{1.1}$$

---

* Dray introduced the felicitous terms "covering law" and "covering law model" in his book, reference 6. To avoid a misunderstanding that might arise from some passages in Chapter II, Section 1 of this work, however, it ought to be borne in mind that a covering-law explanation may invoke more than just one law. Also, while Dray used the term "covering-law model" exclusively to refer to the deductive-nomological model, I am using it here to refer to the probabilistic model as well.

The premises are said to form the explanans; the conclusion, i.e., the statement E describing the phenomenon to be explained, is called the explanandum-statement or briefly the explanandum. For convenience the word 'explanandum' will occasionally be used also to refer to the phenomenon described by E, i.e., the explanandum-phenomenon; this will be done only when the context makes it quite clear which is meant.

Usually—and especially in the case of causal explanation, which is one variety of deductive-nomological explanation, —the particular circumstances specified in the sentences $C_1, C_2, \ldots, C_n$ will be such that their occurrence is prior to, or at most simultaneous with, that of the event to be explained. But some scientific explanations also invoke, in the explanans, certain occurrences that are later than the explanandum-event. Suppose, for example, that the path taken by a light ray between two points, P_1 and P_2, is explained by deductive subsumption under Fermat's law that a light ray's path is always such that the time required to cover it is an extremum: then the statements $C_1, C_2, \ldots, C_n$ will include, in addition to a specification of the refractive characteristics of the optical media involved, statements to the effect that the path in question did contain both P_1 and P_2; hence, in explaining its passage through a certain intermediate point P_3, which then constitutes the explanandum event, reference is made in the explanans to some later event, namely, the ray's going through P_2.

The kind of explanation schematized in (1.1), then, deductively subsumes the explanandum under general laws and thus shows, to put it loosely, that according to those laws the explanandum-phenomenon "had to occur" in virtue of the particular circumstances described by $C_1, C_2, \ldots, C_n$. This procedure is illustrated, for example, by the explanation of mirror images, the broken appearance of an oar partly submerged under water, the size of images produced by lens systems, etc., with the help of the optical laws of reflection and refraction; and by the explanation of certain aspects of the motions of freely falling bodies, the moon, artificial satellites, the planets, etc., with the help of the laws of Newtonian mechanics. Professor Hanson's discussion, in his contribution to this volume, of the HD (hypothetico-deductive) method in science suggests further illustrations; for example, his account of the HD analysis of the problem of perturbations can be used to construct another example of deductive-nomological explanation.

In an inductive-probabilistic explanation, on the other hand, at least some of the relevant laws are not of strictly universal, but of statistical character. The simplest statements of this kind have the form: 'the statistical probability (i.e., roughly, the long-run relative frequency) for the occurrence of an event of kind B under conditions of kind A is r' or, in symbols, '$p_s(B,A) = r$.' If the probability r is close to 1 then a law of this type may serve to explain the occurrence of B in a particular case i by reference to the information that i satisfies condition A or, briefly, that Ai. But this information, together with the statistical law invoked, does not, of course, deductively imply the explanandum-statement 'Bi,' which asserts the occurrence of B in the individual case i; rather, it lends to this statement strong inductive support; or, to use Carnap's terminology, it confers upon the explanandum-statement a high logical, or inductive, probability. The simplest kind of inductive-probabilistic explanation, then, may be schematized as follows:

$$\left.\begin{array}{l} Ai \\ p_s(B,A) = 1 - \epsilon \quad \text{(where } \epsilon \text{ is small)} \\ Bi \end{array}\right\} \quad \begin{array}{l} \text{confers high in-} \\ \text{ductive prob-} \\ \text{ability on} \end{array} \quad (1.2)$$

Let me give a simple illustration of this type of argument. Suppose that a blind drawing made from an urn filled with marbles produces a white marble. The result might be probabilistically explained by pointing out that there were 1000 marbles in the urn, all but one of them white, and that—as a result of thorough stirring and shaking of the contents of the urn before each drawing—the statistical probability for a blind drawing to yield a white marble is $p_s(W,D) = 0.999$. This law, in combination with the information, Di, that the instance i in question was a drawing from the urn, does not deductively imply, but lends strong inductive support, or high inductive (logical) probability, to the presumption that in the case i, the result is a white ball, or briefly that Wi.

It might be objected that after all, the explanatory information offered in this case does not exclude the drawing of a non-white ball in the particular case i, and that therefore the probabilistic argument does not explain the given outcome. And indeed, this kind of objection is sometimes raised. But it presupposes what seems to me a too restrictive construal of explanation: while in deductive-nomological explanation, the explanans does indeed preclude the nonoccurrence of the explanandum event, probabilistic arguments, which make their conclusions no more than highly probable, are surely often offered as scientific explanations. In particular, such probabilistic accounts play a fundamentally important role in such fields as statistical mechanics, quantum theory, and genetic theory. For example, the explanation of certain uniformities that hold at the macro level in terms of assumptions about statistical uniformities at the level of the underlying micro phenomena has basically the logical character just considered, although, needless to say, the details are vastly more complex.

It is also often held that statistical laws can account only for what happens in large samples, but not for what happens in a single case. But this view is not literally correct. Even statements about what happens in large samples can at best be made (inductively) very probable by the relevant statistical laws, but they are never implied with deductive certainty by the latter. In our illustration, for example, the statistical law that $p_s(W,D) = 0.999$ does not conclusively imply any non-analytic statement about the number of white marbles obtained in a given sequence of even 10,000 drawings (after each of which the marble is put back into the urn); rather, it assigns to every number of white marbles that could possibly be obtained in 10,000 drawings, and also to every possible interval—e.g., between 9000 and 10,000 white marbles—a certain, more or less high, probability. And some statistical laws, such as the one just mentioned, assign in the same manner a very high probability to a particular kind of outcome—in our illustration the drawing of a white marble—even for one single trial or test. The difference between a "sample of one" and a "large sample" is, after all, a matter of degree, and it is hardly to be expected that in the context of probabilistic explanation it should give rise to an essential logical difference.

A probabilistic explanation, then, shows that in view of the information provided in the explanans, which includes statistical probability laws, the explanandum phenomenon is to be expected with high inductive probability.

But suppose now that by way of an explanation for the occurrence of B in a particular case i we are offered the explanans considered earlier, consisting of the statements '$p_s(B,A) = 1 - \epsilon$' and 'Ai.' Then even if this information is true, it is still possible that i should also satisfy some further conditions, say A^*, under which, according to a further true statistical law, the occurrence of B has an extremely small probability. For example, in a particular instance of throat infection, it may well be the case that (i) the illness is a streptococcus infection, and the statistical probability of a favorable response of such infections to penicillin treatment is high, and also (ii) the streptococci in the case at hand are of a strain that is highly resistant to penicillin, and the statistical probability for an infection caused by this strain to respond favorably to penicillin treatment is extremely small. If both (i) and (ii) are known, then a quick recovery in the case at hand surely cannot be reasonably explained by simply adducing the information mentioned under (i), even though this does confer a high probability upon the explanandum. Generally speaking: If a probabilistic explanation is to be rationally acceptable, no further information must be available whose inclusion in the explanans would change the probability of the explanandum. In other words, a rationally acceptable probabilistic explanation must satisfy what Carnap has called the requirement of total evidence; i.e., its explanans must include all the available information that is inductively relevant to the explanandum. In a deductive explanation, whose explanans logically implies the explanandum and thus confers upon it the logical probability 1, and whose deductive conclusiveness remains unchanged if to the explanans any further available information is added, the requirement of total evidence is always trivially satisfied.*

These, then, are the two covering-law models of explanation. What is the scope of their applicability? Do they account for all kinds of scientific explanation? It seems to me that between them, they accommodate all the explanations typically provided by the physical sciences; at any rate, I am not aware of any explanation in this area that cannot be quite satisfactorily construed as an instance—which may, however, be elliptically formulated—of deductive or of probabilistic explanation as they are schematically construed in those models.

The issue becomes more controversial when we turn to other branches of empirical science. Indeed, it is widely held that in order to do justice to their characteristic subject matters and their peculiar objectives, some of those other branches must, and do, resort to explanatory methods *sui generis*. For example, biology has been said to require teleological concepts and hypotheses in order to be able to account for regeneration, reproduction, homeostasis, and various other phenomena typically found in living organisms; and the resulting explanations have been held to be fundamentally different from the kinds of explanation offered by physics and chemistry.

Now indeed, some kinds of teleological explanation which have been suggested for biological phenomena fit neither

* This point is discussed more fully and precisely in reference 14, Secs. 10 and 11.

of the covering-law models. This is true, for example, of vitalistic and neo-vitalistic accounts couched in terms of vital forces, entelechies, or similar agents, which are assumed to safeguard or restore the normal functioning of a biological system as far as this is possible without violation of physical or chemical laws. The trouble with explanations of this type—in sharp contrast, for example, to explanations invoking gravitational or electromagnetic forces—is that they include no general statements indicating under what conditions, and in what specific manner, an entelechy will go into action, and within what range of possible interferences with a biological system it will succeed in safeguarding or restoring the system's normal way of functioning. Consequently, these explanations do not tell us—not even in terms of probabilistic laws—what to expect in any given case, and thus they give us no insight into biological phenomena, no understanding of them (even though they may have a certain intuitive appeal); and precisely for this reason, they are worthless for scientific purposes and have, in fact, been abandoned by biologists. The reason for their failure does not lie, of course, in the assumption that entelechies are invisible and indeed noncorporeal entities; for neither are the gravitational or electromagnetic fields of classical theory visible or corporeal, and yet they provide the basis for important scientific explanations. For those field concepts function in the context of a set of general laws and theoretical principles which specify, among other things, under what conditions fields of what characteristics will arise, and what their effects will be, say, on the motion of a given macrophysical object or on an elementary particle. It is precisely the lack of corresponding laws or theoretical principles for entelechies which deprives the latter concept of all explanatory force.

But while vitalistic accounts have had to be discarded, very promising advances towards a scientific understanding of some of the biological phenomena in question have been made with the help of physical and chemical theory, cybernetic and information-theoretical principles, and other means; but these approaches all lend themselves to analysis in terms of the covering-law models.

Several other branches of empirical science use interesting explanatory methods that appear to be distinctly their own. There is, for example, the method of functional analysis as used in cultural anthropology and sociology; there is the method, used by historians among others, of explaining deliberate human actions by reference to motivating reasons; there are the psychoanalytic explanations of dreams, phantasies, slips of pen, tongue, and memory, neurotic symptoms, etc., in terms of subconscious psychic processes; there is the method of genetic explanation. Do any of these modes of explanation differ logically from those we have considered so far? It is impossible, of course, to examine this vast problem in the present context; but I will at least state the answer which I am inclined to give, and for which I have tried to offer support in other essays.[13, 15, 16]

Among the various explanations here referred to, there are some which lack the status of even a potential scientific explanation because they are entirely incapable of any objective test. This is true of neovitalistic and of some psychoanalytic explanations, among others; they do not tell us, even with probability, what to expect under any kind of circumstance. For this reason, they admit of no test and certainly do not offer an explanation of anything. Some other explanatory accounts—including certain instances of functional analysis—are couched in terms of testable empirical assertions which, however, offer no adequate grounds for expecting the occurrence of the explanandum-phenomenon; thus they violate what is surely a necessary, though not sufficient, condition for any scientific explanation. Still other "explanations" have the character of straightforward descriptions: they tell us that, rather than why, certain things are the case. But if we set aside accounts of these kinds, then the remaining explanations—notwithstanding great differences in the explicitness and precision with which they are formulated—can, I think, be accounted for as more or less complex concatenations of arguments each of which is of one or the other of the two basic types considered earlier; and all of them derive whatever explanatory power they possess from universal or statistical laws which they explicitly invoke or implicitly presuppose.

The assessment just outlined of the adequacy of the covering law models for the various sorts of explanation offered in different areas of empirical science implies, of course, no claim whatever concerning the extent to which scientific explanations can actually be achieved for the phenomena studied in different branches of scientific inquiry; and even less does it imply or presuppose universal determinism.

2. Predictive Aspects of the Covering-Law Models

In the preceding section, I appealed, at certain points, to a requirement which must be satisfied, it seems to me, by any account that is to qualify as a scientific explanation. I will refer to it as a *condition of adequacy for scientific explanations* and will now state it somewhat more fully, and then comment on it. The requirement is that any adequate scientific answer to a question of the type 'Why is X the case?' must provide information which constitutes good grounds for believing or expecting that X is the case. Of course, by no means all information that offers such grounds does thereby provide an explanation. For example, a report on the favorable outcome of a thorough experimental test of the hypothesis that X is the case may constitute good inductive grounds for believing the hypothesis to be true, but it surely provides no explanation of why X is the case. Thus, the condition of adequacy just stated is a necessary, but not a sufficient one. Indeed, we might add that the request for an explanation normally arises only when the explanandum-event is known or presumed to have occurred; hence, offering grounds for believing that it has occurred is not the principal task of an explanation at all; but it is nevertheless a necessary condition for its adequacy.

Explanations by covering laws, whether deductive or probabilistic, clearly satisfy this condition; and they have a further feature which seems to me characteristic of all scientific explanation, namely, they rest on general laws. In the explanation of an individual event, these laws connect the explanandum-event with the particular circumstances cited in the explanans, and they thus confer explanatory significance upon the latter. To be sure, in the usual wording of an explanation the laws often are not all explicitly mentioned. An explanation for a particular event, for example, may sometimes be stated by saying that the event in question was *caused* by such and such other events and particular conditions. But a causal claim of this kind presupposes causal laws, and the assumption of such laws is thus implicit in the explanation.

One consequence of the condition of adequacy I have been discussing may be stated as follows: In the explanation of a given event, the explanans must be such that if it had been known before the occurrence of the explanandum-event, it would have enabled us to predict the latter deductively or inductively.* This principle seems to me obvious, and indeed almost trivial; yet it has met with objections. One of these, advanced by Scriven, holds that there are instances of perfectly good explanations which offer no basis for potential prediction. By way of illustration, Scriven (ref. 23, p. 480) refers to the case where "we have a proposition of the form 'The only cause of X is A' (I)—for example, 'The only cause of paresis is syphilis.' Notice that this is perfectly compatible with the statement that A is often not followed by X—in fact, very few syphilitics develop paresis. . . . Hence, when A is observed, we can predict that X is *more* likely to occur than without A, but still extremely

---

* This formulation takes into account the remark, made by Scheffler (ref. 21, pp. 297–298) and by Scriven (ref. 24, pp. 179–181), that one cannot properly speak of "predicting" the explanandum-phenomenon if the latter is not an individual event but, say, a uniformity as expressed by a general law.

unlikely. So we must, on the evidence, still predict that it will *not* occur. But if it does, we can appeal to (I) to provide and guarantee our explanation." But surely, the information that patient B has previously suffered from syphilis does not suffice to explain his having developed paresis, precisely because paresis is such a rare sequel of syphilis. The specification of what might be called a nomically necessary antecedent of an event does not, in general, provide an explanation for the latter. Otherwise, we might argue, for example, that only individuals who are alive contract paresis, and we might adduce B's having been alive as explaining his having contracted paresis. Note that the probability for living individuals to develop paresis is positive, whereas for those who are not alive it is zero, just as in the case of the explanation by prior syphilitic infection.

It might be suspected that this counter-example simply is not an instance of specifying "the only cause" in the sense intended by Scriven. However, Scriven presents us with no precise criteria for what he wishes to understand by "the only cause" of a phenomenon. He does indeed indicate what he means by a cause [24]: "Speaking loosely, we could say that a cause is a nonredundant member of a set of conditions jointly sufficient for the effect . . . , the choice between the several candidates that usually meet this requirement being based on considerations of context. However, many qualifications must be made to this analysis . . . , and in the end probably the best view of *a cause* is that it *is any physical explanation which involves reference to only one state or event (or a few) other than the effect*" (pp. 215–216; italics mine). But—disregarding the point that, even according to Scriven, an explanation of an event is a certain kind of communication about it and must therefore surely be distinguished from its causes—the account thus achieved is simply circular, because the kind of *explanation* referred to in Scriven's paresis example is in turn characterized as specifying the only *cause* of an event. The same characteristic seems to me to vitiate Scriven's general analysis of causal explanation, according to which a causal explanation of a state or event X must specify "the cause of X," and must do so in a manner which meets certain specified requirements of intelligibility (ref. 24, p. 204). For since, as has just been mentioned, Scriven's definition of 'cause' is in terms of 'explanation,' his analysis of the meanings of the two terms plainly moves in a circle.

Among the objections that have been raised against the attribution of potential predictive import to explanations, there are some, however, which are aimed at the stronger thesis, put forth in an article by Oppenheim and myself,[17] that scientific explanation and scientific prediction have the same logical structure and differ only in pragmatic characteristics.* I agree with the observation made both by Scheffler (ref. 21, Sec. 1) and by Scriven (e.g., ref. 24, p. 177) that what is usually called a prediction is not an argument but a statement—or, more precisely, as pointed out by Scheffler, a statement-token, i.e., a concrete utterance or inscription of a statement,† purporting to describe some future event. Our thesis about the structural identity of scientific explanation and prediction should be understood, of course, to refer to the logical structure, not of predictive statements, but of *predictive arguments* that serve to establish predictive statements in science. But I would now want to weaken the thesis so as to assert only that the two covering-law models represent the logical structure of two important types of predictive inference in empirical science, but not that these are the only types. That there are predictive arguments that could not qualify as explanations has been asserted, for example, by Scheffler (ref. 21, p. 296) and by

---

* *Philosophy of Science*, 15, 138 (1948); p. 132 in reprinted text. For an earlier statement, see reference 11, Sec. 4.

† Cf. reference 21, Sec. 1; a fuller discussion of explanation and prediction in the light of the type-token distinction will be found in Kim (ref. 19).

Scriven (e.g., ref. 23, p. 480); the one type of argument in support of this claim that I find clear-cut and convincing is Scheffler's observation to the effect that scientific predictions may be inductively grounded on information that includes no statements in the form of general laws, but only a finite set of particular data, e.g., the results obtained in trying out a given die or a given roulette wheel a finite number of times for the purpose of predicting later results. Predictive arguments of this type, from finite sample to finite sample, clearly are not of the covering-law form.

The preceding discussion cannot, of course, do justice to all the comments and criticisms that have been directed at the theses here considered concerning the predictive aspects of scientific explanation. Several of the points I have been unable to examine here are very thoroughly discussed in Grünbaum's contribution to the present volume (p. 57); further responses to some of the criticisms have been put forward elsewhere.[10, 14, 19]

3. Some Misunderstandings Concerning the Covering-Law Models

In this section, I will survey briefly certain objections against the covering-law models which completely miss their target because they involve misunderstandings or even outright misrepresentations.

(i) In a recent essay,[22] Scriven speaks of "the deductive model, with its syllogistic form, where no student of elementary logic could fail to complete the inference, given the premise" (p. 462). He gives no reference to the literature to support this simple-minded and arbitrary construal, and indeed, this would be impossible; for the deductive model has never been conceived in this fashion by its advocates, and the general form (1.1) of the model clearly allows for the use of highly complex general laws—e.g., laws representing certain quantitative parameters as mathematical functions of others; and the deduction of the explanandum cannot, in such cases, be achieved by syllogistic methods, as any student of elementary logic knows.*

(ii) Referring to writings by Oppenheim and by myself on the subject of explanation, Scriven maintains, again without any documentation whatsoever, that the deductive model as characterized by us "fails to make the crucial logical distinctions between . . . things to be explained, and the description of these things," and he accuses us accordingly of an "incautious amalgamation" of the two †; he adds the diagnosis that "the most serious error of all those I believe to be involved in Hempel and Oppenheim's analysis also springs from the very same innocuous-seeming oversimplification: the requirement of deducibility itself, plausible only if we forget that our concern is fundamentally with a phenomenon, not a statement"; and he goes on to say (ref. 24, p. 195), "It may seem unjust to suggest that Hempel and Oppenheim amalgamate the phenomenon and its description . . . when they make clear that the 'conclusion' of the explanation is 'a sentence describing the phenomenon (not that phenomenon itself).'" In view of the passage he quotes here, ‡ and in view of the fact that the distinction between empirical phenomena and statements describing them is rigorously observed in all our publications, Scriven's suggestion does not only *seem* unjust: it *is* unjust, and indeed, it is an indefensible misrepresentation.

As for Scriven's remark that "our concern is fundamentally with a phenomenon, not with a statement," it is clear that—no matter how the logical structure of explanation may be construed in detail—an explanation will require reference to some explanatory "facts," and that these, as well as the

* This misconstrual is pointed out also by Brodbeck,[2] in an essay which includes a critical study of various aspects of Scriven's views on explanation.

† Reference 24, p. 196 and p. 195.

‡ The passage here quoted, which I had called to Professor Scriven's attention by correspondence, is from Hempel and Oppenheim,[17] pp. 136–137; p. 321 in reprinted text.

phenomenon to be explained, cannot be dealt with, in the context of scientific explanation, without the use of statements describing them.

(iii) Concerning the status of probabilistic explanation, Scriven (ref. 24, p. 228) speaks of "the mistake [Hempel] originally made in thinking that explanations which fit the deductive models are more scientific than statistical explanations." Again, the attribution of the alleged mistake is not documented, and it could not be; for I have never expressed that opinion. Rather, I have presented deductive and probabilistic explanation as different modes of explanation, each significant in its own right.*

(iv) Referring to my analysis of probabilistic explanation, Scriven comments: "Such explanations cannot be subsumed under Hempel and Oppenheim's original analysis as it stands, because no *deduction* of a nonprobability statement from them is possible, and hence it is impossible for them to explain any actual occurrence, since actual occurrences have to be described by nonprobability statements" (reference 24, p. 192). The first part of this sentence is misleading, to say the least; for neither Oppenheim nor I have ever claimed that the deductive model could accommodate probabilistic explanations. And the second part involves a misconception of statistical explanation: In schema (1.2), for example, the explanandum-statement does describe a particular and (if true, as we may assume it to be) an actual event. In an earlier article,[22] Scriven states his idea more explicitly: ". . . one cannot *deduce* from any law of the form 'If C then probably E,' combined with the antecedent condition E, that E occurs. One can only deduce that E

---

* The earliest references to the point are in Hempel,[11] Sec. 5.3; Hempel and Oppenheim,[17] pp. 139–140 (p. 324 in reprinted text); Hempel,[12] Sec. 1. The first two of these articles make only brief mention of probabilistic explanation and then concentrate on an analysis of deductive-nomological explanation; the reason being the difficulty of the logical problems posed by statistical explanation, as is explicitly stated at the second of the three places just listed.

probably occurs, and we are not trying to explain a probability but an event" (p. 457; italics his). But from the premises Scriven mentions, one surely can *not* deduce 'E probably occurs,' for this is not even a significant statement, any more than are such expressions as 'Henry is older' or 'line *z* is parallel.' For the occurrence of E can be qualified as probable or improbable, or perhaps as having such and such a quantitative probability, only relative to some body of information by reference to which the probability of E's occurrence is appraised. Hence, properly constructed, a statement about the probability of E's occurrence will take some such form as 'On information e, the probability that E occurs is high (or low, or has such and such a numerical value).'

This consideration indicates why, in our earlier discussion, the probabilistic explanation for the occurrence of *B* in the individual case *i* is not construed as an argument—deductive or otherwise—with the conclusion 'It is highly probable that *Bi*,' but as an inductive argument showing, in the manner schematized in (1.2), that '*Bi*' is made highly probable by the information adduced in the explanans.

(v) Scriven attributes to me, and expresses disagreement with, the assumption that "probability statements are statistical in nature" (ref. 24, p. 228). He does not amplify or document this attribution, which is seriously incorrect: I regard it as crucially important—and have said so explicitly in several articles—to distinguish, in the manner of Carnap, between two very different concepts of probability. One of these is the empirical, statistical concept, which figures in sentences of the form '$p_s(G,F) = r$,' or 'the statistical probability of G relative to F is r,' which means, roughly, that the long-run relative frequency with which instances of F are also instances of G is r. Thus, the statistical concept of probability represents a quantitative relation between two kinds, or classes, of events. It is this concept which is used in all probabilistic laws of empirical science, and thus in some of the premises of probabilistic explanations. The second concept of probability, the logical or inductive one, represents a relation, not between kinds of events but between statements, e.g., between the conjunction of the explanans statements and the explanandum statement in a probabilistic explanation. This concept is *not* statistical in character, and it is not invoked in the probabilistic laws of empirical science. Exactly how this concept is to be defined, and to what extent it is capable of precise quantitative characterization is still a matter of debate; a rigorous and systematic quantitative concept of logical probability, applicable to certain types of formalized languages, has been developed by Carnap.*

(vi) Another of Scriven's criticisms (ref. 24, p. 209) contends that "Hempel and Oppenheim never deal with the explanation of a particular event instance, but only with events of a certain kind." Since Scriven again does not support this contention, it is hard to offer a pertinent reply other than to point out that it is false. In setting out the deductive model in our article,[17] Oppenheim and I consider first "exclusively the explanation of particular events occurring at a certain time and place" † and then go on to examine the explanation of uniformities expressed by general laws.

I might add, moreover, that while both the deductive and the inductive model clearly provide for the explanation of particular event-instances—for example, Bi in a probabilistic explanation of the form (1.2), or a volume increase in a particular body of gas at a particular place and time, as explained by deductive subsumption under appropriate gas laws—they do not, strictly speaking, attribute a meaning to the notion of explaining a *kind* of event. For a particular event-instance can be represented by a statement describing it, which may become the explanandum-statement of a covering-law explanation; whereas a certain *kind* of event

* See especially Carnap, reference 4. A very clear general account of the basic ideas will be found in reference 5.
† See reference 17, p. 136; p. 320 in reprinted text.

would be represented by a predicate expression, such as 'is a case of a volume increase' or 'is an instance of drawing a white marble,' which clearly cannot form the explanandum of any covering-law explanation.

4. Different Concepts of Explanation

Since limitations of space preclude any attempt at completeness of coverage in this study of criticisms directed against the covering-law analysis of explanation,* I propose to single out for consideration in this final section just one interesting and important group of those criticisms.

As I pointed out at the beginning, the covering-law models are intended to exhibit the logical structure of two basic modes of *scientific explanation,* of two logically different ways in which empirical science answers questions that can typically be put into the form 'Why is it the case that X'?, where the place of 'X' is occupied by some empirical statement. Requests for explanations in this sense are often expressed also by means of other phrasings; but the 'Why?' form, even if not uniformly the simplest or most natural one, is always adequate to indicate—pre-analytically,

---

* The important recent discussions and new contributions with which, to my regret, I cannot deal in this paper include, for example, the precise and incisive critique by Eberle *et al.*[7] of the formal definition, set forth in Sec. 7 of Hempel and Oppenheim,[17] of the concept of potential explanans for languages which have the syntactic structure of the first-order functional calculus without identity. The authors prove that the proposed definition is vastly too liberal to be adequate. An ingenious modification which avoids the difficulty in question has been constructed by one of the three critics, D. Kaplan.[18] An alternative way of remedying the shortcoming in question has been proposed by J. Kim in one section of his doctoral dissertation [19]; his procedure is to be published in a separate article under the title "On the Logical Conditions of Deductive Explanation." Two other illuminating studies both of which raise certain questions about the deductive model of explanation, and which I can only mention here, are Bromberger[3] and Feyerabend.[9] Several earlier critical and constructive comments on the covering-law models are acknowledged and discussed in reference 14.

and hence not with the utmost precision—the sense of 'explanation' here under analysis, and to set it apart from the various other senses in which the word 'explain' and its cognates are used. To put forward the covering-law models is not, therefore, to deny that there are many other important uses of those words, and even less is it to claim that all of those other uses conform to one or other of the two models.

For example, an explanation of why every equilateral triangle is equiangular, or why an integer is divisible by 9 whenever the sum of its digits in decimal representation is so divisible requires an argument whose conclusion expresses the proposition in question, and whose premises include general geometrical or arithmetical statements, but not, of course, empirical laws; nor, for that matter, is the explanandum statement an empirical one. This sort of explaining, though rather closely related to the kind with which we are concerned, is not meant to be covered by our models.

Nor, of course, are those models intended to cover the vastly different senses of 'explain' involved when we speak of explaining the rules of a game, or the meaning of a hieroglyphic inscription or of a complex legal clause or of a passage in *Finnegans Wake*, or when we ask someone to explain to us how to repair a leaking faucet. Giving a logical and methodological analysis of scientific explanation is not the same sort of thing as writing an entry on the word 'explain' for the *Oxford English Dictionary*. Hence to complain, as Scriven does, of the "hopelessness" of the deductive model because it does not fit the case of "understanding the rules of Hanoverian succession" (ref. 22, p. 452) is simply to miss the declared intent of the model. And it is the height of irrelevance to point out that "Hempel and Oppenheim's analysis of explanation absolutely presupposes a descriptive language" (which is true), whereas "there are clearly cases where we can explain without language, e.g., when we explain to the mechanic in a Yugoslav garage what has gone wrong with the car" (ref. 24, p. 192). This is like objecting to a definition of 'proof' constructed in metamathematical proof theory on the ground that it does not fit the use of the word 'proof' in 'the proof of the pudding is in the eating,' let alone in '90 proof gin.' I therefore cheerfully concede that wordless gesticulation—however eloquent and successful—which is meant to indicate to a Yugoslav garage mechanic what has gone wrong with the car does not qualify as scientific explanation according to either of the two covering-law models; and I should think that any account of scientific explanation which did admit this case would thereby show itself to be seriously inadequate.

In support of his insistence on encompassing all those different uses of the word 'explain,' Scriven maintains, however, that they have the same "logical function," about which he says: "the request for an explanation presupposes that *something* is understood, and a complete answer is one that relates the object of inquiry to the realm of understanding in some comprehensible and appropriate way. What this way is varies from subject matter to subject matter . . . ; but the *logical function* of explanation, as of evaluation, is the same in each field. And what counts as complete will vary from context to context within a field; but the logical category of complete explanation can still be characterized in the perfectly general way just given" (ref. 24, p. 202; italics his). But while the general observation with which this passage begins may well be true of many kinds of explanation, neither it nor the rest of the statement specifies what could properly be called a *logical* function of explanation; this is reflected in the fact that such terms as 'realm of understanding' and 'comprehensible' do not belong to the vocabulary of logic, but rather to that of psychology. And indeed, the psychological characterization that Scriven offers here of explanation makes excellent sense if one construes explanation as a pragmatic concept. Before considering this construal, I want to indicate briefly why I do not think that explanation in all the different senses envisaged by Scriven can be held, in any useful and enlightening sense, to have the same "logical function."

One of the reasons is the observation that the objects of different kinds of explanation do not even have symbolic representations of the same logical character: Some explanations are meant to indicate the meaning of a word or of a linguistic or nonlinguistic symbol, which will be represented by an expression that is not a statement, but a name ('the integral sign,' 'the swastika') or a definite description ('the first pages of *Finnegans Wake*'); while other explanations are meant to offer reasons, grounds, causes, or the like for something that is properly represented by a statement; for example, a mathematical truth, some particular empirical event, or an empirical uniformity such as that expressed by Galileo's law of free fall. Thus, first of all, the logical character of the explanandum-expression is different in these two classes of explanations.

Secondly, the task of specifying meanings and that of specifying grounds, reasons, causes, etc., surely are not of the same logical character; and still a different kind of task is involved in explaining how to make Sacher Torte or how to program a certain type of digital computer. And while any of these and other kinds of explanation may be said to be capable of enhancing our "understanding" in a very broad sense of this word, it is worth noting that the requisite sense is so inclusive as to be indifferent to the important distinction between knowing (or coming to know) that p, knowing (or coming to know) why p, knowing (or coming to know) the meaning of S, and knowing (or coming to know) how to do Z. To be sure, the application of any concept to two different cases may be said to disregard certain differences between them; but the differences in the tasks to be accomplished by different sorts of explanation reflect, as I have tried to indicate, *differences* precisely *in the logical structure* of the corresponding explanations.

As I suggested a moment ago, Scriven's observations on the essential aspects of explanation are quite appropriate when this concept is understood in a pragmatic sense. Explanation thus understood is always explanation for someone, so that the use of the word 'explain' and its cognates in this pragmatic construal requires reference to someone to whom something is explained, or for whom such and such is an explanation of so and so. One elementary sentence form for the pragmatic concept of explanation is, accordingly, the following:

Person A explains X to person B by means of Y.

Another, simpler, one is

Y is an explanation of X for person B.

Here, Y may be the production of certain spoken or written words, or of gestures; it may be a practical demonstration of some device; or, perhaps, in Zen fashion, a slap or an incongruous utterance.

The pragmatic aspects of explanation have been strongly emphasized by several recent writers, among them Dray [*] and, as we have seen, Scriven. Indeed, the pragmatic concept may claim psychological and genetic priority over the theoretical nonpragmatic one, which the covering-law models are intended to explicate. For the latter is an abstraction from the former, related to it in a manner quite similar to that in which metamathematical concepts of proof—which might figure in sentences of the form 'String of formulas U is a proof of formula V in system S'—are related to the pragmatic concept of proof, which would typically figure in phrases such as 'Y is a proof of X for person B.' Whether, say, a given argument Y proves (or explains) a certain item X to a given person B will depend not only on X and Y but quite importantly on B: on his interests, background knowledge, general intelligence, standards of clarity and rigor, state of mental alertness, etc., at the time; and factors of

[*] See, for example, reference 6, p. 69, where the author says: ". . . as I shall argue further in this, and in succeeding chapters, there is an irreducible pragmatic dimension to explanation."

this kind are, of course, amenable to scientific investigation, which might lead to a pragmatic theory of proof, explanation, and understanding. Piaget and his group, for example, have devoted a great deal of effort to the psychological study of what might be called the conception of proof in children of different ages.

But for the characterization of mathematics and logic as objective disciplines, we clearly need a concept of proof which is not subjective in the sense of being relative to, and variable with, individuals; a concept in terms of which it makes sense to say that a string Y of formulas is a proof of a formula X (in such and such a theory), without making any mention of persons who might understand or accept Y; and it is concepts of this nonpragmatic kind which are developed in metamathematical proof theory.

The case of scientific explanation is similar. Scientific research seeks to give an account—both descriptive and explanatory—of empirical phenomena which is objective in the sense that its implications and its evidential support do not depend essentially on the individuals who happen to apply or to test them. This ideal suggests the problem of constructing a nonpragmatic conception of scientific explanation—a conception that requires reference to puzzled individuals no more than does the concept of mathematical proof. And it is this nonpragmatic conception of explanation with which the two covering-law models are concerned.

To propound those models is therefore neither to deny the existence of pragmatic aspects of explanation, nor is it to belittle their significance. It is indeed important to bear in mind that when a particular person seeks an explanation for a given phenomenon, it may suffice to bring to his attention some particular facts he was not aware of; in conjunction with his background knowledge of further relevant facts, this may provide him with all the information he requires for understanding, so that, once the "missing item" has been supplied, everything falls into place for him. In other cases, the search for an explanation may be aimed principally at discovering suitable explanatory laws or theoretical principles; this was Newton's concern, for example, when he sought to account for the refraction of sunlight in a prism. Again at other times, the questioner will be in possession of all the requisite particular data and laws, and what he needs to see is a way of inferring the explanandum from this information. Scriven's writings on explanation suggest some helpful distinctions and illustrations of various kinds of puzzlement that explanations, in this pragmatic sense, may have to resolve in different contexts. But to call attention to this diversity at the pragmatic level is not, of course, to show that nonpragmatic models of scientific explanation cannot be constructed, or that they are bound to be hopelessly inadequate—any more than an analogous argument concerning the notion of proof can establish that theoretically important and illuminating nonpragmatic concepts of proof cannot be constructed. As is well known, the contrary is the case.

On these grounds we can also dismiss the complaint that the covering-law models do not, in general, accord with the manner in which working scientists actually formulate their explanations.* Indeed, their formulations are usually chosen with a particular audience—and thus with certain pragmatic requirements—in mind. But so are the formulations which practicing mathematicians give to their proofs in their lectures and writings; and the metamathematical construal of the concept of proof purposely, and reasonably, leaves this aspect out of consideration.

I think it is clear then, from what has been said, that many—though by no means all—of the objections that have been raised against the covering-law models, as well as some of the alternatives to them that have been suggested, miss

* On this point, cf. also the discussion in Bartley,[1] Sec. 1, which, among other things, defends Popper's presentation of the deductive model against this charge. For some comments in a similar vein, see Pitt,[20] pp. 585, 586.

their aim because they apply to nonpragmatic concepts of explanation certain standards that are proper only for a pragmatic construal.

References

1. W. W. Bartley, III, "Achilles, the Tortoise, and Explanation in Science and History," *The British Journal for the Philosophy of Science*, 13, 15–33 (1962).
2. M. Brodbeck, "Explanation, Prediction and 'Imperfect' Knowledge," in Feigl and Maxwell, Eds., *Minnesota Studies in the Philosophy of Science*, University of Minnesota Press, 1962, pp. 231–272.
3. S. Bromberger, "The Concept of Explanation," Ph.D. thesis, Harvard University, 1961.
4. R. Carnap, *Logical Foundations of Probability*, University of Chicago Press, Chicago, 1950.
5. R. Carnap, "Statistical and Inductive Probability." Reprinted, from a pamphlet published in 1955, in E. H. Madden, Ed., *The Structure of Scientific Thought*, Houghton Mifflin, Boston, 1960.
6. W. Dray, *Laws and Explanation in History*, Oxford University Press, London, 1957.
7. R. Eberle, D. Kaplan, and R. Montague, "Hempel and Oppenheim on Explanation," *Philosophy of Science*, 28, 418–428 (1961).
8. H. Feigl and G. Maxwell, Eds., *Minnesota Studies in the Philosophy of Science*, Vol. III, University of Minnesota Press, Minneapolis, 1962.
9. P. K. Feyerabend, "Explanation, Reduction, and Empiricism," in Feigl and Maxwell (ref. 8), 28–97.
10. A. Grünbaum, "Temporally Asymmetric Principles, Parity between Explanation and Prediction, and Mechanism Versus Teleology," *Philosophy of Science*, 29, 146–170 (1962).
11. C. G. Hempel, "The Function of General Laws in History," *The Journal of Philosophy*, 39, 35–48 (1942). Reprinted in P. Gardiner, Ed., *Theories of History*, Allen and Unwin, London, and The Free Press, Glencoe, Ill., 1959, pp. 344–356.
12. C. G. Hempel, "The Theoretician's Dilemma," in H. Feigl, M. Scriven, and G. Maxwell, Eds., *Minnesota Studies in the Philosophy of Science*, Vol. II, University of Minnesota Press, Minneapolis, 1958, pp. 37–98.
13. C. G. Hempel, "The Logic of Functional Analysis," in L. Gross, Ed., *Symposium on Sociological Theory*, Row, Peterson and Co., Evanston, Ill., and White Plains, N. Y., 1959, pp. 271–307.

14. C. G. Hempel, "Deductive-Nomological *vs.* Statistical Explanation," in Feigl and Maxwell (ref. 8), pp. 98–169.
15. C. G. Hempel, "Rational Action," *Proceedings and Addresses of the American Philosophical Association,* Vol. XXXV, The Antioch Press, Yellow Springs, Ohio, 1962, pp. 5–23.
16. C. G. Hempel, "Explanation in Science and in History," in R. G. Colodny, Ed., *Frontiers of Science and Philosophy,* University of Pittsburgh Press, Pittsburgh, 1962, pp. 7–33.
17. C. G. Hempel and P. Oppenheim, "Studies in the Logic of Explanation," *Philosophy of Science,* 15, 135–175 (1948). Sections 1–7 of this article are reprinted in H. Feigl and M. Brodbeck, Eds., *Readings in the Philosophy of Science,* Appleton-Century-Crofts, New York, 1953, pp. 319–352.
18. D. Kaplan, "Explanation Revisited," *Philosophy of Science,* 28, 429–436 (1961).
19. J. Kim, "Explanation, Prediction, and Retrodiction: Some Logical and Pragmatic Considerations," Ph.D. thesis, Princeton University, 1962.
20. J. Pitt, "Generalizations in Historical Explanation," *The Journal of Philosophy,* 56, 578–586 (1959).
21. I. Scheffler, "Explanation, Prediction, and Abstraction," *British Journal for the Philosophy of Science,* 7, 293–309 (1957).
22. M. Scriven, "Truisms as the Grounds for Historical Explanations," in P. Gardiner, Ed., *Theories of History,* Allen and Unwin, London, and The Free Press, Glencoe, Ill., 1959, pp. 443–475.
23. M. Scriven, "Explanation and Prediction in Evolutionary Theory," *Science,* 130, 477–482 (1959).
24. M. Scriven, "Explanations, Predictions, and Laws," in Feigl and Maxwell (ref. 8), pp. 170–230.

PART III

Philosophical Aspects of the Foundations of Mathematics

What Do Symbols Symbolize?: Platonism

Alan Ross Anderson, *Yale University*

The dispute between nominalists and Platonic realists has been with us for a long time—long enough to have assumed many forms. I don't want to rehearse the history of these various debates, or even to look at the matter from a historical point of view. But I would like to begin by distinguishing two quite different skirmishes in the general battle, one of which is new, and one of which is very old. We begin with the new one, which is the clearest.

I

For the most recent form of the fuss we are indebted to Goodman and Quine,[9] but in order to motivate discussion of the issue, we have to go back to Georg Cantor, who in 1883 began to lay the "foundations of mathematics," as that phrase is generally understood at present. Cantor's contribution was to show the importance of sets (classes, bunches, aggregates, *mengen, ensembles*) in mathematics, and indeed to see that the fundamental notion behind our concept of *number* is that of a set, or collection, of (arbitrary) entities. We won't go into the theory of sets at any length, but it will be helpful at least to mention some of the concepts involved.

As logical apparatus we have the ordinary truth-functional connectives "and," "or," and "not," together with quantifiers "for all x" and "for some x." For the present purposes these can be thought of as requiring simply classical mathematical logic: the first-order functional calculus as in (for example) *Principia Mathematica*. But in addition to the logical machinery, we have a two-termed relation symbolized by ϵ, which is the relation between members (or elements) of a set, and sets of which these members *are* members. So that

$$x \, \epsilon \, y$$

is to mean "the entity x (which for all we know may itself be a set) *is a member of* the set y." And though (as I have said) I don't mean to discuss set theory at length, it might be worth the trouble to give a sample axiom of set theory to see what sort of thing is involved:

$$(x)(y)(\exists z)(w)[w \, \epsilon \, z. \equiv .w = x \vee w = y]$$

What the axiom asserts, essentially, is that given any two sets x and y, there exists a set z with the following property: Every w in z (i.e., every w which is a member of z) is either x or y. That is to say, given sets x and y, there is a set z which has as members just x and y, and nothing else.

There are other axioms for the theory of the epsilon relation; generally, about nine or ten suffice for most formal systems of set theory. But in all these formal systems there are variables, x, y, and z (say), which range over *sets,* or arbitrary collections of entities. And in particular, our sample axiom asserts that given x and y, *there exists* a set z (satisfying the stated condition).

Now what are we to mean by "set" or by saying that a set *exists?* How (apart from the axiomatic method) are we to say what we mean by "arbitrary collection"? It is immediately obvious, of course, that sets are "abstract entities": Sets cannot be kicked, pushed, or the like (though some sets have the property that their *members* can be kicked— for example, the *set* or *aggregate* of people in this room). But aside from the fact that sets are obviously not physical or material particulars, what can we say about the concept "set"?

The first attempt at an intrinsic definition of the term was Cantor's own. He begins his article [5] with the words

By a "set" (*Menge*) we are to understand any collection into a whole (*Zusammenfassung zu einem Ganzen*) M of definite and separate objects *m* of our intuition or our thought. These objects are called the "elements" of M. (p. 85)

From a philosophical point of view, one feature of the definition is immediately obvious: it is chockablock with metaphysics. We have "thought," "whole," "separate," "definite," "intuition,"—practically the whole zoo. This fact alone ought to warn us that difficulty is in the offing—but Cantor didn't feel the warning, and as a result the whole enterprise came a cropper with the discovery of Cantor's (and later Russell's) paradox. Russell's problem is easier to grasp, and does not depend on an elaboration of the theory. So we state Russell's difficulty as a paradigm case of the problems that are likely to result when one considers sets.

Ordinarily, we tend to think of a set as defined by a *condition.* That is, the set (collection) of presidents of the United States is defined by the following condition on *x*: *x* is president of the United States. In ordinary formal languages, the set of presidents is expressed as

$$\{x: x \text{ is president of the United States}\}$$

Now it seems clear that this collection, or set, is not itself a president of the United States—it is rather an unkickable abstract entity; that is what sets are. So the set is *not* one of its own members; i.e., it is not a president. And this seems to be characteristic of most sets. The *set* of all pianos is not itself a piano; the *set* of all fishes is not itself a fish; the *set* of all copies of *David Copperfield*[7] is not itself a copy of *David Copperfield;* and so on. We might think of a set as *normal,* if it is not a member of itself (as Russell did).

Now suppose we consider a set as normal under these circumstances: namely, a set is normal, or a member of the set *N* of normal sets, just in case it is not a member of itself, i.e., given any set *x*:

$$x \in N \qquad \text{if and only if} \qquad \sim(x \in x)$$

Russell's difficulty then arises when we ask whether the set N of normal sets is a member of itself. Suppose it is. Then it is one of those sets which is not a member of itself— so it isn't a member of itself after all. But from this it follows that it is a set which is not a member of itself, hence it is one of those sets satisfying the defining condition for normality. Hence it *is* a normal set, and consequently a member of itself. So we have a contradiction: N is a member of N just in case it isn't; i.e., we have a proposition ($N \in N$), which is true just in case it is false.

Now without making any pretense of historical accuracy, I think the dialectical content of the reaction to this unhappy discovery can be covered under the following two headings.

1. [Hilbert, Russell, Zermelo, von Neumann, Gödel, Fraenkel, etc.] The situation must be *fixed*. It is obvious that there *are* sets, and that our theory has an interesting and important intuitive content. But somehow the intuitions that led us to this unsatisfactory situation are in error. It is evident that there are some mathematical intuitions to be salvaged, and what we must do is to try to see what they are, and to formulate some theory or other that will enable us to state the *truths* involved, and let us prove them. This reaction led to set theory as we now know it.

2. [Quine, Goodman, perhaps White and Martin.] The situation is shot. There is absolutely no hope of repair, and indeed it is obvious what got us into trouble in the first place: Anyone in his right mind could see immediately that there are no such things as "sets," hence no such things as abstract entities. It is the assumption that we can allow our variables of quantification to range over allegedly existing "sets" which is at the root of the problem. There "really exist" nothing but concrete individuals, and once this is recognized we can see that the Platonic pretense that there are abstract entities is just what we have called it: a pretense.

This, then, is one version of the nominalist–realist controversy, and it is the version that has particularly occupied our generation. Of course a variety of Kantian conceptualism can be added as a further option; and though I do not plan to consider conceptualism, I cannot forbear quoting the following delightful remark of Quine's [11]:

> Tactically, conceptualism is no doubt the strongest position of the three; for the tired nominalist can lapse into conceptualism and still allay his puritanic conscience with the reflection that he has not quite taken to eating lotus with the platonists. (p. 129)

This first version of the debate concerns what I shall call a "calm" or "casual" sense of *existence:* We ask in a gentle and (sort of) everyday tone of voice whether there are any abstract entities. Platonists say yes; nominalists say no.

II

To introduce the second form of controversy I wish to consider, I will beg your indulgence in allowing me what may look like two irrelevant digressions, having to do with the anthropological category of *culture* and with senses of "exist." I shall try to establish the connection with Platonism later.

The first digression amounts to a summary of a forthcoming paper by Omar Moore and myself. The central ideas are two in number.

In the first place, ever since Tylor [12] introduced the notion of culture in 1871, there have been several sorts of things that the category was to accomplish. Without making any attempt to be comprehensive, we cite simply as examples some locutions in which the term appears: (1) Culture *diffuses;* (2) culture *persists* in a society; (3) cultural objects may be lost, and then rediscovered. As an example of diffusion, we may mention the oriental game of Gō, which is now played in some parts of this country. An entity that *persists* in a society is exemplified by a language, which, though it may undergo some changes, is still recognizable as "the same language" over a considerable period of time. And the Rosetta stone illustrates the case where a technique (namely, the technique of reading it) is lost to the world, and then rediscovered. True, most definitions of "culture" by most ethnologists would preclude them from saying the kind of things that they *want* to say about cultural objects. (They say that culture consists of "bits of behavior," which we note are *not* the kind of thing that can be "handed down from generation to generation"; or they say that culture consists of "all the things that a group of people inhabiting a common geographical region do," which would seem to make *eating*, rather than methods of eating, or of finding food, a cultural phenomenon—in explicit contradiction to the idea that human beings have *cultures*, but animals don't. For further polemics on the matter the reader is referred to Anderson and Moore.[4])

It seems at any rate that the following are examples of things that ought to be regarded as "cultural," in the sense that they can diffuse, persist, etc.: languages, games, methods for making canoes (or making computers; Moore and I have commented elsewhere with irritation upon the short shrift given by students of "culture" to the really elegant and high-powered cultural objects which influence our *own* lives so much), *baskets*, dances, and the like. This is the first observation we would like to make.

And the second is that *all* of these objects are abstract entities in a Platonic sense. No one can kick a jig (though one might kick a particular jig-dancer); no one can kick a method for making canoes (though one might kick a particular canoe-maker); no one can kick chess (though one might kick a chess-player); and no one can kick the English language (though one might kick a speaker). The cultural entities under consideration are one and all abstract. And it is easy to see that they bear an enormous influence on our lives.

This completes the first digression, the moral of which is that items of culture, which in a certain sense make us what we are, are abstract entities.

The second digression has to do with a certain ambiguity in the word "exist," on which I have already commented elsewhere.[2] When we say "That is a *real* collie," or "That is *some* collie," we don't ordinarily mean simply to be acknowledging that the dog in question is a collie. We mean rather to say that this particular animal measures up to collie-hood in a rather more satisfactory way than do most other collies. That is, sometimes when we say that a thing is *real*, or that it *really exists*, we mean to be approving of it, as somehow better, or more important, than other members of the same collection. Senator Kennedy was *some senator*, in a way that some others (I shan't try to cloud the issue with political controversy) weren't. (See Fitch,[3] which is not an article on Senators, but rather mentions the fact that sometimes "exists" is a value term.)

Now I would like to contend that a second version of the nominalist–realist debate has to do with this "honorific" sense of exist. To "exist" in this second sense, it is not sufficient to exist in the first "calm" or "casual" sense: One requires in addition that the calm existing be done in an especially good or approvable way. Existence in the second sense is ascribed only to those things that are *important*, or *really count*, or *really matter*.

Aside from the merits of either side, I would now like to think that I have distinguished sufficiently two forms of the Platonist–nominalist controversy: (*1*) What exists? (in a trivial sense, in which it is perfectly obvious to anyone that there is a blackboard in this room), and (*2*) what Exists? (asked in a deep tone of voice, indicating some anxiety as to what it is important to pay attention to). And though I have thus far tried to consider the issues impartially, I would like now to choose an option in both cases, namely, what I take to be the Platonistic one. We tackle the second issue first.

III

It seems to be a cultural, or sociological, or psychological *fact*, that people everywhere attach a certain special value to *permanence*. I think there are at least two sources of the feeling that permanent things are somehow better than things that change. In the first place, things that can be counted on to be there when we need them (parents, friends, etc.), and even things that we can count on to be hostile, so long as they are predictable (and in that sense have some permanent features), are somehow "friendlier" than chaotically changing, unpredictable, unstable things. The kind of thing that will scare the pants off a person is to meet someone wearing opaque dark glasses, who just stands in front of you and says nothing. What is he going to *do*? The ominous quality of this stranger stems, I submit, from the fact that we can't "read off," from his eyes or his talk, what his intentions are. Maybe he is a hood; maybe he is as benign as they come; what bothers us is the lack of predictability. We want to know what rules he is operating under, where (we pause to note) *rules* are Platonic abstract entities of the very first water. Even if we knew that he was hostile, we would be in a better position as regards knowing how *we* should act. Regularity, permanence, stability, order—these are the things that enable us to see what is coming, and (usually, if possible) to try to take countermeasures.

A second reason for the feeling that permanence is desirable is also a notorious anxiety-provoker, namely, the consideration of our own mortality. One almost gets the idea from reading some existentialist philosophers that they actually enjoy wallowing in this worry. (I am reminded of the fact that once when I was with R. N. Smart, he asked an existentialist colleague about a lecture he had recently heard, and our colleague said "It was *terrible!*" After he had left, Smart looked at me quizzically and asked "I wonder whether that meant that he liked it? You know—waves of *Angst* and *Beklemmung* whooshing over one . . . ?"

Some of us (Platonists), at any rate, like to believe that there are better things to think about, things that are better in two ways: (1) Things that are better to think about because we can *do* something about them (we seem to be able to do precious little about our mortality), and (2) things that are better to think about because they have this important property of permanence (i.e., the possibility of persisting through a much longer time than any of *us* will last).

Now it seems to me that when Plato asked "What Exists?" in the profound or honorific sense of "exists," he was just exactly right in latching onto cultural objects as being the most important for human beings. Languages, sets of rules (for games, or etiquette, or parking cars, or the Nō drama, or canoe-making, or the like), theories (of groups, or games of strategy, or Banach spaces, or braids, or the like)—these items of culture are just what make us human. The required property of permanence is present; cultural objects diffuse, are lost and rediscovered, and so on. And the problems are such that we can *do* something about them: Hilbert's tenth problem [10] has as famous a history as Fermat's last conjecture, or Goldbach's conjecture—and occasionally problems of this sort get solved.

Problems, questions, solutions are *things* we can bequeath to our progeny. We can also bequeath them money, and we are all of us, in our love for our progeny, gladly willing to do that. But our intellectual or cultural objects have to us, unlike money, a beauty that time cannot tarnish, that we cannot lose through ill-advised investments, and which nominalists cannot squelch; our cultural objects are *things*, in the best sense of the word.

I think that Plato, considering his own mortality, was dead right in thinking that the most important things about himself were the things we still have with us: his words. And if "to exist" is "to be important," then he has won that battle. The important things are the cultural things.

IV

But in the calm, or casual, sense of "exists," it seems to me that the matter is not even worth arguing. Of *course* the

Platonists are right. Imagine a man (Quine or Goodman of 1947) who, when asked whether he had played chess last night, said "Yes, and it was an interesting variant of Alekhine's Defense. Chess is one of the games I enjoy most." But then he suddenly coughs and turns pale, and adds, in a dispiriting tone of voice, "But of course I didn't *really* play chess . . . there aren't *really* any abstract entities, . . . so there is no such thing as chess . . . so that isn't what I was doing after all."

The claim that there are no languages, or no games, or no laws about parking cars, simply can't be taken seriously. The claim that such *things* are unimportant or uninteresting can be seriously considered, of course, and I think that such plausibility as nominalist theses have stems in part from confusing these two issues. But there are nonetheless (in the calm sense of "there are") such *things* as parking laws (as many of us well know). I don't mean to be recommending Plato's unhappy view that the forms or ideas provide standards of value. ["How do you decide whether it is a good ship?" "Well, you measure it against shipship." "How do you decide whether he is a good hood?" "Well, you measure him against hoodhood (or perhaps goodhoodhood)."] But it does seem perfectly clear that our language and (what language is a part of) our culture, demand that we recognize the existence of abstract entities.

Of course, one frequently hears that (in the casual sense of existence) we Platonists are "cluttering up the universe" with our abstract entities. Now there is no one who hates clutter more than I do, but as regards philosophical clutter, again it seems to me that the Platonists win. To adopt a point made to me by my colleague Omar Moore, the nominalists' universe is as cluttery as they come. Imagine having to take into account all those plays of a game such as chess. Surely no sane person would want to characterize chess as the collection of *plays* of the game, especially when we have von Neumann's elegant abstract theory of the matter, according to which chess is the set of its rules.

So as regards the calm sense of existence, it seems to me that the Platonists win hands down. In fact, the issue is one of the few I know of for which ordinary Aristotelian syllogistic reasoning *almost* suffices to establish a point of interest. We have the following:

(1) Chess is a game;
(2) All games are abstract entities;
∴ (3) Chess is an abstract entity.

The only non-Aristotelian step required to clinch the argument is to go from 3 to

(4) There are abstract entities.

V

But now if I am correct in holding that the Platonists are victors in both quarters, in both the easy-going *and* frenetic senses of "exist," we are still left with something of a mystery. Why on earth, in the face of these very convincing arguments of mine, should anyone have ever proposed a nominalist view of symbols? I have already offered one explanation of this oddity (namely, a confusion as to the two senses of "exist" involved); I shall now suggest two more.

The second guess as to why people might like nominalism has to do with the notion of *identity criteria*. We are told occasionally that the chief difficulty about possible fat men in the doorway is that there are no satisfactory identity criteria for them. How many of them (and which ones) are bald?[11] In this particular case, I am in sympathy with the objection, but the moral the nominalists have drawn seems to me to be in error. And this for two reasons:

1. It seems to be said by some that we *have* no identity criteria for abstract entities. Now this may well be true for possible fat men in a doorway (though I think that the problem is specious: "there is a possible fat man in the doorway" surely says the same as "it is possible that there is a fat man in the doorway," i.e., says the same as a statement of the form "it is possible that p," or "$\Diamond p$." It is true that there have been problems about identity criteria for propositions, but these problems have recently been licked, I claim, by Belnap and myself (see Anderson and Belnap,[3] and references there listed), with a ten-ton assist from Ackermann.[1] But even if we did have problems about identity criteria for possible fat men, it would still be true that we have identity criteria for extensional *sets*. Indeed, if there is one clear case where we know *exactly* what we mean by saying that A is identical with B, it is where A and B are (abstract) sets, and have the same members. For these abstract entities we have identity criteria *par excellence*.

2. It seems to be said also by the same people that though we have no criteria of identity for abstract entities, we *do* have such for concrete ones. Is this true? How do we tell whether A and B are identical when A and B are concrete? By pointing? Obviously not. Suppose I aim my finger generally in the direction of the chairman of this meeting. What am I pointing at? Him? His belt buckle? The color of his suit? Something on the other side of him? (He happens to be in the way.) Am I pointing at a spatial location just three feet away from him (toward me)? Of course there are sociocultural conventions about pointing at things, and if a great big crane goes by, and I point at it, yelling "Look!" there is little doubt in your mind as to what I am pointing at. But if you said "Do you mean the crane?" I might answer "Yes," or I might say "No, no, I mean the pile-driver on the end of it," or I might say "No, no, I mean the gull up above it," or . . . etc. And I don't know where this would stop. The point I mean to make is that I can point significantly to a physical object only if you can guess, or be told by me (with the help of *abstract* words), what it is I am pointing *at*.

What other criteria of identity for concrete individuals could we have? Identity of spatiotemporal location (i.e., of *sets* of spatiotemporal points)? That of course won't do nominalistically, since nominalistically there aren't any sets.

The upshot seems to be that we are in a miserable state as regards identity criteria for physical objects, and in excellent shape as regards certain abstract entities, namely, sets. So no nominalist moral is plausible in this second case.

The third and final motivation for nominalism is the only one that seems to me to have any plausibility, and for this way of looking at the matter I am again indebted to R. N. Smart. Plato asks "These two things are both red, aren't they?" And we say "Yes." And Plato says "Well, this means they have a common property, doesn't it?" And we say "Yes." And he says "And isn't this common property redness?" And we say "Yes." "So there are abstract entities, or forms, like *redness*, aren't there?" And again we say "Yes." And so far everything seems pretty innocent. But then as the discussion continues, we begin to be socked by the old Dialectic. It turns out that these forms, which we genially admitted as epistemological units, begin to pick up normative power, and provide us with standards of value. And we begin to say of a poor poem that it is not a poem at all, or of a sick man that he is not *really* a man. Or that *in so far forth that he is ill,* he is not a man (or a Man). And not only this; it turns out that some of these forms, like the form of the Good, have a sort of mystico-religious quality. Goodness shines on our behavior like the sun shines on our bodies.

Well, it is not hard to imagine a hard-headed philosopher going home after such an exercise and muttering to himself "That *can't* be right. *Nothing* could do that much work— not even Platonic Forms. Something has gone *gravely* wrong."

So the next day he meets Plato again, and Plato says "These things are both red, aren't they?" And Testadura * says, this time rather grudgingly, "Yes." Plato says "This

---

* Testadura is one of my favorite fictional characters; he is to be found in Danto.[6]

means they have a common property, doesn't it?" And Testadura says "Now hold *on!*" And thus is born a nominalist.

VI

The difficulties about Platonism stem *not* from the question as to whether abstract entities exist (of *course* they exist), or whether they are important (of *course* they are important); the trouble arises rather when one considers the *kind* of importance abstract entities have. Testadura is quite right in wanting to deny that the form of the Good has magical properties, but he stopped Plato too soon. We can admit with Plato that abstract entities exist, and that they are among the most important aspects of our lives, without giving them a magical character.

And this seems to me to be the nub of the matter. We *ought* to be able to say (Platonically) that there are good and bad performances of *La Gioconda*. The nominalists won't even let us have the opera. There are *performances* of it, from a nominalist point of view (though they can't tell us what the performances are *of*, there being no abstract entities, such as operas); but no such opera. Platonistically we can play some games; nominalistically we can't, since games are sets of rules, hence abstract entities. A nominalist will allow me to play my piano, but won't let me play any of Bach's *Partitas*. So before flying into a rage about these nominalistic restrictions, I will simply conclude by saying that I *like* operas, and games, and Bach's music, and in denying them to me, I think nominalists are simply being mean.

References

1. Wilhelm Ackermann, "Begründung einer strengen Implikation," *Journal of Symbolic Logic*, **21**, 113–128 (1956).
2. Alan Ross Anderson, "Church on Ontological Commitment," *Journal of Philosophy*, **56**, 448–452 (1959).
3. Alan Ross Anderson and Nuel D. Belnap, Jr., "First Degree Entailments," Technical Report No. 10, Office of Naval Research Contract SAR/Nonr-609(16), New Haven, 1961.

4. Alan Ross Anderson and Omar K. Moore, "Culture," *Synthese*, to be published.
5. Georg Cantor, "Beiträge zur Begründung der transfiniten Mengenlehre," *Mathematische Annalen*, **46**, 481–512 (1895). [Translated by P. E. B. Jourdain, in *Contributions to the Founding of the Theory of Transfinite Numbers*, Chicago and London, 1915, reprinted by Dover Publications, Inc., New York.]
6. Arthur Danto, "A Note on Expressions of the Referring Sort," *Mind*, n.s. **67**, 404–408 (1958).
7. Charles Dickens, *David Copperfield*, London, 1850.
8. F. B. Fitch, "Actuality, Possibility, and Being," *Review of Metaphysics*, **3**, 367–384 (1950).
9. Nelson Goodman and W. V. O. Quine, "Steps Toward a Constructive Nominalism," *Journal of Symbolic Logic*, **12**, 105–122 (1947).
10. David Hilbert, "Mathematical Problems," *Bulletin of the American Mathematical Society*, **8**, 437–479 (1901–02).
11. W. V. O. Quine, *From a Logical Point of View*, Harvard University Press, Cambridge, 1953.
12. Edward B. Tylor, *Primitive Culture*, John Murray, London, 1871.

Discussion

R. D. Gray (*University of Delaware*): You hold that Forms have no location in time and space, and in that sense, we must mean something a bit different when we say that abstract entities have an existence than we do when we say that this chair has existence. Is that correct?

A. R. Anderson: You mean, are we using different senses of "exist"? I myself would prefer to use the calm sense of existence to include both chairs and Forms. I think certainly there is a distinction to be made between the fierce sense of existence as regards the Forms and as regards the chairs.

Mr. Gray: Shouldn't we be a little careful about making rules for doing things to things that exist—if we don't actually mean the same thing by "exist" in the two cases?

Professor Anderson: From a logician's point of view, if you grant me two senses, exist$_1$ and exist$_2$, I can always fox you in the following way: I will define exist$_3$ to mean by definition, exist$_1$ or exist$_2$. Then exist$_3$ is the one I am interested in. I can grant you the distinction, and grant that for certain philosophical purposes it might be useful. I don't mean to deny that; but exist₃ is what I had in mind.

W. Reese (*University of Delaware*): You started out with Russell's paradox. Now does this constitute no problem for a Platonist?

Professor Anderson: In order to get Russell's paradox from standard logical systems, it is required that the following be provable. There exists a set N, such that N has as members just those sets which are not members of themselves. This is the assumption needed in order to get the paradox in standard systems of logic. In Zermelo set theory, it turns out that you can't prove that there is any such set. That is, the axioms for the construction of sets allow for the existence of a lot of sets, some of them just enormous; but there is no universal set, and there is no set satisfying the condition just mentioned for N. So from that point of view, if set theory is consistent (and there is certainly every reason to believe it is), this problem is whipped.

You see, Platonists needn't admit the existence of *any* old abstract entity. There are certain kinds of abstract entities (or things that would be abstract entities if there were them), but they don't exist (if you will forgive me for putting the matter in this virtually unintelligible way). As examples we might consider a decision procedure for the first-order functional calculus, or a method of squaring the circle. If there were a method for squaring a circle, then we would want to call that an abstract entity in the same way that we want to call a method for bisecting an angle an abstract entity. But we have been able to prove geometrically that there is no abstract entity satisfying the "circle-squaring" condition. Many proofs in mathematics involve showing that there is no such thing as an abstract entity satisfying certain conditions.

T. Bynum (*University of Delaware*): If you think of N, at the bottom of the blackboard—is this thought an idea? How do you distinguish between an idea and existing abstract Forms? Can there be an idea which is a non-existent abstract Form?

Professor Anderson: By "idea," do you mean the idea in what I take to be the classical Platonic sense, or at least one Platonic sense, namely, an abstract entity? Or do you mean by "idea" something I am thinking?

Mr. Bynum: Well, I am confused about the definition of "idea" now, because before, I would have thought that the idea of N, even though we say N can't exist, exists. Well, that makes the idea different from an abstract Form.

Professor Anderson: Do you mean that I have to have some idea of what it would be like for it to be there? Consider squaring the circle. It is perfectly clear what is wanted. It is a method (with ruler and compass) of taking a circle and finding a square with the same area. And we can imagine what it would be like to have somebody come in and say, "I have a method." He sits down with some paper and he horses around with rulers and compasses and makes some constructions, etc., and after he gets through, he says, "See, now I have got a proof." You know what you would like in a proof. You know what sort of thing to expect; but in point of fact, there is no such proof. There is no such method.

Mr. Bynum: Is the thought of being able to square a circle an idea?

Professor Anderson: Sure, I think so.

Mr. Bynum: It's not an abstract entity?

Professor Anderson: I think one gets confused about "thinking the thought." "Thoughts" are certainly quite different from anything that I mean to talk about here. Set theory *exists*, in the Platonic sense of existing—with you all the time, even though you can't really stomp on it.

Mr. Bynum: In other words, you are saying that the idea of N as defined exists, but that N as an abstract idea does not exist. Are you making a distinction between idea and abstract entity?

Professor Anderson: Yes, certainly. The defining conditions for N exist; that is: X is not a member of itself. Here is the defining condition: X is not an X. As a matter of fact, in some theories one can prove this: that *no* set is a member of itself. But there is no universal set. We can't admit the existence of a set that has *everything* as a member, without getting into trouble. In set theory, the universe is sort of cone-shaped. You start down here at the bottom with a set that doesn't have anything in it at all; we use the notation "Λ." This set is empty, and then you start constructing sets out of this empty set—you first get a set with one member, namely, the empty set. (Is that at all intelligible?) The empty set is a perfectly good set just like all the other sets, only it doesn't have anything in it. It is like the set of people in this room after a while.

Now, here's a different set $\{\Lambda\}$. This is a set that has just one member, namely, the empty set. A member that doesn't amount to much; but at least the new set $\{\Lambda\}$ is different from the empty set because this Λ, the empty set, doesn't have any members, and $\{\Lambda\}$ has one member. Now, what do we do? We form another set with two things in it, namely, the empty set and the set that has one member, namely, the empty set. And we just keep on building things up, and they are all different because they have different members. You start out down here, and you build enormous, enormous, enormous sets; but the universe of sets sort of disappears into a fog. There is no one big set which has *everything* as members, and that is why we conclude that it is true of all sets that none of them is a member of itself. So the defining *condition* exists, and indeed holds for all sets.

W. Busse (*du Pont; University of Delaware*): I don't see how you are able to slip from an operation to an idea or an abstract entity. It seems to me you are using "operation" and "abstract entity" interchangeably.

Professor Anderson: Yes, by "abstract entity" I mean what I take certain philosophers to have meant, namely: anything that isn't concrete—anything that you can't step

on. Now, addition can be thought of as an operation, and
certainly you can't step on addition; and you can't step on
numbers, and you can't step on dances. By "abstract entity" I mean anything that you can't touch, including operations on numbers, or techniques for doing things, or the
like.

Dr. Busse: Is an operation what *I* am aware of, or what
at least someone can be aware of?

Professor Anderson: There is a point of view that, as
Quine indicated, is sort of midway between nominalism and
Platonism, called "conceptualism," which I just didn't discuss. According to this position, the fact that a theory exists
at all depends upon the fact that we know something about
it. If we knew nothing about it at all, then there would be
no such theory. Now from a Platonic point of view, I would
say that that theory existed (in the calm sense) long before
the earth did. It was there, and we discovered it. The objections I have to saying that its existence depends upon
the fact that *we know* it (or that the theory is mind-
dependent somehow: "If we didn't know it, it wouldn't be
there"), is that I can't see how to answer certain questions,
from the conceptualist point of view. Is it sufficient for *one*
person to know a theory for it to exist? Or how many—40?
And which ones? I don't see any way of adjudicating the
issue. So for that reason, I would not like to say that the
existence of the theory depends upon the fact that we
know it.

B. Baumrin (*University of Delaware*): Let's say that
next week it turns out that some theory falls before a paradox. It was only thought to have been an entity. It was
really just an idea—just psychologically opted for by a
group of individuals; then surely it must have always not
existed?

Professor Anderson: No, I disagree with you. I think there
are inconsistent theories. For example, Frege's foundations
of mathematics is a theory, but it is an inconsistent one: it
is an inconsistent abstract entity. But if I say that this fell

to the ground next week because we discovered a contradiction, then we would know something more about the theory. It would be just a new fact about it. You see, one of the psychological reasons why people who work in logic and mathematics can have a Platonistic outlook is that it always looks to them as if what they learn (or very frequently it looks to them as if what they learn) is something they *discovered*. It was already there. That is, we define the natural numbers in Peano's way and then we prove Euclid's theorem, say, that there are infinitely many prime numbers. Did we make them up? Weren't they there yesterday and I just didn't know it? What kind of an attitude are we going to take about this? This is why it seems to me that the conceptualist outlook is unsatisfactory; again one has a hard time answering these questions. There is a certain school of mathematicians, called "intuitionists" (they all happen to be in Holland) who take the position that to say that a theorem has been proved, or to say that something is a theorem, *means* that you, or I, or someone we know, has proved it. But certainly most mathematicians take the attitude that they are *discovering* things about the system they are considering; it looks as if the truths are already there, as completed entities. You run through the entities and discover more and more properties, and they *already had* those properties a long time ago. It is not that they suddenly *acquired* them on Tuesday morning at 11:00, when someone finally wrote the proof.

Dr. Busse: Wouldn't it be equally consistent to say that these theories satisfied something in their minds?

Professor Anderson: I think that it's true that most mathematicians tend to feel very good when they have proved a theorem. They have a considerable amount of satisfaction and even more important, theorems sometimes suggest very good questions. Asking good questions and finding interesting answers are very gratifying things to do; but I don't think that any of us feel that the *gratification* is what we mean when we say the thing existed. For example, if I prove the existence of a function, satisfying certain conditions, then if it's a nice proof, I might feel very happy about it and people might say: "My, that's well done." But they would all take the *fact* that I was trying to prove as being objective in a stronger sense. The function was already there, and I or someone else went out and found it, or proved that it exists. Here's a case in point. There's a conjecture (sometimes erroneously referred to as a "theorem") called the "twin prime theorem." (I assume that "prime number" is a familiar notion: A prime number is one divisible only by itself and 1, so that 4 is not prime because it is divisible by 1, 2, and 4, but 5 is prime because it is divisible evenly by 1 and 5 only.) Now, we have 5 and 7, which are both primes; 11 and 13 are both primes; 17 and 19 are both primes; 29 and 31 are both primes; and so on. But notice that these are split by just two. Now here is a problem which has been unanswered for many years: Does this continue to happen? Are there infinitely many twin primes, primes that are separated by just two? This is a very elementary problem; there is no difficulty in stating the problem, or in understanding what is involved. Nobody knows the answer to this question, although it is a very elementary or simple question, in the sense that it can be easily understood. Certainly most number theorists think the twin prime conjecture is either true or false. They don't know which, and someday somebody may discover whether it is true or false. But it isn't a matter of some brilliant mathematician discovering that there are infinitely many twin primes, and that *from then on,* there are infinitely many such. There were *always* infinitely many (or finitely many) twin primes, or else there *never* were. If somebody finds out that there are only a finite number of twin primes, certainly most mathematicians will look at the matter as if that had always been true.

That's not an argument. I was just trying to express what I take to be the intuitive feelings behind the almost universal acceptance of Platonism by most mathematicians (if they think about it at all). If they consider the matter, it is usually not hard to convince them that they are Platonists in outlook even though they might never have studied Philosophy.

W. McCormack (*du Pont*): If the rules of chess are an abstract set and I take the rules of chess and program them on a computer so the computer can now play chess, are the rules of chess now still an abstract set in spite of the fact that I can now kick the computer's memory?

Professor Anderson: I would say so, for from this point of view it is just a matter of following the rules. If I get a person or a chimpanzee to play chess, it is still true that following the rules is *behaving* in a certain way; and just as you kicked the computer, you could also kick the person who played. I think that most Platonists would say that the set or collection of rules *is* the game.

Dr. Reese: Back to the possible fat man in the doorway: This calm sense of Platonism becomes less calm the further the argument goes here. What about this? In mathematics, it seems very sane to talk this way, but what about when you get outside of mathematics?

Professor Anderson: I think that Quine's problem is specious in the following sense. What would you want to say about this: "The possible fat man in the doorway has spats"? Now, what I would like to ask is, how does the meaning of this utterance, such as it is, differ from the following: "It is possible that there is a fat man in the doorway wearing spats"? I would take it that if one of these is true, then the other one is. They seem to have the same content, and I think that when you ascribe possibility to any kind of entity like "the fat man," you can always rephrase this without losing any content in such a way that the possibility attaches not to the fat man but to a certain proposition. Now if you grant that, then it becomes apparent that we never have to attribute possibility to anything except propositions. We just throw away all the possible fat men, and we don't get Quine's problem.

What Do Symbols Symbolize?: Nominalism

Richard S. Rudner, *Washington University*

In this essay I should like to make as clear as I can just what is the nature of the issue between contemporary platonists and contemporary nominalists. The first thing that needs to be established is that there *is* an issue.

That there is an issue *requires* emphasizing because many platonists apparently believe it is so self-evident that platonism is correct, that the only thing one needs to do to establish this is to repeat three times or so, rather waspishly, "Of course, there are sets!" or, "Of course the claims of nominalism can't be taken seriously!" or, "Our culture demands that we recognize the existence of abstract entities!"

There seem to be three dominant reasons for the fact that platonists frequently proffer such *non-arguments* as a substitute for a discussion of the issue. The first reason is, that since there are a very great many more platonists than nominalists among those who have at all addressed themselves to the problem, the platonists are exhibiting that sense of false security, so often manifested by individuals in mobs, which leads them to exclamation instead of mentalization. (*Why* there are so many more platonists than nominalists, is a topic which I shall eschew—since I do not wish to bore you with a disquisition on the general prevalence of error in our unhappy times. It may suffice simply to note the sad fact, true of our own epoch as it has been of most others, that very many more people are wrong than are right at any given time about most things. This I believe is what extentialists must mean by "the human condition.")

The second reason for the reliance on non-arguments by

platonists may well be due to feelings of helplessness or unfamiliarity which nominalist polemic may have inspired in platonists; or it may be found in some subtlety of argument which platonists have particular difficulty in countering. Of course I am not a very good judge of this aspect of the behavior of platonists. Having been brought up, so to speak, in a nominalistic household, and having learned the rhetoric of nominalism at the knee of one of my philosophical papas, the language of nominalism does not have for me the terror of unfamiliarity. Moreover, since in examining my platonistic friends closely I have found them to embrace with delight arguments as subtle as any which the nominalists have ever offered, I am, accordingly, usually unsure about the occasions when this reason for non-argument is the one to be blamed. I do think, however, that there are such occasions. And one of them, if I am not mistaken, occurred rather recently on this platform.

Platonists are sometimes made uncomfortable by the charge that their position imposes a great deal of unnecessary clutter upon the universe. Thus, for example, if, as he typically does, the platonist holds that for every element (i.e., for every individual or class), there *exists* some *class* which has that element as its only member, it can easily be seen that he must hold the universe to be, to put it mildly, immensely populous. For it follows from this position that if there is some element *A*, then there is a class, *B*, which has *A* as its only member; and, moreover, that there is a distinct class *C* which has *B* as its only member; and, moreover, that there is a class *D*, distinct from all of these, which *C* as its only member; and so on and so forth—to put it mildly. Now, apparently, some platonists are so nettled by the charge of a cluttery universe that they may be led to the thoughtless rejoinder that "the nominalists' universe is just as cluttery as they come." By which, one supposes, the platonist means not to concede the correctness of the nominalist view, but rather to claim that a nominalistic universe *would* be at least as cluttery as a platonistic one. For example, a part of this platonistic rejoinder seems to be that the nominalist must countenance the existence of all of the different plays of the game of chess, while the platonist has available to him "von Neumann's elegant abstract theory of the matter, according to which chess *is* the set of its rules."

Yet even the slightest reflection makes clear that this is a pathetic rejoinder to the original charge. The platonist's engorgement of chess as an abstract entity *doesn't disembarrass his universe of a single play of the game.* Every play of the nominalist universe is a play of the platonist one. The platonist universe has, however, at least one piece of furniture in addition to and distinct from individual plays of the game; namely, the game as an abstract entity.

A moment ago, I described this self-vitiating platonist rejoinder as "pathetic." I used the term advisedly, for there has always seemed to me to be a certain pathos in this aspect of the platonist position *vis-à-vis* nominalism. The fact is, that the contemporary platonist is in no position to cavil at anything whatever in either the nominalist's universe or in the nominalist's linguistic apparatus for describing it. For the platonic universe *includes* everything in the nominalist's universe and more, and the platonic descriptional apparatus includes everything in the nominalist descriptional apparatus and more (it is, in fact, the "more" which generates the controversy).

The platonist is thus not only barred from a legitimate "your universe is more cluttered" rejoinder, but also from any rejoinder to the effect that there are obscurities in nominalistic treatments which are avoided in platonistic ones. This latter point has, to be sure, sometimes been lost sight of, with bizarre results. Thus, it has been recently alleged by some platonists that while "we are in miserable shape as regards identity criteria for physical objects," since such criteria are obscure, we are, on the other hand, "in excellent shape as regards" identity criteria for such abstract entities as sets or classes. But this must be counted as a very odd claim indeed. For the criterion of the extensional identity of classes, as this author, curiously enough, himself points out, is just the identity of the members of the classes. Thus, if we are confronted with classes of physical objects, a demonstration that class A is extensionally identical with class B presupposes our demonstration that each physical object member of A is identical with some physical object in B and that each physical object member of B is identical with some physical object in A. The criterion for the identity of such classes can thus surely be no *less obscure* (in the sense the author is propounding) than can the identity of the physical objects concerned. *

Of course, in calling attention to the pathos of this aspect of the platonist position *vis-à-vis* nominalism, I do not intend to suggest that there are no types of objection against nominalism which place platonists in a *less* pitiable plight. The third reason for some of the platonists' recourse to nonargument, for instance, seems to be one for which some mitigation in bafflement or ignorance may be pleaded. As I see it, the third reason lies in ignorance about just what the nominalist position comes to. And ignorance is not always pitiable. In this case, though, it seems to me that a modicum of mitigation for the ignorance is to be found in unfortunate locutions which contemporary nominalists adopted in their early work, and in the fact that for a time two distinct branches of contemporary nominalism seemed to be developing. The explanation of this circumstance will give me the opportunity both to nail down the point that there is an issue between platonists and nominalists and also to give some more precise indication of its nature.

Traditionally, the roots of the controversy have been obscured by the confusions which have surrounded three pairs of presumably polar terms: "Abstract" and "Concrete," "Class" (or "Set") and "Individual," and "Universal" and "Particular." In order to understand both some of the bafflement which platonists may have felt as well as some of the

* This point was called to my attention in a conversation with my colleague at Michigan State University, Dr. Robert Barrett.

actual (as opposed to pseudo) issues which separate the two camps, it is necessary to convey a notion of the distinction which holds among at least the first two pairs.

Presystematically and loosely (in his book, *The Structure of Appearance*, Nelson Goodman gives a rigorous and systematic account of these terms), a *concrete* entity is one which is spatiotemporally localizable. We can associate it with some specific spatiotemporal stretch. Accordingly, this building and these chairs are all concrete entities, as am I. Entities which are not thus localizable, for example, *color qualia*, are abstract.

We will return to the concrete–abstract distinction in a moment; for the time being, however, let us consider the class *vs.* individual distinction.* An individual is something which is such that if it is different from something else then it has different basic or "atomic" constituents from that something else. In contrast, a class or set may be such as to be different from something else (e.g., another class) without having different basic constituents from that other thing. To see what is meant by the assertion that two *classes* may be different although they are composed of the same *basic* constituents, consider a system which has the four basic, or atomic, elements: a, b, c, and d. They are described as basic or atomic in the sense that they themselves have no other elements as constituents. Now consider the class K which has as its two members the class of a and b and the class of c and d. Further, consider the class L which has as its two members the class of a and c and the class of b and d. According to platonism, K and L are distinct entities even though their *systematically* ultimate basic constituents are the same. Nothing which is an individual could fulfill such a condition.

* In the explication which follows, I have tried to adhere closely to the one presented by Goodman in "A World of Individuals" (see ref. 1, p. 19). That illuminating essay likewise anticipates, as must be obvious to those familiar with it, most of the other arguments for nominalism adduced in this essay.

Given this distinction, the branch of nominalism with which I am here concerned may be described as holding the position that *there are no non-individuals*. Alternatively, and somewhat more positively, the program of contemporary nominalism may be described as that of showing that it is possible to develop a *nominalistic* language which is adequate to science and mathematics; that is to say, a language which is adequate to the *description* of the universe and which does not commit its users to the claim that there are any non-individuals.

Goodman has aptly described the nominalist position as "super-extensionalism." Its relationship to classical extensionalism (see ref. 1, pp. 19–20) may be seen from the following considerations: Classical extensionalism may be construed as a restriction upon the indiscriminate multiplication of entities by *its* stricture to the effect that any two classes which have, so to speak, the same *proximate* constituents are identical. Nominalism adds a further restriction on the multiplication of entities by its stricture to the effect that any two entities which have the same systematically ultimate entities are identical.

With this much characterization of the individual *vs.* class distinction we can return to the abstract–concrete distinction and the mitigated puzzlement of some platonists. First of all, it should be noted that it is not the case that an abstract entity need be a non-individual. Accordingly, a nominalistic position construed as a renunciation of abstract entities and a nominalistic position construed as a renunciation of non-individuals need not be identical positions. Hereafter, I shall call the latter of these two nominalistic positions G-nominalism after Goodman and the former of the positions Q-nominalism after Quine (though I am not at all sure that it is a position to which Quine does subscribe, or ever has subscribed).

In the introductory passage of an early and otherwise quite brilliant joint article,[2] Quine and Goodman lapsed

into the assertion that they did not "believe in abstract
entities." Although, as Goodman has pointed out, this assertion was "intended more as a headline than as final doctrine,
and although some reservations concerning it were almost
immediately indicated" (ref. 1, p. 16), and although Goodman has painstakingly made clear the G-nominalist position
in several other works since 1947, nevertheless that initial
assertion has, as he says, "been fair game for critics ever
since."

This, then, is the source of the modicum of mitigation
which may be conceded to those platonists who are puzzled
or misled about what the position of nominalism comes to.
How slight the mitigation is, may be seen from the fact that
Goodman's *The Structure of Appearance,* in which he clearly
delineates G-nominalism and indeed constructs a G-nom-
inalistic system which is not Q-nominalistic, appeared more
than ten years ago, while his essay "A World of Individuals"
which again explicitly and clearly discusses the whole point,
appeared some six years ago.

The question is sometimes raised whether a nominalism
which renounces abstract entities is closer to traditional
nominalism than one which renounces non-individuals. The
answer depends, of course, on which strand of the tradition
you have in mind. It seems pretty obvious that G-nominalism is closer to that part of the tradition embodied in the
animadversions of Berkeley and Hume—both of whom
clearly admitted *individual color qualia,* for example, into
their ontologies. In a similar vein, it would probably not
be too unfair to conclude that of our final pair of polar terms,
"Universal" and "Particular," the former seems most often
to have been used to refer to those abstract entities which
are non-individuals and the latter to those concrete entities
which are individuals—although this practice has been by
no means unexceptional. In any case, the current controversy
does not here require us to draw upon the third pair at all.

All in all, such considerations are chiefly of historical interest; and, indeed, when we come down to the heart of the present issue, the problem of whether the platonist is venting spleen on G-nominalists or on Q-nominalists turns out to be of no great moment. For whatever difference there may be in fine between the two nominalist positions, it is quite evident that they are in complete agreement on their renunciation of classes or sets. The Q-nominalist renounces classes on the grounds of their abstractness, the G-nominalist on grounds of their non-individuality. The platonist joins issue with both in his claim that classes are both actual and indispensable.

In joining issue on the question of the existence of classes, it seems to me that the platonist has typically done so by leveling certain charges at the nominalist. Three such charges in particular seem to be recurrent—and worth consideration in their own right for the illumination thus thrown on the nature of contemporary nominalism; although I shall hold that two of these objections are ill-founded and the third not truly an objection at all. The first of these objections may be indicated by a statement like "Nominalists are mean—they want to deprive us of culture and cultivation— if they were right we would be deprived of Bach partitas." The second objection may be indicated by some such statement as "Nominalism is trivial—even if its esoteric program were successful, it would make no difference of any significance whatever for, say, the serious concerns of science; indeed, the dry and tortuous work of nominalists, their overwhelming preoccupation with the minutest details of language, is simply a distressing modern example of the worst faults which have been attributed to medieval scholasticism." The third objection may be indicated by some such statement as "Nominalism is a failure—the nominalist program has shown itself so far unable to cope with serious problems which confront it, and there is no reason to believe it will ever be successful."

I shall devote the remainder of this essay to an attempt at meeting each of these objections in turn.

I. Are Nominalists Mean?

Although my allusions earlier to a platonist fright reaction to nominalistic rhetoric were intended semi-humorously, I must confess that I am at a loss about how else to account for the widespread and persistent inability to understand a relatively uncomplicated point of the nominalist thesis. It is this: If the nominalists are "correct," then the universe is not poorer by a single, solitary, individual thing which would have been in it were the platonists "correct." Not one play of the game of chess, not one portrayal of *Hamlet*, not one rendition of an aria, not one performance of a partita is lost. To be sure, the nominalist universe will not contain the archtypal *Hamlet* or some archtypal Bach partita as these entities are construed by contemporary platonists. But no one's aesthetic life will have thus been in the least impoverished. For, as construed by platonists, such entities are *not* the kinds of things that can be presented for aesthetic response. What we aesthetically respond to are individual performances or renditions, perceived or imagined, of art works.

To give a detailed demonstration of the point that the nominalist program is not dedicated to the death of cultivation or even to the abandonment of what anthropologists might cogently and usefully be referring to as culture in such locutions as "culture diffuses," lies well outside the scope of our present discussion. Perhaps, however, attention to just one example will suffice to yield an inkling into a nominalistic treatment of the general problem.

More years ago than it now makes me comfortable to remember, I wrote an article [3] which was concerned with the analysis and resolution of certain puzzles that seem to be involved in some of our typical uses of names of art works. In this article I tried to trace how the grammar of such locutions as *"Beethoven's Fifth* is a great symphony but that was a poor rendition of it,"* may have misled some philosophers or patrons of the arts into hypostatizing the existence of an abstract entity to stand as the referent for the expression *"Beethoven's Fifth Symphony."* For, locutions like "That was a poor rendition of *Beethoven's Fifth Symphony*" seem to suggest that there *is* something, properly called by the title, over and above any individual musical rendition. I tried to show that such hypostatizations were not only unnecessary in order for us to make sense out of, and properly employ, such titles, but also that platonic hypostatizations would make hash out of any theory of aesthetics. And I did this by considering in turn several of the different kinds of abstract entity which had been hypostatized. All of this is by way of background for the treatment of the one platonistic view which *is* relevant to our present concern. This is the view which construes the referents of names of art works like *Beethoven's Fifth* to be certain classes or sets; and which construes the relationship between, say, Beethoven's fifth symphony and any rendition of it to be strictly analogous to the type–token or symbol–token relationship. On this page of my manuscript there are several occurrences of the inscription or token "to." Platonists distinguish such tokens from the abstract type or form of word, of which they are said to be tokens. This distinction, it is said, is demanded by the propriety with which we claim that all these *different* occurrences are different occurrences of just one word. On this platonic construal, then, the individual tokens are taken to be physical objects and the corresponding types are defined as classes of similar tokens. Analogously, the title *"Beethoven's Fifth Symphony"* is taken to denote *a certain class of similar musical renditions.*

However, I pointed out in that old essay, what still seems plausible to me today, that such an analysis has the untenable consequence that no one could possibly respond aesthetically to, e.g., *Beethoven's Fifth Symphony.* For abstract entities like classes can not only not be kicked, they can't be seen, touched, smelled, tasted, or *heard!* But we need not accept such a platonistic analysis, with all of its unacceptable consequences, of the problematic locutions. We are not required to claim the existence of a referent for the expression *"Beethoven's Fifth Symphony"* when we truly assert "That was a rendition of *Beethoven's Fifth Symphony"* any more than we are required to claim the existence of a referent for the expression "Zeus" when we truly assert "Some Greeks worshiped Zeus." Both the expressions "Zeus" and *"Beethoven's Fifth Symphony"* may cogently be taken to occur syncategorematically in their respective contexts.

Expressions occur syncategorematically in contexts when their occurrence is meaningful without being denotative. A great many expressions in English always occur syncategorematically without causing the least uneasiness to their users. Expressions like "the" and "a" and "if," etc., are perfectly good, meaningful, expressions of English; yet we should instantly recognize someone to be an atavism from some epoch of language magic if he insisted on looking for referents for *these* words.

The result of this nominalistic analysis,* then, is to construe the occurrence of the title in the Beethoven sentence syncategorematically, and to construe the sentence itself as being paraphrasable into one which does not employ the title but which connects a given rendition causally with some of Beethoven's activities.

It is immensely important to notice that the fact that the

* An alternative nominalistic technique for handling this and similar problematic locutions is suggested in Quine and Goodman.[2] Following them, the title might be construed as denoting not the class whose members were certain renditions, but rather the scattered *whole* whose parts were certain renditions. There is, incidentally, no reason to believe that the expression "culture," in typically anthropological locutions, would be any more recalcitrant to nominalistic analysis than are titles of art works. For example, *the nominalistic alternative* to construing the locution "the *x* method of cooking" as denoting a behavior *pattern* (i.e., as denoting a presumably finite class of similar behaviors) in such sentences as "The *x* method of cooking is an item of French culture which has diffused," was already well known more than fourteen years ago. Similar analysis would take care of such assertions as "Culture diffuses," for again the term "Culture" denotes at most an entity with a finite number of *basic* (or atomic) constituents.

relatively brief Beethoven sentence can be nominalistically paraphrased by a much more cumbersome sentence, does not in any way *force* the nominalist to employ the cumbersome paraphrase instead of the ellipsis. On the contrary, he can, once the innocuousness of the original ellipsis has been established, use the briefer sentence quite freely; i.e., with a clear philosophical conscience. It is important to notice this because some platonists believe or pretend to believe that nominalists advocate the use of intolerable circumlocutions. Nothing could be further from the truth and this simple-minded error surely deserves to be buried once and for all. The nominalist does *not* advocate nor is he confined to the *use of* his complicated, unpacked paraphrases—no more than is the mathematician who insists that an expression like "10,000!" is definable by a very long and cumbersome expression confined to the use of such a cumbersome expression. On the contrary, the imputation to the nominalist of such a linguistic perversity puts the cart before the horse: A main point of the nominalist program is to *earn* the freedom to use otherwise suspicious expressions whose brevity or elegance makes their use worthwhile.

Some platonists have recently taken a related tack (a new one to me, I must confess), which also seems to have the fragrance of red herring about it. In this tack the platonist arrives at the conclusion, that the nominalist is barbarically arrayed against what is good or important, by reasoning from some interesting premises. The first of these is that there is a "special value to permanent things" or that "permanent things are somehow better than things that change." The second premise is that abstract entities like classes are more permanent than individual things like sticks and stones and ice cream cones. Since the nominalist obviously prefers things like the latter to things like the former, the conclusion that the nominalist perversely prefers the less to the more important seems inescapable.

But this *is* a very obscure argument—and surely the two initial premises are false, if intelligible at all. Whether a permanent thing is better or more important than an impermanent thing is obviously going to depend on what the things in question are. A permanent excrutiating pain is *not* in general better than a pleasure—however ephemeral. The moon, though it may well turn out to be a more permanent phenomenon than the one biologists refer to as the human species, is not more important. The fact is that people do not believe that something is good because it lasts a long time. On the contrary, they want it to last a long time when they believe it is good, and a short time when they believe it is bad. So much for the first premise.

It is also in general false that classes, even if there were any, are more permanent than every individual. Even in the platonist universe, there surely cannot be anything more permanent than that good old *individual* universe itself. The argument thus is specious. Nominalists as such do not prefer the worse to the better part.

The upshot of this discussion, I hope you will agree, is that nominalists aren't really mean. They do not conspire to deprive us of art or culture. They do not desire that anyone should talk in intolerable circumlocutions, and they *do* believe that important things are important.

II. Is Nominalism Trivial?

The objection indicated by this question is not so much an objection against nominalism, I think, as it is against the nominalist–platonist controversy itself. The objection amounts to the claim that the controversy is nothing but a metaphysical quibble wholly remote from such matters of significance as science; and that, accordingly, a nonmetaphysician can be supremely indifferent to either a nominalist victory or a nominalist defeat in the controversy.

I must, perforce, treat this objection much more briefly than its importance warrants. For, I *do* think that it is a very serious, though ill-founded, objection. Unfortunately, in the compass of this essay, I can only *outline* an argument which meets it. And I shall have to rely heavily on allusions

to matters which have been treated elsewhere in the literature of the philosophy of science to accomplish even that
much.

The objection, I believe, is met by showing the important
consequences that the nominalist position does have for both
philosophers of science and scientific theorists. In the philosophy of science there is already a very sizeable literature
devoted to the problem of dispositional predicates. Such
predicates are frequently construed as referring to non-
observable properties or dispositions which objects may
have. The problem they pose arises from their recalcitrance
to adequate analysis or definition by so-called "observable
predicates." Though dispositionals are recalcitrant, they are
also, apparently, indispensable components of a great many
important scientific theories. This fact, as evidenced by increasing attention scientific theorists have given it in their
own discussions of operationalism, is not, of course, a remote
matter to scientists. Now, Scheffler has shown [4] that some
of the difficulties which attend the problem of achieving an
adequate analysis of dispositionals are exacerbated by a
platonist construal of dispositionals and helped toward solution by a nominalist one. If, as I believe to be the case,
Scheffler's views are correct, then we have here at least
one instance in which the outcome of the nominalist–platonist controversy makes a significant difference.

But there is an even more important instance of the significance which the nominalist–platonist issue has for science. This instance has to do with the logic of induction
itself. The function of a logic of induction is to provide
methodological canons which will enable the scientist to
make valid choices among alternative hypotheses or theories.
In making such choices—indeed, in deciding on the scientific
acceptability of any theory—it is clear that the scientist must,
and in fact has always attempted to, take into consideration
weights other than that of evidential strength. There is perhaps no more hoary cliché of the scientific literature than

that to the effect that the scientist attaches greater weight to a more simple theory than to a less simple one.

The difficulty about simplicity as an inductive weight over and above that of evidential strength, has always been the obscurity of the relevant notion of simplicity. Until the relatively recent past, the obstacles in the path of an adequate notion of the degree of simplicity of theories seemed well nigh insurmountable. During the past two decades, however, results achieved and increasingly refined by Goodman have given great promise of a means for objectively measuring the formal or structural simplicity of scientific theories.* Goodman's *calculus of structural simplicity* enables us to compare the relative economy of any pair of formalized theoretical systems and thus to have some valid basis of choice between them. But of two theoretical systems, one platonist and one nominalist, which are otherwise equally adequate to a given subject matter, the nominalist system turns out to be structurally or formally more simple than the platonist one. Accordingly, it seems fair to conclude that the outcome of the platonist–nominalist controversy is not without significance for science.†

III. Is the Nominalist Program Incomplete and Incompletable?

Of the apparent objection suggested by this question I can really make very short *Schrift*. The program of nominalism is surely incomplete and it may very well be incompletable. But even if this *is* true of the program, I do not think that the implicit suggestion that the program should be

---

* For a bibliography on this subject, see reference 5.

† An important example of this may be seen in the attempts by philosophers of science to assess a logical device for handling theoretical terms in theories, which was initially suggested by F. P. Ramsey. If the nominalists are correct, then "Ramsey's way out" of the theoretician's dilemma is clearly unacceptable. If the nominalists are moderately successful, then "Ramsey's way out" is not likely to be necessary. For a lucid exposition of the Ramsey technique, see reference 6.

abandoned is a justifiable one. In the first place, while it is undoubtedly the case that nominalists have not solved all of the problems which confront them—and in particular have not succeeded in showing how the whole of mathematics may be generated on a nominalistic basis—it is equally the case that platonists have not solved all of the problems which confront *them*. If encountering difficulties were a sufficient condition for abandonment of programs, it is perfectly obvious that very few worthwhile programs would ever have been accomplished.

In the second place, the suggestion that nominalism as a program is incompletable—is merely that. No demonstration of incompletability has ever been forthcoming. And the probability that such a proof *could* be given in the foreseeable future seems for obvious reasons to be vanishingly small. What, for example, would be the nature of the system within which such a proof could be offered? On the other hand, the difficulties confronting the completion of the nominalist program are so massive that the prospects of completion in the foreseeable future are also negligible. But, even if the nominalist program should turn out to be incompletable, I would agree with Goodman that the value derived from continuing work on it makes abandonment the poorer strategy. On this point I should like to quote a passage from his essay "The Revision of Philosophy." [7] In this passage he is speaking of the program of *phenomenalism;* yet, what he says there patently applies to the program of nominalism as well:

> Usually phenomenalism is taken to be utterly discredited once its incompletability is acknowledged. It is just this step in the argument—a step commonly passed over as obvious—that I want to challenge. I am ready to maintain that the value of efforts to construct a system on a phenomenalistic or any other narrow basis is very little affected by whether or not the system can be completed. Euclid's geometry is not robbed of value by the fact that the circle cannot be squared by Euclidean means. Indeed, acceptance prior to Euclid of the

impossibility of squaring the circle with compass and straight-edge would not in the least have diminished the importance of developing Euclidean geometry. . . . But my point is not just that it was psychologically necessary or helpful to work in this way. What is accomplished in the incomplete system has permanent value when incorporated into a fuller system. Indeed after a system like Euclid's has been developed as far as possible, questions concerning what can be accomplished with even fewer means (e.g., without a straightedge or without a given postulate) often still have interest.

The analogy, I take it, is transparent. Incompletability by itself is no decisive objection against the attempt to build a system on a phenomenalistic basis. Only by positive efforts with severely restricted means can we make any progress in construction; only so can we discern the exact limitations of a basis and the exact supplementation needed. And what we achieve may be retained in an expanded system, and will help solve parallel problems in alternative systems.

So much for objections and pseudo-objections against nominalism. In conclusion, I hope you will forgive my inability to resist the temptation both to answer the question posed by the title of this lecture and to close with what in "show biz" has become a classical blackout line: The nominalist's answer, Mr. Bones, to the question "What do symbols symbolize?" is: Individuals—because, for the nominalist, *that's all there is, there isn't any more.*

References

1. Nelson Goodman, "A World of Individuals," in I. M. Bochenski, Alonzo Church, and Nelson Goodman, Eds., *The Problem of Universals*, The University of Notre Dame Press, 1956.
2. W. V. O. Quine and Nelson Goodman, "Steps Towards a Constructive Nominalism," *Journal of Symbolic Logic*, 12, 105–122 (1947).
3. Richard Rudner, "The Ontological Status of the Esthetic Object," *Philosophy and Phenomenological Research*, X (No. 3), 380 (1950).
4. Israel Scheffler, "Prospects of a Modest Empiricism," *Review of Metaphysics*, 10 (No. 3), 383 (1957); *ibid.*, 10 (No. 4), 602 (1957).

5. Richard Rudner, "An Introduction to Simplicity," *Philosophy of Science*, 28 (No. 2), 109 (1961).
6. C. G. Hempel, "The Theoretician's Dilemma," in H. Feigl, M. Scriven, and G. Maxwell, Eds., *Minnesota Studies in the Philosophy of Science*, Vol. II (*Concepts, Theories and the Mind–Body Problem*), University of Minnesota Press, 1958.
7. Nelson Goodman, "The Revision of Philosophy," in Sidney Hook, Ed., *American Philosophers at Work*, Criterion Books, New York, 1956.

Discussion

D. W. Oplinger (*du Pont*): Would you mind defining what you mean by the nominalist program and what would constitute completion of it?

R. Rudner: The nominalist program consists of an attempt to develop a language; that is, a linguistic basis of a specific character, which is adequate to science. In particular, the nominalist language in which the theories of science are to be framed or constituted would be such as not to commit a scientist to holding that there existed any such thing as a non-individual in the universe. The point that this is not an odd or absurd program to undertake may be seen from the following: Mathematics, which is an important part of the language of science, makes ontological commitments. It makes the claim, among other things, that there exist such things as classes; and classes, by the criteria that I put on the blackboard, are non-individuals. Accordingly, contemporary language of science is platonistic in character. Among *its* claims is the claim that there are such things as classes. The nominalist program is an attempt to see whether such a commitment is dispensible. After all, if we can construe our theorizing in science as talking about just objects which are not classes, we will have made less of a claim about the nature of the universe than one which made the claim that there were these objects and also classes. The platonist claims that there are both individuals and classes; the nominalist attempts to construct a language which makes the claim that there are only individuals.

Dr. Oplinger: In physics, we believe that a gas consists of a set of particles, a bunch of particles, and if you wanted to, you would put labels on each one of them. When we observe the properties of this body, we can measure what we recognize as pressure, temperature, and so forth, which are aggregate properties. Would the nominalist permit us to talk about these properties or would he require us to identify the individual motions of each particle rather than talk about the properties of the body as a whole?

Professor Rudner: The nominalist probably wouldn't choose to talk about properties at all without some analysis available which made it possible for him to recognize that talk ostensibly about properties was really a short way of talking, in the same way in which "10,000!" is a short way of talking. But within those limits his point, with respect to any gas with a finite number of particles, would be that discourse about it presents no special difficulty. Nominalistic ways have already been developed for talking about such particles and of talking about what you called aggregates of them as well. So, there would be no difficulty for the nominalist position of that sort; and if this program were successful, wholly successful, there would be no difficulty about using any mathematical terms, any numbers, since if successful, the nominalist would have construed such mathematical terms nominalistically as shortened for rather more cumbersome expressions and which make no reference to non-individuals.

Question: Beethoven's Fifth Symphony takes on meaning only in performance. That is your position, is it not?

Professor Rudner: No, not exactly. You see, I think an equivocation on the term "meaning" is developing. The *term* "Beethoven's Fifth Symphony" has meaning only in the context of an expression like "Beethoven's Fifth Symphony is a . . .", or "that was a good rendition of Beethoven's Fifth Symphony." The term "Beethoven's Fifth Symphony" is syncategorematic in the same way in which the term "of" in that sentence is syncategorematic. When saying, in locutions of this sort, that the word "of" is a perfectly good meaningful word, but that it doesn't denote anything (and similarly, when saying the title "Beethoven's Fifth Symphony" does not refer to some abstract entity over and above the rendition, and in fact that it doesn't refer at all), we are claiming that the word "of" is meaningful *in a linguistic context;* we are claiming in short that it is syncategorematic. What the exact meaning of the whole context is might be spelled out by an intolerably long circumlocution. In the case of "Beethoven's Fifth," for example, the circumlocution would, to put it roughly, have traced this *rendition* causally to some specific ones of Beethoven's activities, while no other one of the renditions of Beethoven's other symphonies are so related and no other pieces of music by other composers are so related. So that what the ostensible title turns out to be is simply a very compact expression which as such doesn't have a referent. I am sorry to have said all this again but I saw that we were going to go off if I didn't repeat it.

Question: Would you kindly give explicit definitions of what you mean by "exist"?

Professor Rudner: Well, I don't know if this will be explicit or satisfactory enough. This is a definition of "exist" in terms of "all" and some other logical terms: To say that there exists something such that it has a certain property, is the same thing as saying it is not the case that all things are such that they do not exemplify by that property, to put it very platonistically.

M. Primack (*Lincoln University*): I have two disconnected questions. First of all, your criterion of individuality; an example occurred to me which I think might be incompatible with it. Take the case of two different organizations. You see that they have the same basic constituents, yet are different individuals.

Professor Rudner: Two different organizations that have the same members? Suppose we take these as classes in some home town. For example, consider the class of East Lansing

Rotarians and the class of East Lansing Lions. You may find that these have the same membership. Assume they have exactly the same members, then according to *platonism* itself they would be the same organization! Accordingly if this is a problem for nominalism, it is also a problem for platonism—at least of the kind we have been discussing. And so the platonist has the difficulty of being able to say how these are two organizations even though they have the same members. Actually, I think that a solution for the difficulty is possible for both camps; although the exact analysis of any organization, or the concept "organization" in social science generally, is going to be a rather complex one. A nominalist solution could proceed somewhat as follows: one might say that the segment of the life histories of those people we ordinarily call the East Lansing Rotarians, i.e., the sum of those segments that are given over to participation in Rotarian-like activities, is distinguishable from (the sum of) those segments of the life histories, of the same people to be sure, given over to Lion-like activities and that the members of the distinguishable classes are the distinguishable segments. Consider Jones, the one lonely person in the East Lansing Rotary and Jones the one lonely person in the East Lansing Lions. Some part of his life's activities is given over to roaring and other parts of his life's activities are not. These are life segments which are distinguishable. In this case, the East Lansing Lions, the disconnected whole which comprises his activities as an East Lansing Lion, are distinguishable from the disconnected whole which comprises his activities as an East Lansing Rotarian. And really, there is nothing terribly mysterious about this. We regard each of ourselves as individuals, but as we well know, we are *spacially* discontinuous parts—in fact, compared to the atomic or even sub-atomic level, the spaces between the parts are a good deal—relatively—a good deal greater than the size of the parts themselves. So, there should be no great strain in thinking of some spacially discontinuous or even temporally discontinuous object as being one individual object. Spacial discontinuity and temporal discontinuity are no more problematic for nominalism than they are for platonism in this sense.

Professor Primack: What terms would you say are not syncategorematic in the example that you have given of the nominalist treatment of "Beethoven's Fifth Symphony"?

Professor Rudner: I would say that "the rendition" was not syncategorematic.

Professor Primack: Anderson gave us the impression that one of the problems that a nominalist faces is how to handle mathematics, and the impression is reinforced by what you described as the nominalist program. I wonder if you would comment briefly on how the nominalist does face mathematics.

Professor Rudner: The problem generally is this: One of the most important accomplishments in philosophical analysis, as you know, in this century was the development, or the generation, of mathematics on the basis of certain logical notions. This was accomplished by Russell and Whitehead in *Principia Mathematica*. Among the things due to Russell and Whitehead and Frege is a definition of the concept of number and indeed a definition, or the provision of a method for defining, any given number. Numbers, by Russell, Whitehead, and Frege are defined as certain classes of classes. So that if one uses the Russell-Whitehead-Frege definition (and no terribly plausible substitute has come along) and one *also* asserts many of the locutions that occur in scientific theory, one finds oneself committed to the assertion that there *exist* classes. In addition to the *numeral 3*, there is held to be something, presumably a class, which the *numeral 3* denotes or designates; and this is an abstract entity of a certain sort. Now, it is perfectly possible to give a nominalistic definition, or to show how to give a nominalistic definition for any finite number in terms of logical operators which do not carry the nominalist beyond the austere equipment he allows himself. But it is not possible, or at least so far it hasn't been accomplished and may not be possible, for the nominalist to handle all of non-finite mathematics. And this is the issue to which Professor Anderson must have been referring. It is the case, then, that the nominalist program includes as one of its goals the generation of mathematics on a nominalistic basis; *that* certainly has not been accomplished. Yet, Quine and Goodman published their article "Steps Towards a Constructive Nominalism" in 1947; before that date, a good deal of what they then accomplished, such as definitions of *theorem* and *proof* in a mathematical system, were held to be impossible or insurmountable obstacles. Since that time, things that have been said to be too difficult for nominalists to accomplish in terms of a nominalistic program have been accomplished by them. The view that the nominalist program is incompletable—can never possibly be completed—is itself one that stands solely without proof; no demonstrations have ever been forthcoming for it. Yet, even if the program were incompletable, this would still not be sufficient reason for abandoning it; because the work which is done, the progressive analysis of key notions from a very austere or very narrow basis, turns out to be immensely fruitful not only for nominalist programs but for platonist programs as well. Parallel problems occur in the platonist programs to ones which occur and may be solved in the nominalist ones. Again, here, a mine of examples of this sort can be found in the book by Goodman that I mentioned, *The Structure of Appearance*.

R. Ackermann (*University of Pennsylvania*): I would like to see one thing clarified here. Admission of the nominalist program as incomplete and perhaps incompletable seems to suggest, an unfortunate suggestion, that the platonist program is completed or completable.

Professor Rudner: It would be an unfortunate suggestion, indeed.

Dr. Ackermann: I would like to point out that even if platonism is granted, even then, with respect to certain problems (for example, the two that you have raised) platonism is not in any sense completed and there are equally strong grounds for holding that their program will not be completable. For example, in mathematics, take the one case of set theories themselves. Formal systems of set theories, even if they are known to be complete, are not known to be consistent. There is no straightforward way at the present time of showing their consistency and this is something which is certainly not done in the platonistic program. Also if you take dispositional predicates and even grant the platonist license to talk about classes, platonists themselves, or at least the less absurd ones, would not be able to complete an analysis that is entirely satisfactory even on their own grounds. I think it is important perhaps to clarify the fact that this incompletability is not just a feature of nominalism.

B. Baumrin (*University of Delaware*): Since we are at the point of dislodging misconceptions, let me dislodge one very small one. Professor Rudner has claimed that the nominalists are in a tremendous minority, as though submerged beneath untold numbers of Platonists . . .

Professor Rudner: And their classes, yes.

Dr. Baumrin: Perhaps submerged beneath an indefinite number of empty classes, but not active classes. I think the situation has changed in recent years and I think that it is now generally agreed that the nominalists have the better story to tell, particularly on the point with respect to the notion of consistency and completability.

Professor Rudner: Well, I think that more and more good and able people have become nominalists in the past few years but they are still clearly in the minority, I'm afraid.

Question: Suppose for a moment those whole positive numbers between zero and 10. Do you think we are thinking about the same thing now? Have I defined it sufficiently well? I may have missed one definition somewhere.

Professor Rudner: Well, we might or might not be. The chances are that we are not thinking about the same thing but I wonder how relevant it is that we are thinking about the same thing.

Question: I might be wishing to call this a "set" or a "group" or a "class" but I take it you don't hold to call it a "set" or a "group" or a "class."

Professor Rudner: That's the end of the quarrel, huh?

Question: No, I'm asking a question.

Professor Rudner: At least, it is the case that whatever it is I am talking of, I don't want simply to call it a "set" or a "class."

Question: I am thinking of what we call the numbers 1, 2, 3, 4, 5, etc. But what do you want to call these things I'm thinking about?

Professor Rudner: No, notice this, are you talking about the *numerals?*—because there is no problem about that. This is a string of calcium particles shaped on the board. If you are thinking about the *numerals*, then we might well be thinking about the same thing and there is no problem at all. But if you are thinking of what this numeral *refers to,* then my question is, what does it refer to?

Question: Well, can we think about the same thing for a minute; the numerals? Can we call them "numerals" and think about them?

Professor Rudner: I would like to call them individual calcium configurations on that blackboard.

Question: We are now thinking about the same thing but using two different words. I call it a "set." You object to this.

Professor Rudner: No, I wouldn't object to it unless in so doing you were also maintaining that the set of these things existed. For, the set of them is, notice, something over and above the things as well. No platonist holds that a class of objects is identical with the objects of which it is a class. The class has different properties from the objects. A class is an abstract thing. The things I am thinking of over here have mass and momentum. If you are calling them a set and mean by it (e.g., make deductions using the word *set*) things which indicate that you are using set in the sense in which, say, a mathematician would use the word *set*, then what you are talking about is something abstract; something which doesn't have, for example, any mass at all.

Question: You are saying that mass is a criterion for existence.

Professor Rudner: No, but I am saying that mass is not a characteristic of abstract entities.

Question: Still, you don't like these numbers on the board, and yet can't come up with a satisfactory explanation that we are both perceiving the same thing. Now, we can't *just* call it a pile of calcium on the board. Now what shall we call it?

Professor Rudner: I think the question you are raising is a very important question, because this kind of point comes up again and again in the discussions between nominalists and platonists and if this *were* the issue, the whole thing would be obviously trivial. If in using the term "set" as you just have, you are simply saying that *this* is synonymous with *that*, then there isn't any problem at all. You can call it "calcium configuration." You can call it "this set of chalk marks" and if, indeed, you *are* using the terms synonymously to refer to the individual numerals, there is no problem at all. But if you say "this is a set"; or "these chalk marks are, after all, a set," and moreover assert it has some of the characteristics which sets have and which no non-sets have, then that's where the difficulty comes in. In that latter case, you are not merely using one term as short for another nor confronting the trivial question "Who's to be master, the words or you." Not at all! If you begin saying that the fact that this is a set of chalk marks implies so and so about it, then you are saying that over and above these individual calcium configurations, there is another entity hovering some place, an abstract entity, the *set* of chalk marks which is different from the chalk marks. That's a distinction between the nominalists and platonists in this case. It is not a trivial difference about words.

D. Doehlert (*University of Delaware*): I can give the set that I take is hovering somewhere and I think that this gentleman might have well given it—that is, the set of positive integers—and this will remain hovering for some considerable time. And you have already suggested that handling the problems of infinite quantities as such is rather difficult for nominalists. Now, in expanding this gentleman's question in asking about this set of positive integers, do you want to discuss the problem of handling infinity itself?

Professor Rudner: Let me discuss it, at least in this way. You are quite right in suggesting that what the nominalist lacks at the moment is a way of giving an analysis in nominalistic terms which would be adequate to mathematics, at least in the sense that all theorems could be proved in the nominalist language for certain concepts of mathematics. This is perfectly correct. Now, the nominalist, however, might well be in the position of somebody, say in 16th century medicine, who is skeptical of the humors theory of personality (that highly developed and well-constructed theory of personality according to which, if anybody acts sad or melancholy, this is due to the fact that there is a dominance of his body's melancholy humors). Now, if you were someone who was skeptical of this as a personality theory in the 16th century, you might well be challenged to construct an alternative theory for it. You might begin to set out on the program of constructing the alternative theory. And you might even make some progress in it, but you might not have completed it. It might well be the case that this parallels the situation the nominalist faces in mathematics. Nobody can offer or has offered a proof that the nominalist program is incompletable; i.e., that it won't be able to handle the non-finite concepts of mathematics.

K. F. Traumann (*du Pont*): You have distinguished between nominalists and platonists, such that if one is wrong, the other is right. Is there some third group?

Professor Rudner: Well, traditionally, there is a third view called conceptualism, which has been put forward; and oh, I will have to make almost a parody of oversimplification of it—the primary notion of conceptualism is that although classes may not exist (or, better, abstract entities may not exist) in the real world, yet they exist in our minds; we have thoughts of them. They are thought creatures. Abstract entities appear for some purposes to be very useful thought creatures and that has made conceptualism, as sort of a middle course, awfully appealing. But I think the position rests on a confusion about what the issue is; for the nominalist and the platonist raise the question, as they must, for *all* of the furniture of the universe. Are these psychological entities, our thoughts now, are they individuals or classes? Is a *thought-of-a-class* an individual or is it a class?

Dr. Oplinger: When you mention a table, aren't you really giving a word for the class of atoms comprising the table and perhaps really talking in terms of classes here?

Professor Rudner: This, I think, comes back to the objection which I tried to take up a little bit in the paper; that is, the view that the nominalist can't use proper or common nouns in his discourse about things. No, as Quine again has demonstrated, I think, the use of platonistic terminology is innocent for any nominalist up to the point that he says that *there are* referents for his platonistic terms. So, if I assert "that table is brown" as an example, I have used the word "brown" and I have used the word "table." Those locutions, so long as the person using them doesn't commit himself to referents for them, are innocuous. Just as in the case of "Beethoven's Fifth Symphony" and just as in the case of the grammatically proper name in the locution "the Greeks worship Zeus" there need be no ontological commitment. To assert *truly* of the Greeks, as we do, the last-mentioned sentence, doesn't commit us to holding that Zeus exists. For the locution "the Greeks worship Zeus" is translatable into a sentence about certain activities of the Greeks that itself doesn't mention Zeus at all. So too, in the locution "that table is brown," or in a locution like "there exists an X such that X is brown and X is the table." This does not commit us to assert the existence of referents for the predicate terms, the so-called property terms that occur. Such locutions claim only the existence of an individual, an X.

Mathematical Objects

Joseph Ullian, *University of Chicago*

I remember once long ago when I was prompted, for
reasons which either never existed or are long forgotten, to
try to explain a little bit about number theory to a young
lady who knew nothing about number theory. All you need
to know about her is that she had lived for a considerable
time in the State of Nevada. I had to start somewhere, so I
found myself saying, "We are going to talk about the natural
numbers. By these we mean whole numbers, like one, two,
three, and so on—*all* of them—and also we are going to count
zero as one of these numbers." Her attentive pose blossomed
quickly into a question and she asked: "How about double
zero?"

We too are going to talk about the natural numbers. We
will find that inquiries into the nature of mathematical objects, if you will allow me that phrase, become quickly involved with the problem of mathematical truth. We will
find ourselves wishing to see things both mathematically and
philosophically, and this may bring on a kind of intellectual
jarring, since the intellectual moods demanded by these
disciplines are ordinarily so very different. I shall avoid in
what follows many technicalities relevant to the issues, but
I claim that my remarks lose no force in the full light of the
metamathematical detail. And let me here express my in-
debtedness for stimulation and suggestions provided by my
friends John Myhill, Robert McNaughton, and Paul Ziff.
They are not, however, to be held in any way accountable
for my views, and in fact the stimulation received was the
greater since their agreement with me on controversial
points was minimal. And so we begin.

What are numbers? Now I am not asking for names, nor

for an answer like "things we use in counting," though that may certainly be relevant. And I don't want the answer, "those things which arithmetic is about," though I am willing to say on a common-sense level that arithmetic is about numbers—on a common-sense level, I repeat, for I do not wish by this acknowledgment to contradict the deeper contention of extreme formalists, according to which mathematics consists wholly in the manipulation of meaningless marks on paper. Let me interject the comment that the phrases "those which" and more typically "that which" are among the most abused I know of in philosophy. Introductions of terms or explications of terms which employ them ought to carry a red flag, and perhaps the flag should even bear the words "Watch out for verbal tricks." But back to our problem. What we are seeking are comments about what kinds of *objects* numbers may be said to be, if indeed they may be said to be objects at all.

Very bad cases have been made for the identification of numbers with numerals, or with ideas in the mind, though variants of the second of these views are still with us. For Frege, numbers were extensions of concepts, but you need his rather elaborate metaphysics to get much out of that. To say that a number is a class of classes or the set of all numbers preceding it is to presuppose a resolution which can properly be made only after a very detailed study, the resolution to construe the question as a demand for the kind of explication achieved in the "reduction" of mathematics to logic. We want to begin closer to the beginning. And we begin by noting that sooner or later, in asking what numbers are, we will have to look at the properties and relations which we want to ascribe to them. It might happen that once we have done this we will be in a much better position to comment on the original question.

While we are not looking for names, it might help to give a characterization of the natural numbers by saying that zero is one of them, where "zero" is an undefined constant term, and that whatever is one of them has a unique successor which is one of them, where the successor relation is also undefined. We can say, moreover, that zero is not the successor of any number, and that distinct numbers have distinct successors. We can add that any property which belongs to zero and also belongs to the successor of every number to which it belongs, belongs to all the numbers. These statements are easily recognized as Peano's Postulates,[1] and they give us the very minimum, so to speak, which we want to insist upon. Put another way, we should want to discard immediately any notion of natural number which did not lend itself to the fulfilment of these stipulations.

Moreover, we want to be able to use the operations *plus* and *times* upon our numbers. We want a number x plus zero to equal x, and we want x plus the successor of y to equal the successor of the quantity x plus y. Similarly for *times*. We want x times zero to be zero, and x times the successor of y to be x times y, all plus x. This is the least that we should wish to require of these operations *plus* and *times*. As is well known, it is sufficient.

In fact, the various postulates or axioms given above are, properly formalized, a sufficient extralogical foundation for elementary number theory. (I use "elementary number theory" and "arithmetic" as synonyms.) Importing quantification, truth functions, and identity, with appropriate axioms and rules, we have all the ingredients on hand. We can define a great many further notions, such as that of being a prime number. Intuitively we want x to count as prime just in case it is at least two and is divisible by no numbers save one and itself. The formal definiens in terms of our ingredients might be one which would upon "translation" into English read: There is a number y such that the successor of the successor of y is equal to x, and, for any numbers z and w, if z times w equals x then either z equals x or z times any number u equals u.

Given such a system we can prove all the familiar theorems of arithmetic. We can prove Euclid's result that there is no greatest prime number by showing that for any number x, some number in excess of x (and in fact some such number no bigger than $x!$ plus 1) is a prime. So there are shown to be infinitely many prime numbers, as we ordinarily put it. Given any number, we can easily enough establish whether or not it is a prime, so that we can show that the number pairs $(3, 5)$, $(5, 7)$, $(11, 13)$ each exhibit two primes, the second of which exceeds the first by 2, that is, is the successor of the successor of the first. And we can add to the list of such pairs, say $(17, 19)$, $(29, 31)$, and $(41, 43)$. Given a pair it is easy enough systematically to test whether or not it belongs in this list. How many such pairs are there? To say that there are infinitely many is to say that for any number x there is a larger number y such that both y and y plus 2 are prime. That this is so is called the Twin Prime Theorem, but it is much better to call it the Twin Prime Conjecture (hereafter TPC), since it stands unproven. And it is unrefuted. Popularly this comes to saying that we do not know whether TPC is true or TPC is false, and popularly there is no question but that one of these is so, that TPC is true or that TPC is false. You will note that the sentence just concluded contains my first uses of the words "true" and "false," which have been carefully avoided in what has gone before. A large part of what follows will concern itself with exploring the rationale of applying these words in such contexts.

If we accept, in some sense, our various postulates, and resolve to accept the logical consequences of whatever we accept, then we are bound to accept all our theorems. Indeed, insofar as we are agreed on the acceptability of our postulates, we might be tempted to think of just those arithmetic sentences as true which are provable in a formal system such as the one which we are imagining ourselves to have constructed. Surely we will want to count at least these as true, if we are going to allow the notion of truth to attach itself to our arithmetic at all.

But now we must face Gödel's Incompleteness Theorem. We call a system *consistent* if not all its sentences are theorems. Gödel's result tells us that in any consistent formal system S which is as strong as ours there are sentences neither provable nor refutable by means of proof available in S. This is to say that there are sentences such that neither they nor their denials are theorems of S if S is consistent. Moreover, such undecidable sentences can be effectively discovered for any given system and those so discoverable are sometimes called Gödelian sentences. Arithmetic is thus incomplete, and since the result applies equally to any extension of a system such as ours, it is incompletable. So if we were to identify truth with provability in some system S, we would be forced to conclude, if we assume S consistent, that there are arithmetic sentences which are neither true nor false.

One frequently hears it claimed that Gödel has shown there to be arithmetic sentences which are true but unprovable. This claim is supported by more than the wish to retain the principle of excluded middle, according to which each sentence must be either true or false. For given a system S containing elementary number theory, we can construct a syntactic model J of S under which some of the sentences of S themselves express facts about syntactic properties of sentences of S. This construction uses the procedure known as the arithmetization of metamathematics, to which the technique called Gödel numbering is central. For example, let A_1 through A_6 be sentences of S. Under J, A_1 might be interpreted as saying that A_2 is an axiom of S; A_2 might be interpreted as saying that A_3 followed by A_4 constitutes a proof in S of A_5; A_3 might under J say that there is a proof in S of A_6, that is, that A_6 is a theorem of S. Now we can find a sentence G which expresses, under the syntactic model J, the fact that G itself is unprovable in S. G is a Gödelian sentence in the very strong sense that if there were a proof of G in S, we could from that proof construct a proof of G's denial in S, and, similarly, from a proof of G's denial in S, we could construct in S a proof of G. So either both G and its denial are theorems of S, from which the inconsistency of S would immediately follow owing to S's closure under the usual logical inferences, or else neither G nor its denial is a theorem of S. This simply states, of course, that G is an undecidable sentence in S. But now, insofar as G expresses its own unprovability, as it does under the interpretation J, there is reason to say that if S is consistent G is true, since G *is* unprovable if S is consistent.

G is unprovable if S is consistent, but not, so to speak, because of the *meaning* of G under J. G's unprovability follows by the strictly combinatorial argument in which we show that from a proof of G in S one could construct a proof in S of G's denial. Now insofar as we have reason to "accept" G, we might wish to consider an extended system S_1 exactly like S except for containing the additional axiom G, and thus additional theorems (if S was consistent), one of them G itself. G, recall, was a sentence of S and so built up by logic from numerical equations involving at most *zero, successor, plus,* and *times.* Its sentencehood in no way depends upon its interpretation under J. Nor, since we are imagining S to be a formal system, does G's sentencehood depend upon the arithmetic interpretation which it would receive by understanding "zero," "successor," "plus," and "times" in the ordinary arithmetic way. That too is an interpretation, but it differs from J, which provides a mirroring of the syntax of S within itself.

It is easily shown that S_1 is consistent if S is, for inconsistency of S_1 would imply provability of G's denial in S, hence inconsistency of S. To S_1 we can apply the Gödel argument again, discovering an undecidable sentence G_1 which, under a suitable syntactic interpretation J_1, expresses its own unprovability in S_1. Since the syntax of S_1 differs from that of S, there being an additional axiom, J_1 must differ from J. S_1 is as incompletable as S was; iteration of the process of appending axioms will clearly not yield a completed system to which the Gödel argument no longer applies.

Now, what of G? G is an axiom, and so a theorem of S_1.

J_1 does not inflict an untoward significance upon G, that is, G does not express under J_1 its own unprovability in S_1, though G does assert under J its own unprovability in S. G is true under J and provable in S_1. So, under J, G is now a provable truth. Since S_1's sentences are just those of S, J makes true the same sentences in S_1 which it made true in S. The theorems of S_1 are just those of S together with the consequents of those conditionals with G as antecedent which were provable in S. (One can construe this in terms of appropriate counterparts of conditionals if S contains no conditionals.) It follows that no theorem of S_1 can be false under J unless there were theorems of S false under J. Still, J is not a full-fledged syntactic model for S_1.

S_1 differed from S by having one further axiom G. Now consider an alternative extension S^* of S, also equipped with but a single additional axiom. But this time let the denial of G be the new axiom. S^* is consistent if S is, for inconsistency of S^* would imply provability of G in S, hence inconsistency of S.[†] To S^* as to S and S_1 Gödel's argument applies, so that we can find an undecidable sentence G^* which, under a suitable syntactic model J^*, expresses its own unprovability in S^*. Recall that under J, G's denial expresses G's *provability*—not *absolute* provability, whatever that might mean,[‡] but *provability in S*. And if S was consistent, G was *not* provable in that system, which is to say that our new axiom, G's denial, is false under J.

But we cannot straightaway conclude from these observations that S^* is a system in which falsehoods are provable. We could, alternatively, repudiate the interpretation J as inadequate to S^*, since sentences false under J are provable in S^*. This is oversimplified, in view of questions involving ω-inconsistency. But the point remains that interpretations,

---

† S^* is, however, ω-inconsistent, to use a term introduced in the following paragraph.

‡ An invigorating and incisive discussion of what it might mean appears in John Myhill's paper "Some Remarks on the Notion of Proof," *Journal of Philosophy*, LVII, 461–471 (1960).

like *J*, have no more claim upon us than their suitability allows them, that we are not barred from rejecting them and accepting sentences which, under them, express falsehoods. Truth and falsehood accrue to sentences of a formal language *only* through interpretation. So in accepting certain sentences we may think of ourselves as disqualifying certain interpretations, namely, those falsifying the sentences accepted—though in the light of ω-inconsistency there is rather more to be said.

Roughly, a system of arithmetic is ω-inconsistent if it contains a proof of an existential quantification and also contains a disproof of each of the instances of that existential quantification. An inconsistent system is thus ω-inconsistent, since it contains proofs and disproofs of everything, but ω-inconsistency is compatible with consistency. A system which is not ω-inconsistent is called ω-consistent. Now Gödel's Theorem has a remarkable consequence which we have not yet noted. It is shown that if *C* is a sentence which, under a suitable syntactic model of *S*, say *J* again, can be taken to express the consistency of *S*, then, if *S* is ω-consistent, *C* is undecidable in *S*. In fact, on the weaker assumption that *S* is consistent, *C* must be unprovable in *S*. So a consistent system cannot prove its own consistency, or, to state the ironic contrapositive (irony in metamathematics!), a system which purports to demonstrate its own consistency thereby provides proof of its inconsistency. If *S* is ω-consistent, *C*'s denial cannot be established in *S* either, but if *S* is consistent without being ω-consistent, it is possible that *C*'s denial may be provable within *S*. This, then, would be the strange case in which a theorem of *S* would appear to be false under a seemingly acceptable syntactic model of *S*; for we would in an assumed consistent *S* be able to prove a sentence which, under *J*, appeared to express *S*'s inconsistency. The phenomenon of ω-inconsistency provides many such paradoxes and leads to the consideration of what are called *nonstandard models*. The study of these raises rather deep questions concerning "limitations of our notation," but they are beyond the scope of the present paper.

Now, then, *C* fares very much like *G*. Indeed, since consistency of our system is of great concern to us, it is of much more interest to introduce *C* as a new axiom than it was to introduce *G* in that role. If we add *C* as a new axiom, the resultant system, if consistent, will still be vulnerable to the Gödel argument, in fact to the Gödel *arguments,* counting now the corollary of the previous paragraph. Note here that *S*'s consistency does not guarantee consistency of the extension. And note that while *C* expresses under *J* the consistency of *S*, it cannot express consistency of the new system lest that new system be thereby inconsistent. As before, we can iterate the process of adding to each system in turn a sentence expressing its consistency, thus obtaining a sequence of systems, but we cannot hope thereby to ascend outside the scope of the Gödel arguments. And we may, in fact, generate an inconsistent system in this way, even if *S* was consistent.

And as before, we can play the game "against interest." We can get an extension of *S* by taking *C*'s denial as our new axiom, and we can iterate this process, appending to each system what was interpretable in that system as a statement of that system's *in*consistency. Of course, we will not escape the scope of the Gödel arguments in this way either, and we will again want to throw away, in general, each old syntactic model as we ascend. Indeed, incredibly enough, this "against interest" procedure is actually safer, in terms of preserving simple consistency, than the corresponding "with interest" procedure of appending axioms affirming, in effect, consistency. We can show that if *S* is consistent, addition of an axiom expressing its inconsistency will yield a system which, though not ω-consistent, is still consistent, while we have seen that addition of assertions of consistency can lead to inconsistency. Such are the treacheries of formal systems and their interpretations.

What of the arithmetic interpretation through these many

extensions? It is easy to forget while dealing with sentences expressing under special interpretations real-life properties of the systems involved that those sentences are still sentences of arithmetic built from equations in the usual way. And put crudely, each sentence expresses, or appears to express, a fact about numbers, a fact apparently independent of the various syntactic interpretations. One can say the following. Insofar as what the arithmetic interpretation requires is prescribed by the postulates originally adopted, *every* consistent extension of S admits the arithmetic interpretation (though extensions which are ω-inconsistent will require nonstandard models, and there are reasons for regarding these as unacceptable for arithmetic). For every consistent extension of S has among its theorems all those sentences which follow by logic from the postulates and no denials of such sentences. To restate the content of the Incompleteness Theorem, the postulates for number theory leave us with many degrees of freedom; and chop away as we might, degrees of freedom must remain unless we fall into the total bondage of inconsistency.

To free us from thoughts of arithmetic for a moment, think of plane geometry. Think of Euclid's Parallels Postulate, that through any point not on a given line there is exactly one line parallel to the given line. Now is this postulate true? I suspect that anyone who is at all acquainted with the developments in modern physics will have the reaction that this is an absurd question, or at best a very incomplete one. Recall, however, that the postulate was once held to be self-evidently true, though admittedly to a lesser degree than the other usual postulates of plane geometry. We now know, and accept with equanimity, that assumption of alternative axioms in place of the Euclidean Parallels Postulate yields geometries which can be shown to be consistent if Euclidean geometry is consistent. Further, there is reason to consider one of these alternative geometries, Riemannian, as an instrument better designed to fill the needs of physical theory than its Euclidean counterpart.

Points and lines are no longer supposed to have objective existence; these terms acquire reference only through application of the various geometries. One may say that they are idealizations, but this, then, is just to say that the various geometries apply only approximately to the physical world. If one is troubled about the truth of a statement of geometry, one is concerned either with its provability in a given geometric system or with its applicability in a given physical context.

In set theory one can state the existence of extraordinarily large ordinal numbers known as inaccessible ordinals. It has been shown that the assumption that such ordinals exist is consistent with the other accepted axioms of set theory; whether or not it is independent of those other axioms is not known. Do such ordinals exist? If their existence were somehow shown to follow from the other accepted axioms, the answer would be Yes. Failing this, the answer, the only answer, will be embodied in the decision of practicing set theorists as to whether or not the assertion of their existence should be added as an axiom to the rest of set theory. Such a decision will be based on practical grounds, or at least what set theorists think of as practical. If results deemed desirable follow from the assumption that there are inaccessible ordinals, then there are inaccessible ordinals. If not, then not.

What sets exist? One's answer depends on many considerations, not the least of which is how one construes the epsilon which is primitive in set theory. Those of us who want to say that the epsilon receives its significance, its entire significance, from the development of the theory in which it occurs, will clearly not attempt to answer *a priori*. One considers the uses to which one wants set theory to be put. These, of course, are essentially uses in pure mathematics, which makes the case quite different from that of geometry. In this general connection I shall quote from Bertrand Russell's 1924 essay "Logical Atomism," [2] though from the full context it is not clear that Russell's position is fully in the spirit of my own:

The logically first principles of logic—at least some of them—are to be believed, not on their own account, but on account of their consequences. The epistemological question: "Why should I believe this set of propositions?" is quite different from the logical question: "What is the smallest and logically simplest group of propositions from which this set of propositions can be deduced?" Our reasons for believing logic and pure mathematics are, in part, only inductive and probable, in spite of the fact that, in their *logical* order, the propositions of logic and pure mathematics follow from the premises of logic by pure deduction.

In 1926, Hilbert introduced the distinction between *real* and *ideal* statements of mathematics. The real statements are supposed to be those with intuitive meaning. For Hilbert, a statement about an infinite collection would count as ideal. As Kleene [3] remarks, "The addition of 'ideal elements' to a system to complete its structure and simplify the theory of the system is a common and fruitful device in modern mathematics." Now among those who still make this distinction it is currently popular to count as real only statements of elementary number theory. For our purposes I imagine we can identify arithmetic *statements* with the sentences of an appropriate formalization of arithmetic. That arithmetic statements alone be regarded as real is reminiscent of Kronecker's remark that God made the natural numbers and man made the rest.

While drawing at elementary number theory the line between real and ideal statements, Hartley Rogers, Jr., [4] writes regarding the possibility of adding an axiom which we can think of as our *C* above:

Whether or not we decide to adopt it *can only depend* upon some form of external evidence . . . At this point an investigator often says, "I will take *C* and call it *true* on the basis of certain empirical evidence—namely, that after many and varied explorations no one has found an inconsistency." In other words, we are inclined to adopt the *real* statement *C*, because (in part) of results of a certain finite amount of experiment. . . . A person attempting to extend elementary number theory is in the position of a natural scientist attempting to widen a theory in order to describe and predict a wider range of natural phenomena. In such activity, criteria of simplicity and elegance as well as factual evidence appear to play a role.*

This calls back to mind Russell's, "Our reasons for believing logic and pure mathematics are, in part, only inductive and probable," though Russell was writing without knowledge of the Gödel Theorem and was not making quite the same suggestion as Rogers. Reading it a certain way, there is something of a paradox in Rogers' view. Real statements, statements of arithmetic, are to be accepted or rejected, judged true or false, on empirical grounds. It is as if we have gone the whole way around the circle and come back to John Stuart Mill!

But the air of paradox can be made to disappear quickly if we will only be hard-headed. Real truths about real objects, be they mathematical or not, are independent of our thought, purposes, and powers only to a degree. In another connection, but fully applicable here, Norman Campbell [5] notes, "I should suggest to (the questioner) that he calls those things real because they are necessary to make the world intelligible to him." For one who works in the foundations of mathematics it is, locally, the world of mathematics that must be made in some sense intelligible. Compare Carnap [6]: "The acceptance or rejection of abstract linguistic forms (e.g., those representing the framework of numbers), just as the acceptance or rejection of any other linguistic forms in any branch of science, will finally be decided by their efficiency as instruments, the ratio of the results achieved to the amount and complexity of the efforts required." For Carnap this accompanies a denial of the

---

* See reference 4. Italics are his. I find extremely enlightening the detailed discussion of extensions of elementary number theory which Rogers gives in this work.

meaningfulness of extrasystematic ascriptions of reality, in particular of reality to numbers. But even for those of us in basic sympathy with Carnap's thoughts on ontology, it might also be taken as providing a way of making sense of just such ascriptions.*

Are Peano's Postulates and the postulates governing *plus* and *times* true? If this question seems different from the corresponding questions about axioms for plane geometry or for set theory, I submit that it is largely because geometry and set theory, unlike arithmetic, present cases in which there is reason to consider alternative foundations—for geometry because it has different dimensions of application and for set theory because that field is still highly fluid. There is no serious reason to consider radical alteration of the well-accepted fundamental principles of arithmetic, say as embodied in the Peano postulates. So we can say straight-away that these postulates are true. But that arithmetic statements are alone among mathematical statements in having clear intuitive meaning seems to me to be false, partly because I appear not to have been given the ironclad intuition of numbers which some claim, and, more seriously, because it is my experience that how much intuitive mean-ing a mathematical statement has to me is more or less directly proportionate to the amount of thinking I have done about the particular area of mathematics in which it lies. Of course, the notion of intuitive clarity is not one without difficulties in its own right. Much more important, it is not clear to me that intuitive meaning of a set of statements or, to use Carnap's term, a "framework," gives it a valid claim on our attention. Intuitivity surely does not rule the roost in choice of geometry for physics, and what seemed intui-tively acceptable led to all kinds of trouble in set theory. Where we have intuitions that we can harness in the doing of mathematics and in its application, let us welcome them. But let us on no account confuse mathematics, its founda-

* See footnote, p. 204.

tions, or its justification with questions belonging properly to psychology.

Certainly we accept our arithmetic postulates. But this not through homage to a singularly untouchable mathematical world. Were our methods of measurement and counting sufficiently different, we might, as Gasking shows,[7] have 4 times 3 coming to 24, and not just by way of a patently verbal or conventional maneuver. Or we might want to stop the numbers with 10^{100} and just not go any further (a modern extension of the tribal "one, two, three, many"). One might say that in such cases we would be in a position of not really knowing arithmetic. But one might also say that we would be in a position of having, knowing, and using a different arithmetic.

In a recent article, Goddard [8] observes that "it is not that we check the (arithmetic) axioms against the objects of the model, as we might check statements about cows by looking in fields, but rather, by supposing them to be true (i.e., by interpreting them in a certain way) we define a set of 'objects.' That is, we create the model by making the assumption, not the truth of the assumption by taking the model." I think there is much to be said for this account, though it oversimplifies the case to suggest that we get *a model* by making the assumptions which our postulates, as they are ordinarily understood, express. What we have seen at great length is that we get very many models, among which we cannot choose on the basis of the postulates alone. If we are to narrow down the field, we must use considerations of other kinds. By attending, for example, to syntactic properties of the system, we gain grounds, through metamathematical arguments carried out in a suitable metalanguage, for regarding some initially unprovable sentences as acceptable and desirable. In particular, there is good reason for accepting sentences, like G and C above, whose denials can be shown to generate ω-inconsistency. Other analytical arguments, transcending what can be proved arithmetically, may provide reasons for accepting still more sentences. Such arguments lie always within some formal or formalizable system, but their application to arithmetic is often far from automatic and it is not always clear what one wants to conclude from them regarding the acceptability of particular arithmetic sentences. Now, acceptance of additional sentences may be counted as a decision to regard them as true. When we do this, we limit our choice of a model, or, more in the spirit of Goddard, we sharpen the characterization of the objects of our model. On one reading, Gödel's Theorem tells us that we can never get these objects into perfect focus. As Rogers observes, additions to the stock of acceptable arithmetic sentences must be made with an eye open to empirical findings, most notably discoveries of inconsistency, so they are best made in a somewhat tentative spirit. In seeing the variety of canons which are relevant to ascriptions of truth to sentences of arithmetic, we see, I think, all that is relevant to the question of what arithmetic sentences are about. As far as I can see, the militant claims now popular for the reality of numbers are best understood in this light. We may think of ourselves as limited on several fronts as to what we may ascribe to numbers, so that numbers pass what is perhaps the most basic test of (objective) reality open to empiricists: intransigence.*

What, then, of TPC? If TPC is neither provable nor refutable within our system S, it is still possible that the extensions of S which we elect to make will decide whether the conjecture is to be accepted or rejected. Note that its acceptance or rejection would then be subject to revision, as it were, in the light of further evidence. But there is no assurance that TPC would be decidable through suitable extensions of S. In such a case, it seems to me that there would be no strong ground for insisting that either TPC is true or TPC is false (i.e., that TPC has a truth value). Indeed, the general pronouncement to the effect that each

---

* My use of this word in this connection was suggested by a helpful remark of Elizabeth Flower.

arithmetic sentence either is true or is false carries with it a picture in which, for arbitrary sentence A, there is an objective fact expressed either by A or its denial. And this picture may be misleading. It might be that the intuitions, or whatever, distilled in our axioms and strengthened by our grasp of higher mathematics simply fail to determine A one way or the other. That is, while seeming to make an assertion, A may in fact be a contentless composite of partially defined ingredients.

So may be TPC, but there are two arguments against its so being. In a recent talk, James Guard * noted that all those sentences of arithmetic which have been found to be undecidable within arithmetic have been in a certain sense pathological; that is, they have been in a sense self-referring under a syntactic interpretation superimposed upon them. Thus there might be said to be inductive evidence against TPC's undecidability. And we have observed that such evidence is not by any means irrelevant in assessing the status of arithmetic sentences. Secondly, TPC seems to have very clear content. Primeness is quite well defined. Indeed, for each number it is trivial (in principle) to demonstrate either primeness or compositeness. And claims of the "there is no greatest number such that" kind seem clear enough, though there do arise in this connection problems of constructivity. So if our intuition be any guide, TPC, under an ordinary arithmetic construal, seems to have the kind of content that ought to be fixed one way or the other, that ought not to figure in one of our degrees of freedom. How good an argument this is taken to be depends on how we feel about such intuitions.

Of course, it could turn out that there are no absolutely undecidable sentences of arithmetic, that any A is acceptable or rejectible on some acceptable ground. (This would not, however, lead us to a completed formal system, which remains an impossibility.) In this case we might want to

* At the Moore School of Electrical Engineering, University of Pennsylvania, 7 February, 1962.

reinstate the picture questioned above, but it would even then be well to remain aware of its quilted character.

The picture might serve one other purpose. To a practicing mathematician, it might be a sound heuristic principle to suppose each arithmetic sentence determinate as to truth. Such a supposition might well facilitate discoveries of proofs. For, analogously, it is interesting how quickly a proof or disproof can be found in mathematics once one knows which of these to look for. Knowing which to look for, the work seems much less than half that of finding the one or the other. And now we are touching upon psychological questions of a kind, though considerations not at all like those involving intuitivity.

I do not know what the right label is for the position I hold. It is a form of pragmatism. It stands against the psychological component of Intuitionism, and it is not at home with the absolutes of Mathematical Platonism, the eternal and immutable realms of mathematical objects and truths. Not that I mind abstract entities. My view on these is more or less Carnap's.* If it helps to talk in certain terms, let us talk in those terms, by all means. Finally, I am not quite a Formalist, though but for its rigidity I might find that position attractive.

The intellectual history and the non-intellectual history of man show his unending search for absolutes to have been

---

* It is perhaps more accurate to say that my view follows the spirit of Carnap but the letter of Quine, as given in "On What There Is," *Review of Metaphysics*, 2 (1948), and reprinted in Linsky (reference 6). Quine's pragmatism extends beyond Carnap's in that it applies pragmatic criteria to ontological questions themselves. Quine says, "Our acceptance of an ontology is, I think, similar in principle to our acceptance of a scientific theory, say a system of physics. We adopt, at least insofar as we are reasonable, the simplest conceptual scheme into which the disordered fragments of raw experience can be fitted and arranged" (pp. 35–36 of the original article, pp. 203–204 of Linsky). But in view of the extensive and rather restrictive ontological preferences which Quine's writings reveal, I have considered it less misleading to identify my view as a variant of Carnap's.

more unlucky than lucky. But for the questioning of absolutes in mathematics, we gain a reward of some importance. For now there need be no comparisons under which our knowledge of matters of fact stands poor and pale.

References

1. Bertrand Russell, *Introduction to Mathematical Philosophy*, Allen & Unwin, London, 1919, pp. 5 ff.
2. Bertrand Russell, "Logical Atomism," in Robert C. Marsh, ed., *Logic and Knowledge*, Allen & Unwin, London, 1956, pp. 324–325.
3. Stephen Kleene, *Introduction to Metamathematics*, Van Nostrand, New York, 1952, p. 55.
4. Hartley Rogers, Jr., *Theory of Recursive Functions and Effective Computability*, Vol. I, mimeographed by the Massachusetts Institute of Technology, 1956–57, pp. 148–149.
5. Norman Campbell, *What Is Science?*, Dover, New York, 1952, p. 105. (First published 1921.)
6. Rudolf Carnap, "Empiricism, Semantics, and Ontology," *Revue Internationale de Philosophie*, 11, 40 (1950); reprinted in Leonard Linsky, ed., *Semantics and the Philosophy of Language*, University of Illinois, Urbana, 1952, p. 228.
7. Douglas Gasking, "Mathematics and the World," *Australasian Journal of Psychology and Philosophy* (1940); reprinted in Anthony Flew, ed., *Logic and Language*, 2nd Series, Blackwell, Oxford, 1955 (see especially pp. 214–215).
8. L. Goddard, "Proof-Making," *Mind*, LXXI, 77 (Jan., 1962).

PART IV

Philosophical Aspects
of Biology

Scientific Explanation—Chance and Antichance in Organic Evolution

Theodosius Dobzhansky, *The Rockefeller Institute*

Classical Hindu art often represents the god Siva engaged in what, as Einstein thought and as most of us probably will agree, would be an odd pastime for a deity. Siva and his consort Parvati are shown playing with dice. Should not a god know beforehand which way the dice will fall? Or is the world a gigantic wheel of chance to gods as well as to men? Prevalence of chance, of chance which is not a surface appearance only, not a remediable lacuna in our knowledge, but which reaches deep down in the scheme of things, is intensely repugnant to most minds. It was this kind of chance that Laplace tried to exorcise in his famous dictum in 1820:

> An intelligence knowing all the forces acting in nature at a given instant, as well as the momentary positions of all things in the universe, would be able to comprehend in one single formula the motions of the largest bodies as well as of the lightest atoms in the world, provided that its intellect were sufficiently powerful to subject all data to analysis; to it nothing would be uncertain, the future as well as the past would be present to its eyes.

But Laplace concludes with an anticlimax:

> All the mind's efforts in the search for truth tend to approximate to the intelligence we have imagined, although it will forever remain infinitely remote from such an intelligence.[1]

When, 102 years ago, Darwin's theory of evolution burst into the world, it faced hostility on two counts. Religious fundamentalists could not overlook the fact that Darwin's

209

views did not tally with their understanding of the first chapter of Genesis. But, after all, Darwin was not the first to suggest that the living world has had a long evolutionary history. It was Darwin's account of what brings evolution about that seemed a century ago, and still seems, staggering to some thoughtful people. Evolution is not guided by God, as Robert Chambers supposed in his *Vestiges of the Natural History of Creation,* not even by efforts or strivings of the organism itself, as supposed by Lamarck. The whole of evolution, from viruses or amoebae to man, is a "mechanical" process in which a predominant role is played by "chance." Evolution has neither purpose nor goal, and yet it results, often though by no means always, in adaptation, i.e., in fitting the organism to its environment. René Dubos, certainly no anti-evolutionist, nevertheless wrote in his recent book "evolutionary theory in its present form does not account for the emergence of man from the inanimate world." [2]

Darwin pointed out that every living species shows individual variation; some people, or *Drosophila* flies, or pine trees are taller, or bigger, and others shorter or smaller, some more and others less heavily pigmented, some more and others less resistant to diseases, or to starvation, or to desiccation. The variation gives scope to natural selection, since in some environments the taller, or darker, or more resistant individuals have better chances to survive or to leave progenies than do their opposites. Darwin recognized that variation is the fountainhead of evolution, but acknowledged that he did not know just how variation arises. We are at present in a somewhat better position; hereditary variation arises by mutations; we are beginning to discern the physicochemical basis of mutation; we even know how to speed up the process of mutation, but, with rare exceptions, not how to induce a specific mutation in an individual and at a time of our choosing.

The nature of mutation can be most generally described as an error in self-reproduction. Normally, genes serve as templates for synthesis of their exact copies, but very occasionally the process of replication goes wrong; the imperfect copy, if it retains the ability to replicate itself, is a new, mutant, gene. It would, then, seem that what evolutionary changes will occur will depend on what mutations will happen to arise. The fountainhead of evolution is, consequently, a medley of accidents of gene misreplications, giving rise to a mass of mutations. Most of the accidents are unlucky ones, and mutants are as a rule incapacitating the organism in which they occur to some extent, often making it completely inviable. It is fair to say that the outcome of mutation is usually a hereditary disease. But there are some, a small minority, of lucky accidents; some mutants improve the fitness of the organism in some environments. Natural selection will perpetuate these and cast out the detrimental ones, thus making the evolution as a whole maintain or even advance life.[3]

The view that evolution results essentially from interaction of mutation and natural selection is at present known as biological, or synthetic, theory of evolution. The evidence on which this theory rests cannot be discussed here in detail. In my opinion, this evidence is fairly convincing, at least insofar as so-called microevolutionary changes are concerned, i.e., genetic changes within a species involving alterations of one or a few genes. Mutations do arise, apparently in all organisms, and they arise at random with respect to their usefulness to their carriers. In other words, nature has not been so kind as to arrange things that only mutations that are most likely to be adaptive in the available environments would appear where and when they are needed. The process of mutation would by itself produce an array of freaks and cripples, not evolution. It is the natural selection which converts the mutational raw materials into genetic endowments, genotypes, that are fit to perpetuate themselves in the world as it actually exists.

Natural selection has often been compared to a sieve which retains the rare useful and lets go the more numerous harmful mutants. This is good enough analogy when applied to microevolutionary changes; it leads to difficulties when used as a model of macroevolution as well, i.e., of the emergence of new orders and classes of organisms, development of complex new organs and functions, involving many changes in many genes and thorough reconstruction of whole genotypes. Darwin himself wrote in *The Origin of Species* that "to suppose that the eye with all its inimitable contrivances for adjusting the focus to different distances, for admitting different amounts of light, and for the correction of spherical and chromatic aberration, could have been formed by natural selection, seems, I freely confess, absurd in the highest degree," and in a letter to Asa Grey that "the eye to this day gives me a cold shudder."

A cold shudder indeed, if one imagines that every tiny detail of the eye structure had to be produced by a separate mutation in a separate gene, and that all these mutant genes had to come together in just the right combination to add up to a functioning eye. This is too improbable an event to ask for, even given the two billion years plus that geologists allow us for organic evolution. Its improbability is sometimes illustrated by the so-called "monkey analogy"—a million monkeys pounding a million typewriters for a million years would not produce a great poem, say Dante's *Divine Comedy*.

Quite properly, some biologists are looking for possible alternatives to the modern biological theory of evolution. A number of such alternative theories have been proposed, variously called by their authors orthogenesis, nomogenesis, aristogenesis, hologenesis, or, collectively, autogenesis. All autogenetic theories have this much in common—they assume that evolutionary changes are preformed in the organism itself. The genetic basis of the organism changes, perhaps gradually but relentlessly, in a definite direction. Environment and natural selection can only accept or reject the changes that occur; and indeed, the changes that occur may go against the welfare of the organism, resulting in "evolutionary senescence" and "evolutionary death" or extinction of the species. So, for example, the ammonites, dinosaurs, and mastodons died out because their genes were at a certain stage of their evolution changing in a wrong direction.

Autogenetic theories of evolution are really part and parcel of the venerable doctrine of preformation. Classical preformationists of the seventeenth and eighteenth centuries believed that organic development is essentially growth, and some even claimed to have seen in the head of the human spermatozoon a homunculus, a diminutive figure of man. Modern preformation is a more subtle notion; Weismann thought that every body part is represented in the sex cells by something called a determinant; some modern chemical geneticists assume that every gene produces one and only one enzyme, and that every enzyme is responsible for a "trait" or a syndrome of "traits." Applied to evolutionary problems, preformation means that evolutionary, phylogenetic, developments are somehow built in the living organism or in its genes. Man and every other form of life now existing were infolded in the primordial protoplasm, and evolution was basically an unfolding of what had been there in a concealed state from the start. Once you accept this assumption, you can, if you so desire, ascribe the unfoldment to the guidance by a superior power, or psyche, or vital force. Or you can be a simon-pure mechanist, and theorize that genes have to undergo certain changes in a certain order as inexorably as do atoms of radioactive elements.

The trouble with autogenesis is that it is a fancy name for something that needs explanation, and not an explanation of anything. To say that the living world has evolved as it did because it was constructed to evolve this way would only be meaningful if we were told something about the construction which makes the evolution proceed as it does. Nobody has claimed to have found anything about this construction, or ventured to predict how evolutionary changes will go in the future (excepting forecasts of trivial evolutionary events, namely, probable extinction of some species owing to man's interference with their habitats). Worst of all, autogenesis simply takes for granted the outstanding characteristic of living organisms and of their evolution— their adaptedness to the environments in which they live. The indisputable advantage of Darwin's natural selection theory is that it does give an account that is free of at least overt inconsistencies of how adaptation takes place. Even Berg, the author of the most nearly mechanistic theory of autogenesis (nomogenesis), had to assume an inherent purposefulness of the living matter.[4] Such assumptions seem to be inherently pleasing to some authors who defend them with admirable eloquence (e.g., Joseph Wood Krutch), but as an arid-minded scientist I find them unprofitable.

Rejection of autogenetic theories certainly does not automatically vindicate the system of views that constitutes the biological theory of evolution. Let us, however, consider further the difficulty of the latter theory which gave Darwin the "cold shudder." Mutation rates in most genes are small, say of the order of 10^{-5}. Now, to suppose that all the thousands of genes which play some roles in the development of the human eye mutated simultaneously to just the states which give an instrument of a complexity and perfection that the eye actually is, would tax one's credulity (the probability would be something like 10^{-500} or 10^{-1000}). But no such wildly incredible surmises are called for.

The difficulty lessens or falls away if we are reminded that the eye did not appear suddenly in all its present perfection. Every one of us, and also every mouse, fly, and every blade of grass, is a scion of the same majestically ancient family—the living world. Philosophers and biologists who are quite properly impressed by the wondrous variety, complexity, and harmony of the organic forms should keep in mind that these forms have resulted from roughly two billion years of evolutionary history. And this history was not a mere "Atoms casually together hurl'd"; nor was it the work of a psyche, or a vital force, or an autogenesis; it was under a relentless control of natural selection, a process which makes probable what otherwise would be in the highest degree improbable.

Our close, as well as fairly remote ancestors, had eyes for something like half a billion years. For perhaps twice as long, our still more remote ancestors had some organs, or some physiological functions, that enabled them to perceive light. Perception of light, and later vision, were unquestionably important for their evolutionary survival and success. Natural selection accordingly exerted pressure to maintain, and whenever genetic materials were available to improve, the organs concerned. The point can perhaps be made clearer by considering one wrong and one right analogy of the biological evolution. It is wrong to compare the evolution of the eye to building a modern automobile on an assembly line. The analogy is wrong because the automobile does not start being used until the last bolt and the last speck of paint are where they belong, while our ancestors certainly were using their eyes. A better analogy is the gradual "evolution" of automobiles from the first internal combustion engine, or even from the invention of the first wheel, to the modern models.

Without going into biological technicality, I want to forestall two possible misunderstandings. The role of the engineer, or the inventor, in the above analogy is played in biological evolution by natural selection. This ascribes neither foresight nor volition to natural selection, which is, of course, a "blind," mechanical process, acting through differential survival and reproduction of the carriers of different genetic equipments in certain environments. Natural selection is thoroughgoingly opportunistic—it alters the organism in whatever ways happen to be advantageous in a given place at a given time, even if these alterations are liable to lead to extinction when conditions change. Furthermore, the emergence in evolution of the genetic basis of the human eye should not necessarily be envisaged as a gradual acquisition of one after the other of the genes which now exist in the human species. Although there is no way at present to verify this hypothesis experimentally, it is probable that similar functions, such as vision, are sustained in organisms that are not very closely related (say, mammals, birds, and fishes) by different sets of genes. In other words, the genotypes of our ancestors underwent thorough reconstructions repeatedly in their evolution.

We must now return to the allegation that the type of scientific explanation represented by the biological theory of evolution "makes too great demands on chance" to be credible. Nagel has justly remarked, "the word 'chance' is notoriously ambiguous as well as vague," and "that saying an event 'happens by chance' is not in general incompatible with asserting the event to be determined, except when 'happening by chance' is understood to mean that the event has no determining conditions for its occurrence." What, then, is the role of chance in evolutions?

The simplest evolutionary event is appearance of a mutant which is better adapted to the environment than the ancestral form, and which replaces the latter owing to the action of natural selection. This can easily be observed when a microbial culture, such as that of coli bacteria, is exposed to an antibiotic, such as streptomycin. Mutations to streptomycin resistance take place in normal, i.e., sensitive, bacteria at rates of the order of 10^{-8} per cell division; with a proper concentration of the antibiotic only the resistant cells survive, multiply, and form new colonies. Now, under ordinary conditions we cannot tell when and in which particular cell the mutation will occur; however, if we expose inocula of, say, 10^{10} cells to the antibiotic, most of them will contain some mutant cells, and therefore we can predict that resistant strains will be obtained. The probability can be calculated of obtaining a resistant strain with an inoculum of any given size.

The possibility of prediction is, thus, contingent on the occurrence of a chance event, mutation, which we can handle in probability terms, and of an anti-chance process, selection, which in some instances we can contrive at our discretion. The nature of mutation is still insufficiently known, although studies on the chemical basis of inheritance have made spectacular progress in recent years. The specificity of the gene apparently resides in the structure of its deoxyribonucleic acid (DNA) component. The genetic "information" is "coded" in the DNA molecules by means of different linear sequences of four chemical radicals, nucleotides. These nucleotides may conveniently be pictured as four "letters" of the genetic "alphabet." A gene may then be analogized with a word or a sentence in print; four letters are sufficient to spell virtually an infinity of words and sentences, just like the "letters" of the Morse code (dot, dash, gap). Mutation may be pictured hypothetically as a substitution, rearrangement, addition, or deletion of one or more "letters" in the genetic message. In principle, though not in actual fact, it may be possible to induce a desired mutation when and where needed. This reductionist explanation of mutation may, if confirmed, bring the process of mutation conceivably under human control.

Pushing the process of reduction to the next higher level, we might picture the organic evolution as a sequence of elementary evolutionary events, each event being a mutation–selection–replacement triad. This is indeed the picture drawn by some geneticists, and not only in popular lectures and articles. But this is an over-simplification; to forget this fact is to miss understanding some of the most interesting aspects of the evolutionary process. In addition to mutation and selection, three factors of capital importance in evolution must be considered. These factors are gene interaction, sexual recombination, and adaptation to environmental heterogeneity. Our account of these factors in the present article must be necessarily very brief.[5]

The genetic information passed from generation to generation is atomistic—it is coded in more or less discrete genes. But the development, the ontogeny, is unitary—it is brought about by all the genes acting in concert. There are no separate genes for eyes, for fingers, for digestion, or for intelligence. The genotype as a whole, interacting with a certain sequence of environments, engenders a process of development extending from fertilization to death, which evolves eyes, fingers, digestion, intelligence, and everything else which an individual has or does. We do not inherit the genotypes of our parents, we inherit only some of their genes. But what we are is, and what our parents were was, determined by the genotypes, by the gene patterns interacting with environmental patterns. An analogy may here be helpful—genes act in development as members of a symphony orchestra, not as solo players.

In composition of the genotype, of the gene pattern, the genetic orchestra, an important role is played by the gene recombination in the process of sexual reproduction. With asexual reproduction, as in bacteria which divide by simple fission or in fruit trees which are propagated by grafting, the whole progeny has, barring mutation, exactly the same genotype as the parent had. Not so with sex. Every individual human is heterozygous for many genes, because he has inherited somewhat different variants (alleles) of many genes from his mother and his father. Gregor Mendel has shown almost a century ago that an individual heterozygous for n genes is potentially capable to produce 2^n kinds of sex cells with different gene complements; if both parents are heterozygous for the same n genes, 3^n different genotypes may arise in their offspring; and if each is heterozygous for n different genes then 4^n genotypes are potentially possible.

There is unfortunately no way at present to tell for how many genes a given individual, or an average individual, is heterozygous. For higher organisms, 50 or 100 are more likely to be underestimates than overestimates. However, 2 to the 50th or the 100th power, not to speak of 3 or 4 to these powers, are numbers far exceeding the numbers of individuals alive in any existing species, of at least the higher organisms. Sexual reproduction is more efficient a mechanism than it needs to be; it is capable of engendering numbers of genotypes, genetic endowments, potentially vastly greater than can in reality be incorporated in living individuals.

The most interesting consequences are two. First, among sexually produced individuals, no two are likely to have the same genes; my genotype, and yours (unless you have an identical twin), is probably unique, unprecedented, and nonrecurrent. Secondly, some potentially possible genotypes, in fact a great majority of them, will never be realized. Is it, however, a matter of chance, of the same sort of chance which we face when playing roulette or card games, which genotypes will and will not come into existence? This is a fascinating, but also an immensely complex and as yet not fully solved, problem, which has received less attention than it deserves.

If life existed in only a single uniform and constant environment, evolution might conceivably have produced a genotype optimally fitted to that environment and then come to a standstill. In reality, living creatures dwell in a great variety of environments, in water and on land, in different climes, and follow different ways of life. Different individuals of the same species, and in fact a single individual at different times, face somewhat dissimilar environments. And finally, no environment remains constant in time. It must be kept in mind that natural selection is an environmental agency; Schmalhausen and other authors have pointed out that, in terms of cybernetics, there is a feedback connection between the genetics of living systems and the environment, via the process of natural selection.[6]

The biological theory of evolution is environmentalist, in the sense that it regards adaptation to the environment the chief stimulus of evolutionary change. Herein lies a profound difference between the biological theory and the autogenetic theories, the latter regarding the environment as at most an arbitrator assessing the fitness of what has arisen through the action of autonomous organic causes. But the role of the environment in evolution must be understood correctly. Suppose that the climate of a certain region grows more and more arid. What evolutionary changes will occur in the plant species composing the flora of this region? Judging by what we observe among the inhabitants of existing arid regions, this is quite unpredictable.

In the first place, the species may fail to undergo adaptive change and become extinct. But if it does change, it turns out that it is possible to become adapted to the same environment in quite different ways. Some plants, among them cacti and euphorbias, replace leaves with thorns, and carry on photosynthetic activities in their fleshy stems. Others, like the creosote bush, keep their leaves but cover them with a protective resin. Still others produce tender unprotected leaves, but keep them on only while the danger of desiccation is not too great. And many others do very well by growing, flowering, and maturing their seeds all during a short humid season. Any naturalist will be able to give other examples of multifarious adaptive responses of organisms to the challenges of on the whole rather similar environments. It looks almost like some sort of spontaneity, or free will, or plain chaos.

My collaborator Pavlovsky and myself have made experiments in which a germ of such "spontaneity" is observed in a way that makes analysis hopefully possible. The story is, very briefly, this.[7] Many natural populations of *Drosophila* flies are chromosomally polymorphic, i.e., are mixtures of individuals with differently constructed chromosomes. Experimental populations can be set up in the laboratory, having initially any desired proportions of two chromosomal types. Since the carriers of some chromosomal types are better and others less well adapted to the laboratory conditions, natural selection, acting in obviously very "unnatural" environments, changes the frequencies of these types accordingly. The experiments go differently, however, depending upon whether the ancestors of the parents of the laboratory populations came from the same geographic locality or from different localities. The results in experimental populations of geographically uniform origin are uniform and predictable within the limits of sampling errors; in those of geographically mixed origins they are quite variable, and in this sense indeterminate.

So, not to be outdone by quantum physicists, we have our biological indeterminism. But its explanation, in our experiments at least, seems relatively simple. Suppose that the geographic races of the flies which we cross differ in only 50 genes. As stated above, as many as 3^{50} different genotypes are potentially possible in our populations of geographically mixed origins. But the experimental populations contain only 1000–4000 flies. Therefore, only a minutest fraction of the possible genotypes will be realized, and they will almost certainly be different ones in different experimental populations. The indeterminacy is the outcome of the disproportion between the great power of the sexual process to create novel genotypes and the limited power of the experimenter to create large laboratory populations.

We can predict the average result and the variance observed in the experimental populations of geographically mixed origins. We cannot predict what any given population will do. It is like predicting the results of tossing coins or dice. We may say that the results of a single toss could be predicted exactly if we knew exactly the initial conditions. But, as justly remarked by Philipp Frank, for this purpose we need the Laplacian omniscient intelligence. "From the scientific point of view, predetermination of the future is either a tautological concept, or it assumes the existence of causal laws connecting few variables by simple relations."

Organic evolution is a series of unique events, because, as we have seen, in sexual forms, the same genotype is not likely to arise more than once. But it is not merely the operation of "the dice of destiny." The sovereignty of chance is kept within bounds by the antichance factor, natural selection. This antichance process has a remarkable quality —by and large it maintains or furthers the harmony between the organism and the world in which the latter lives. It enables life not only to endure but to gain ground and to press onward.

Evolution has produced a multitude of remarkable creatures, including man. Were these outcomes of the evolutionary process predetermined and predictable? Yes, they were, but only to a Laplacian omniscient intelligence. However, within a narrower compass both prediction and retrodiction of evolution are possible. What is more, control and direction of evolution within a similar compass are also possible. As we learn more about evolution, the predictability and directability expand. Herein lies the promise of biology.

References

1. Quoted after E. Nagel, *The Structure of Science*, Harcourt, Brace, New York, 1961.
2. R. Dubos, *The Dreams of Reason*, Columbia University Press, New York, 1961.
3. T. Dobzhansky, *Evolution, Genetics, and Man*, Wiley, New York–London, 1957.
4. L. Berg, *Nomogenesis or Evolution Determined by Law*, Constable, London, 1926.
5. T. Dobzhansky, "Evolution of Genes and Genes in Evolution," *Cold Spring Harbor Symp. Quant. Biol.*, 24, 15–30 (1959).
6. I. I. Schmalhausen, "Evolution and Cybernetics," *Evolution*, 14, 509–524 (1960).
7. T. Dobzhansky, "Variation and Evolution," *Proceedings of the American Philosophical Society*, 103, 252–263 (1959).
8. P. Frank, *Philosophy of Science*, Prentice-Hall, Englewood Cliffs, N. J., 1957.

The Relation of the Physical Sciences to Biology—Indeterminacy and Causality

Bentley Glass, *The Johns Hopkins University*

Introductory Analysis

One might explore the relations of the physical sciences to the life sciences by surveying the deepening extent of the dependence of biologists upon physical and chemical techniques and the remarkable growth in our time of molecular biology. To do that would, I believe, have less interest (for philosophers of science) than to consider the current status of a much-debated question that has long troubled, and even now intensely concerns, biologists: the question of causality, the conflict of determinism and purposiveness, of the concept of the organism as machine with the concept of the organism as a system in which the whole is "more than the resultant of the activities of independent components" (Ernest Nagel).[1] The question may be posed succinctly in the following form: *Do the laws of physical science comprehend all the laws of biology?*

There is frequently semantic confusion in the discussion of this question. If physics and chemistry be defined as the realm of matter and energy, then by definition all biological phenomena are embraced within physics and chemistry, since no scientific observations can be made except of matter and the changes in matter attributed to physical forces. It may be helpful to rephrase the question in several alternative forms, as follows:

(*a*) Do the laws of physics and chemistry which are demonstrable in nonliving systems also hold true in living systems? To this question the modern biologist gives an unqualified Yes.

(*b*) Do the laws of physics and chemistry which are demonstrable in nonliving systems constitute all the presently demonstrable laws of living systems? To this question the answer is an equally unqualified No.

(*c*) Can the laws of physical science which are demonstrable in nonliving systems be expected ultimately to explain all the laws of living systems? This is the aspect of the question where differences of opinion arise. But the reasons given are often quite different and require scrutiny. Those who would give an affirmative answer to question (*c*) point to the steady extension of physical law in the realm of biology as research proceeds, and they maintain that since problems once held to be inexplicable in physicochemical terms can in many instances now be explained quite satisfactorily in such terms, it is only a matter of time until all biological phenomena will be embraced by and be explicable in terms of physical and chemical laws. This prediction is, of course, based simply on the extrapolation of a persistent trend. On the other hand, those who give a negative reply to question (*c*) do so for a variety of reasons, some of which are clearly based more on faith than on reason.

Four Bases of Distinction between Biology and the Physical Sciences (*after Nagel*)

Ernest Nagel, in *The Structure of Science*,[1] Chapter 12, discusses four arguments advanced by some biologists to support the belief that biology inherently cannot be reduced to physicochemical terms. The first of these is simply the claim that biology deals with characteristics and laws which do not occur among nonliving systems, and that the techniques of observation and analysis are often very different. At first sight this argument seems entirely circular: the claim assumes the very point at issue. Nagel rightly disposes of this argument very briefly—and yet we will find, I think, that in one particular form it will come back to trouble us again. It may, in fact, be the most significant of all the arguments presented.

The second argument is not, I believe, sufficiently distinct from the third in Nagel's treatment of the issues. It is, in brief, that biologists must deal not only with *structures,* that is, with organized forms of matter as seen in living systems, but also with *functions.* Functions may be considered in two aspects. On the one hand, a biological function is an organized form of action as seen in living systems. In this sense, it is strictly physicochemical in nature. Thus, in the contraction of muscle there is a chain reaction in which each step is the cause of the next one. The delivery of chemical energy from the high-energy phosphate bonds of adenosine triphosphate molecules to the actin and myosin molecules of a muscle fibril results in formation of a shorter actomyosin complex and in consequence in the shortening of the muscle fibril. This effect is multiplied by occurrence in the numerous fibrils making up a muscle fiber and by the numerous fibers making up a muscle, and finally culminates in the appropriate contraction of the muscle that moves certain parts of the skeleton in relation to others. This series of steps seems in no way different from many chain reactions in nonliving systems, such as (*a*) the transmission of momentum from one billiard ball through a series of others to a final ball which moves away with the speed and trajectory of the first—now motionless—ball; or (*b*) the transformation of mechanical vibrations into electrical variations, the amplification of electrical effects in a triode tube or transistor, and the subsequent conversion of electrical variations into sound patterns that reproduce the original sounds which have been frozen into patterns in the grooves of a phonograph disk. Function in this sense is no different in biological and physical systems. It describes the relation of the final term in the causal chain to its antecedent steps.

But there is another aspect of function, its purposive, or teleological, aspect. Nagel discusses quite fully this aspect of function, and its dominating position in biological thinking, but, I fear, unsatisfactorily. His argument and explication are limited to the causal, chain-reaction relationship just discussed, and he readily succeeds in showing the similarity of the biological chain of steps to those of the physical sciences. He concludes that the distinction is largely semantic, a matter of emphasis upon the "*consequences* for a given biological system of a constituent part or process" in the case of the teleological explanation, and of the "*conditions* under which the system persists in its characteristic organization and activities" in the nonteleological formulation of the same system (p. 405). I believe that a more important distinction relates to the evolutionary origin of the adaptations of living beings which have always so profoundly impressed the biologist and the philosopher. Is there a valid distinction here, in that, for the most part, nonliving systems do not evolve, are not subject to the increasingly greater adaptiveness which results from the action of natural selection? This problem will be considered more fully later.

The fourth argument considered by Nagel is that of the proponents of some form of holistic view of organisms. This is the view that there are emergent qualities in living systems which disappear upon analysis and dissection of the system into its component parts, and which are not simply the products of the interactions of the parts in physical ways. For some biologists this organic whole is the entire organism; for others it is the individual cell (Commoner, 1961).[2] As E. S. Russell (1930)[3] has stated, the cardinal principles held by the organismic biologists are as follows: "The activity of the whole cannot be fully explained in terms of the activities of the parts isolated by analysis"; and "No part of any living entity and no single process of any complex organic unity can be fully understood in isolation from the structure and activities of the organism as a whole" (pp. 171–172). Here I believe most biologists of the present time will agree fully with Nagel's conclusion:

> organismic biologists have not established the absolute autonomy of biology or the inherent impossibility of physico-

chemical explanations of vital phenomena. Nevertheless, the stress they place on the hierarchical organization of living things and on the mutual dependence of organic parts is not a misplaced one. (p. 444)

The value of the latter, however, relates to a "wise strategy of research" which may be necessary in biology for a long time to come, to the extent to which there are biological sciences which remain inexplicable in terms of *current* physical and chemical theory. But this is not to admit what some of the organismic biologists would claim, that the method of analysis of an entity into its parts is inapplicable or is less valuable in biology than in the physical sciences. Analysis remains the necessary method of science. Treatment of entities as wholes remains entirely descriptive, and leaves the organism a "black box." One may carry the argument further. The modern biologist who deals with ecological relationships treats not the individual organism, but the population, the community of different organisms, and the entire ecosystem as parts of the increasing hierarchy of life. Carried to its logical end, the insistence of some organismic biologists on study only of the "whole" would lead only to contemplation of the universe in its full cosmic extent. Yet not even these organismic biologists will deny that consideration of the whole organism, abstracted from its environment, leads to a degree of understanding impossible if one must deal with an entire population, or community, or ecosystem as an indivisible unity.

The Borderline between Life and the Nonliving

In 1935 Wendell Stanley succeeded in crystallizing tobacco mosaic virus. In crystalline form the virus could be bottled and kept inert and "lifeless" indefinitely. Redissolved in water and placed on the surface of a tobacco leaf, the virus particles infected the leaf, used the leaf's stores of organic compounds, and rapidly multiplied. This discovery quickly brought about a great debate among biologists regarding the criteria of life. Was the virus alive or not? Can an organized chemical system at one time be lifeless and at another be alive? or is multiplication of an organized system not only a necessary but also a sufficient criterion of life? The discussion was well pointed up in an essay written by N. W. Pirie in 1937 and entitled "The Meaninglessness of the Terms 'Life' and 'Living,' " [4] although with his conclusion that they are indeed meaningless by no means everyone would agree.

During the ensuing quarter century a great deal of scientific study of viruses has been carried out. The result has been rather surprising. Virus particles are far more complicated in organization than was first thought when it was discovered that they could be crystallized, supposedly a criterion of chemical purity. They consist of protein and nucleic acid, and the electron microscope reveals an elaborate arrangement of parts, including an injection apparatus, at least in some viruses. The conclusion that they represent the borderline between the living and the nonliving holds good; but viruses seem far too complex to have come into existence without an evolutionary process of many steps and a long history. Hence the argument has shifted. On the one hand we find the biochemist Isaac Asimov now saying, in answer to the question, "At what moment in evolution did life appear?" the following: "Then, eventually, must have come the key step—the formation, through chance combination of a nucleic acid molecule, capable of inducing replication. That moment marked the beginning of life." [5] On the opposing side, Barry Commoner replies that it is nonsense to say that "modern science has all but wiped out the borderline between life and non-life," as Asimov claims. On the contrary, says Commoner,

> Since biology is the science of life, any successful obliteration of the distinction between living things and other forms of matter ends forever the usefulness of biology as a separate science. If the foregoing sentence is even remotely correct, biology is not only under attack; it has been annihilated. [2]

That remark leaves untouched the question of the line of demarcation. Commoner places this at the level of organization of the cell: "Analysis of living systems, based on modern physical and chemical theory, leads to the conclusion that life is unique and that it cannot be reduced to the property of a single substance or of a system less complex than a living cell." [2]

Many biologists hold that life cannot be defined in terms of a single characteristic property, but all of them, I think, are agreed that reproduction is a necessary characteristic of any form of life that survives more than a single generation! If we look at the reproductive process, it is very clear that it is indeed a cellular phenomenon, that genetic continuity has its basis in the ability of a single cell to grow, divide, and make two cells. Cells without nuclei, that is, lacking the deoxyribose nucleic acid (DNA) which is the hereditary material, are unable to divide. This DNA may be organized into chromosomes, as is usually the case, or dispersed in the cell, as in blue-green algae. Studies of cell division indicate unmistakably that duplication of the DNA precedes, and perhaps triggers, the other complicated events of cell division. Consequently, many biologists have come to think that the capacity of DNA to replicate itself is the ultimate basis of reproduction.

There is, consequently, ground for believing that DNA is the substance possessing the ultimate reproductive power, just as it is demonstrably the hereditary material. Yet one might still say—and this is perhaps the essence of Commoner's argument—that DNA cannot replicate itself except within the very special environment of a living cell. Even the virus DNA must be injected into a living cell before it can find the supply of very special compounds required for its replication. It turns out replicas of itself and sheathes them in proper coats of protein by deforming and misdirecting the normal metabolism of the DNA in the host cell, like a robot tank that might get into a factory designed for making trucks and that somehow succeeded in shifting the controls so that henceforth tanks instead of trucks came off the assembly line.

Yet the argument that the entire living cell is therefore the smallest living unit that can reproduce, the least common denominator of life, has a hollow ring. It strangely reminds us of the century-old argument that organic compounds could never be produced outside of living organisms—an argument quickly shown to be false by the synthesis of urea, and subsequently of many other organic compounds, in the laboratory. Clearly the cell provides the necessary environment for the replication of DNA, but is the entire cell necessary for that? May the biologist not discover just what substrates and enzymes are required, and subsequently duplicate *in vitro* this essential process of life? Frankly, I think we are on the verge of this discovery. Arthur Kornberg's [6] discovery of a system that will synthesize DNA in the test tube is virtually complete. One needs, in this system, the four kinds of nucleotide triphosphates of which the DNA is composed; one needs an enzyme—and this has been extracted from the common colon bacillus; one needs a chemical source of energy—adenosine triphosphate will serve beautifully; and finally, one must have a model, a small amount of native DNA that will serve as a primer, or template, for the new molecules to copy. Given all these, DNA molecules are synthesized in the test tube abundantly, and are indistinguishable from the kind of DNA molecules that are used as a model. Take the primer from the colon bacillus, and one obtains colon bacillus DNA; take it from the thymus gland of a calf, and one gets bovine DNA. This process is surely what Asimov had in mind when he made his seemingly rash statement. If even the replication of the hereditary, all-controlling DNA can be carried out in a simple nonliving system, is there reason to suppose that eventually one cannot isolate and carry on all other significant living processes *in vitro?* The photosynthesis of green plants, for example, can now be carried on in suspensions of isolated chloroplasts. Respiration and the generation of an abundant supply of ATP can be performed in isolated mitochondria. What more fundamental to life than these three processes?

If, on the other hand, one says that life is no single state or process, however complex and indispensable to life it may be, but is precisely that complex interrelationship of processes that occurs only in a living cell, one ends not with an explanation but with a tautology. Nor can one be sure that in the end human ingenuity may not produce a system with even that level of complexity of organization. The creation of life from the nonliving might well be the ultimate demonstration of the meaninglessness of the distinction, of the fallacy of the borderline.

There is another aspect of this question which has received much attention from biologists during the past quarter century. First introduced by Haldane and Oparin,[7] this is the theory of the evolutionary origin of life from the nonliving. Oparin espouses the idea of coacervates, globular droplets of complex protein nature which form when oppositely charged colloidal particles in suspension are mixed. The coacervates grow in size by adsorbing and absorbing materials from the solution about them; they divide into two when they reach a maximum size; they have a boundary, like the membrane of a living cell. Other theorists have championed the view that the nucleic acid molecules came first, and then organized about themselves, from the primeval soup, a more concentrated protein environment in which they could replicate themselves. To decide between these theories is very like trying to answer the riddle of the chicken and the egg—which came first? As the biologist believes that egg and chicken must have evolved together, so it seems to me most reasonable to believe that life commenced with the incorporation of DNA into coacervates. For this to have happened, obviously both must have had a prior existence! The important matter is the presence in the world of natural selection from the very beginning of these steps. Oparin's chief originality consists in his sugges-

tion that natural selection antedated "life." Whatever coacervates were most stable, could grow most rapidly, and
when they divided most successfully passed on to their
progeny their own superior characteristics—these types
would soon outnumber the less stable, less rapidly growing
and dividing, less hereditary forms. Moreover, in a situation where the supply of organic compounds formed by long
ages of random molecular changes under the influence of
heat and radiation must have been very scanty and very
dilute, there would be a strong premium upon these qualities. Soon the supply of organic compounds would be cor-
nered by the better endowed forms, for as the others dissolved, their materials would rapidly be taken over by the
former. Predatory attacks on other "living" forms would
introduce a more active struggle for existence. In short,
there would be a continuous, strong pressure of selection
leading to the evolution of better organized, more efficient
cells that could produce enzymatic systems at the direction
of a single, or moderately replicated, coordinated pattern
of nucleic acid molecules.

With the extension of the principle of natural selection to
the preliving, chemical environment, Darwin's destruction
of the ground for teleological explanations in biology becomes complete. As Ernst Mayr [8] points out, there are two
ways of looking at the function of DNA. One is to trace from
some part of the coded information transmitted in the DNA
from each generation to the next the consequences, step by
step, until one arrives at some end product. This is the
teleonomic aspect, and is indeed all that Nagel [1] discusses
in his treatment of biological function and its apparent purposiveness. But the real question is why these causal chains
leading from genes to end products should be appropriately
fitted to the needs of life, why the chemical, physiological,
and behavioral systems, like the structures, should be adaptive. This question Nagel ignores; but it is the heart of the
issue. Its answer must lie in evolutionary biology, in the

second way of looking at DNA. This is to study the changes that go on in the DNA itself from generation to generation, and to observe their hereditary consequences. The occurrence of such changes, or mutations, so the geneticist reports, are random, that is, are unrelated to their significance in the environment. After selection has taken place for eons, most of the changes in the DNA inevitably are destructive and harmful; yet occasionally a mutation may occur that aids an organism in leaving more offspring of its own kind than the average number of offspring produced by its competitors. Natural selection thus works, with almost infinite slowness but sureness, through differential reproduction. Adaptation to the existing environment is the result. Hence the history of the DNA explains its present state. Natural selection, before and since the advent of life, produces a semblance of purposiveness in the causal chains, though there has been only a blind, purposeless agency at work.

Cause and Effect in Biology

Henri Bergson, in *Creative Evolution*,[9] distinguished between three kinds of "causes" in an instructive way. In one case, the effect which is produced varies both quantitatively and qualitatively with the cause; in a second case, the effect varies quantitatively with the cause but not qualitatively; in a third case, the cause is merely a releasing mechanism, and the effect varies neither quantitatively nor qualitatively with the magnitude of the agent. One may illustrate these three cases quite simply:

1. A number of pierced billiard balls are strung on wires so as to be perfectly balanced and nearly frictionless; then variable numbers of balls are placed in contact at the center of the wire, and impact is made by varying numbers of balls set in motion. It is readily observed that the number of balls which move from the center toward the far end of the wire is always equal to the number set in motion. In biology, this causal relation is represented by a chain reaction in

which each step is both necessary and sufficient to set off
the next step:

$$A \rightarrow B \rightarrow C \rightarrow D \rightarrow E$$

as, for example, in certain biochemical syntheses or in an
unbranching chain of neurons. Such examples are rare in
biology.

2. A rheostat is placed in the electric circuit leading to a
lantern slide projector. By varying the rheostat, it is demonstrable that the image projected varies quantitatively with
the amount of illumination, regulated by the electric current; but the character of the image depends only on the
particular slide which is interposed in the beam of light.
In this type of causal relation, the cause is necessary, but
not sufficient, to evoke the effect. Biology affords many cases
of this kind, especially where branching of a chain-reaction
occurs:

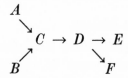

E may vary quantitatively with A or B, but the qualitative
nature of the final response may differ greatly, especially
when a transformation of energy is involved. Thus, to return to an example used earlier, the energy of contraction
of a muscle is different in kind, being motion, from the
chemical energy in the preceding terms.

3. The trigger of a pistol is pressed. Whether the pistol
fires or not will depend upon whether it is loaded and
whether the safety catch is open. The effect depends, both
as to quantity and quality, upon the loading of the system.
It has nothing to do with the energy with which the trigger
is pressed, provided that it exceeds a minimum. The response is all or none. Probably the great majority of causal
chains in biology are like this—at least the most familiar
ones. All stimulus and response mechanisms where a change

in the environment produces a response in the organism are initially of this sort, all reflexes such as a blink of the eyelids following a flash of light, a jerk of the hand when it touches a hot object, a flow of saliva when food is placed in the mouth.

Bergson goes on to say that only in the first case does cause really *explain* effect. Inasmuch as causal relations of the first type are far less numerous in biology than in the physical sciences, and far less numerous than the cases of types 2 and 3, we are presented immediately with one of the principal distinctions between the biological and the physical sciences. The physicist commonly attempts to set aside the role of the releasing mechanism or trigger, and to press forward to an explanation in terms of causes of type 1. The biologist is often unable to get beyond cases of types 2 and 3, and anyhow, because of the complexity of the causal chains he faces, is basically interested in the release type of causation.

Braithwaite,[10] following Hume's thesis, which was adopted in succession by Ernst Mach, Karl Pearson, and many later philosophers of science, regards the idea of "necessary connexion" (that is, cause) to depend only on "constant conjunction." This position raises the question of the distinction between cause and correlation. Let us assume a causal chain, such as frequently occurs in biochemical and biological systems, of the following sort:

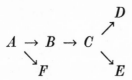

If F regularly follows A, and D and E regularly follow A but after steps through B and C, the criterion of constant conjunction is readily seen to be entirely fallacious. F will always be in constant conjunction with D and E, and in addition will always precede D and E if the step $A \rightarrow B$ takes as much time as the step $A \rightarrow F$. Yet what actually exists here is complete correlation between F on one side and D and E on the other, and no direct causal relation between them. It may be pointed out that this situation is precisely what keeps going the still heated argument as to whether heavy cigarette smoking produces an increased liability to lung cancer. And, note well, that *insofar as prediction is concerned, it does not matter*. Complete correlation with an event, that is to say, "constant conjunction," is entirely as adequate a basis for prediction as direct causal connection. Mayr [8] points out that Bunge, in his recent book *Causality*,[11] still maintains that "the touchstone of the goodness of a causal explanation [is] its predictive value," or in Bunge's own words: "A theory can predict to the extent to which it can describe and explain." Mayr's cutting remark on this is, "It is evident that Bunge is a physicist; no biologist would have made such a statement." The position assumed by Bunge is wrong on two counts. In the first place, I must agree with Mayr [8] and Scriven [12] that "one of the most important contributions to philosophy made by the evolutionary theory is that it has demonstrated the independence of explanation and prediction." As will be shown hereafter, the evolutionary theory very clearly explains, in terms of mutation and natural selection, isolation and adaptation, what it can in no wise predict. But there is a second fallacy in Bunge's position. To return to the example used above, where complete conjunction exists but no direct causal relationship, as between F and D (or E), let us suppose that the nature of A is entirely unknown. The observer would then be in a position, from the occurrence of F, to predict D (or E), but he would lack any explanation for the seemingly causal relation of F to D (or E). The existence of A as a causal link effecting both F and D, in place of the theory that F causes D, can be demonstrated only if the step $A \to F$ can be blocked independently of the step $A \to B$. To a biochemical geneticist this model is among the commonest sorts of branched system. The real steps in a direct

causal chain are actually discovered in experiments by observing the action of mutations that block specific steps.

We may find it worthwhile to examine this example further, in terms of the three types of causes discussed above.
If A represents a compound that is convertible into either
B or F, several possibilities exist. Both B and F may be produced. The two reactions will then compete with each other,
in which case the quantities of B and F produced are less
likely to depend on the quantity of A than on other factors
in the total situation. Qualitatively, B and F may be similar
to or different from A. A second possibility is that the production of F may have priority over production of B, or the
converse. Then F, let us say, is produced until a sufficiency
is formed, whereupon the step $A \rightarrow F$ is shut down and production of $A \rightarrow B$ is initiated. In this case the quantity of F
is fixed and independent of the quantity of A, but the quantity of B will depend upon the excess of the quantity of A
above a certain threshold (determined by the amount
needed to form F). This is an instance of regulation of a
biological process which will be explained shortly. A third
possibility is that of reciprocal regulation. In this relationship the steps $A \rightarrow F$ and $A \rightarrow B$ are alternately turned on
and off. In such a case both F and B may vary in quantity
directly with the quantity of A. It would seem to follow
that one and the same causal chain or system can behave
differently in respect to quantitative variation of "cause" and
"effect." If so, then this aspect of causality is not essential,
in spite of the fact that it is the classic type of causality
sought by the physicist and long made the basis of mechanical determinism.

A word should be said about the developments in biology
that in recent years have clarified the nature of the regulatory or reciprocal regulatory processes referred to in the
preceding paragraph. These regulatory actions, in biochemistry or neurology, are now seen to result, at least most frequently, from positive and negative feedbacks in the causal
system. The system is thereby converted from a chainlike

array of steps to a circular process. For example, systems are known in which the end product inhibits the formation of the enzyme catalyzing one of the antecedent steps in the chain:

$$A \;-\|\!\!\rightarrow\; B \;\longrightarrow\; C \;\longrightarrow\; D$$

This is an example of so-called negative feedback. It regulates the amount of end product that is formed and prevents too great an accumulation of it.

On the other hand, in genetics more and more examples are being found in which the combination of a substrate molecule with an enzyme molecule *induces* the formation of additional supplies of the enzyme, which at first is present in very small amounts.

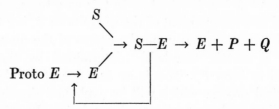

where S = substrate, E = enzyme, and P and Q = products. This type of regulatory process insures that cells will not produce large amounts of particular enzymes in the absence of use for them. The phenomenon is a positive feedback. Such feedbacks probably lie at the basis not only of much physiological adaptation to changing conditions, but also of the developmental changes occurring in cells as the cells differentiate and become specialized. One of the major problems of current biology is to discern the nature of the forces or factors that bring genes into play at appropriate times during life and in different tissues. These releasing mechanisms are now thought to belong to the class of positive feedback mechanisms just described.

The "purposive" or teleological semblance of these systems that so marvelously control the development of an embryo into the appropriate type of adult plant or animal is thus purely physicochemical. Its regulatory aspect is that of feedbacks, acting analogously to a thermostat regulating a heating or cooling system or to the governor of a steam engine. Such are the causal systems whereby the DNA exerts its hereditary control over metabolism and development. They are appropriately called teleonomic to distinguish them from the evolutionary aspect of teleology which, as Mayr [8] says, "deals more broadly with the over-all harmony of the organic world" (p. 1504).

Indeterminacy in Biology

To this point my argument has fully supported the view that the laws of physical science which are demonstrable in nonliving systems might be expected ultimately to explain all the laws of living systems. The distinctions made with respect to causality show up weaknesses in the conventional analysis based largely on physical systems, rather than imply any basic difference in kind of causality. Yet there are good grounds for maintaining that the answer to our major question should be negative rather than affirmative.

Nagel points out (Ref. 1, p. 364) that the reduction of one science to another can be conceived only "as the deduction of one set of empirically confirmable *statements* from another such set"; that is to say, one may be able to reduce the laws of one science to those of another but one cannot reduce one science to another by deducing *properties* from other *properties*.

> The deduction of the "properties" studied by one science from the "properties" studied by another may be impossible if the latter science postulates these properties in terms of one theory, but the reduction may be quite feasible if a different set of theoretical postulates is adopted.

This seems very true, and yet I believe another aspect of the relation between the sciences is even more important. I refer to the statistical nature of scientific laws, the dependence of law upon probability rather than upon determinate certainty.

Bunge has recently discussed some aspects of this matter.[18] He says: "The realization of the statistical nature of all macroscopic laws, and of the objective nature of chance, has not led us to believe in uncaused events: it has only shown that not all relations are causal bonds." After defining what he means by "causal," he says: "There is always, as a matter of fact, some amount of spontaneity, mutual action, and randomness . . . *there are no purely causal laws.*" He proceeds to decry the equation "Causality = Lawfulness" and also the equation "Causality = Determinism." In the case of the first of these equations, it is clear that the sciences now abound with purely statistical as well as with classic causal laws. In respect to the second equation, however, the assertion that causality does not equal determinism seems to rest merely upon an arbitrary redefinition of determinism, such that even chance falls within the scope of "noncausal determiners."

Purely statistical laws are based on "random behavior," whether of the movements of molecules of a gas, the fertilization of a given population of eggs by a given population of sperms, or the number of "reds" and "blacks" that turn up in a simplified roulette game where only those two possibilities may occur. Randomness of behavior does not mean that specified conditions and measurable forces do not enter the situation—only that they are uniform for all the events. Thus in an ideal Pascal apparatus it is assumed that all balls are identical in mass and perfectly symmetrical in distribution of mass and in shape, that the apparatus is oriented true to the gravitational field, that all the balls fall from the same initial position with the same force, etc. It is, however, not necessary to make all these assumptions, since Poincaré demonstrated that in the simplified roulette game mentioned previously, "reds" and "blacks" would turn up with equal frequency no matter what the initial positions and velocities of the marble might be. The fundamental aspect of the situation is that there are always, in any real system, unmeasured random forces and unspecified random conditions that result in ordered distributions characterized by equal "choice" of equally probable alternatives. A perfectly flipped coin will fall "heads" and "tails" equally often; a perfectly balanced die will land with the 5-spot uppermost one-sixth of the time; and so on.

Statistical behavior of this kind exists at all levels of organization, from elementary particles to galaxies. It clearly operates at all biological levels, from the molecule to the organism, from the cell to the population, community, and ecosystem. The occurrence of osmosis in physiological processes depends upon the random distribution by diffusion of the molecules in a solution on both sides of a membrane, provided it is permeable to them. The Mendelian ratios depend upon the equal probability of an egg's fertilization by any one of two or more kinds of sperms when these kinds exist in equal numbers. The Hardy-Weinberg Law, basis of all our modern evolutionary statistical predictions, is based on the random mating, with respect to certain specified characteristics, of individuals in a population containing different genotypes. Random behavior may be exhibited by the individuals composing a group that as a whole is undergoing an ordered shift, as in the Brownian movement of colloidal particles in a gas or liquid that as a whole is drifting in a current. Or conversely, a population as a whole may exhibit random behavior, as in the exploration of their local environment by a colony of numerous bees, even though the movements of the individual bees are very highly directed and determined.

It seems that statistical laws express an aspect of nature that depends upon randomness of behavior of the individual units whether these be atoms, molecules, cells, organisms, or higher entities in the levels of organization. What is more, the randomness of behavior of the units involved at one level does not necessarily depend upon the randomness of units at lower levels of organization. The statistical law does not depend on the relations between levels of organization. The probability that a particular face of a die will land uppermost is one-sixth simply because the die has six faces and not some other number; the probability that the egg will be fertilized by a Y-bearing sperm and give rise to a male, instead of being fertilized by an X-bearing sperm and giving rise to a female, is one-half because the two sorts of sperms are present in equal numbers and are equally motile. If they are not present in exactly equal numbers, or are not equally motile, then the probability will be different.

Such laws of science as these, arising directly from the nature of chance and the mathematical expression of probabilities, do not seem to be reducible to laws at a lower level of physical organization, because they describe the random behavior of entities at one particular level of organization. This is true both intraordinally (for example, within the biological sciences but at different levels of organization), and also interordinally (for example, between biology and chemistry, biology and physics, or chemistry and physics). A particularly clear example is afforded by the relation between the Mendelian laws and the Hardy-Weinberg law. Both express a statistical randomness in the transmission of genes from one generation to the next. The same biological processes are involved in both cases. But the Mendelian ratios arise from the randomness of fertilization of eggs provided by a particular female by means of sperms supplied by a particular male. The randomness here is at the level of the *cell*. On the other hand, the Hardy-Weinberg gene frequency equilibrium depends upon the randomness of mating between male and female individuals of various genotypes present in an interbreeding population. It depends upon the relative frequencies of these genotypes in the population, although the randomness of fertilization is implicitly assumed. One cannot derive the Mendelian ratios from the Hardy-Weinberg equilibrium, or the reverse, because the fundamental randomness each law describes is randomness at a different level from that in the other. The *random* behavior of sperms is simply not the same as the *random* behavior of mating multicellular individuals, even though sperms and mating obviously have a great deal to do with each other.

If this line of reasoning is correct, we may conclude that the statistical laws of one level of organization are not reducible to the statistical laws of another. By reduction directly to the mathematical laws of probability, any reduction to other levels of organization of matter and energy is obviated. In this sense we arrive at a negative answer to our main question: Can the laws of physical science which are demonstrable in nonliving systems be expected ultimately to explain *all* the laws of living systems? The answer is No— the statistical laws that describe random behavior are irreducible.

The second reason for doubting the reducibility of all biological laws to those of physics and chemistry is in fact a simple one, analogous to but by no means identical with the principle of indeterminacy in physics. It derives from the nature of the evolutionary process which affects all life.

The principle of indeterminacy in physics relates to single quanta of energy and single elementary particles. There is no reason to try to introduce this principle into biology, as some thinkers—I believe foolishly—have tried to do, in order to explain will or consciousness. Whatever material events lie at the basis of mental phenomena, they seem surely to depend upon a multimolecular basis. Like the events of chemistry, they involve the statistical behavior of millions or billions of molecules. But there is nevertheless a significant analogy between indeterminacy in physics and that in biology. The indeterminacy in physics arises because a single quantum or elementary particle cannot behave statistically at a given instant. It is unique—and the very operations performed to determine its position in space and its energy unavoidably alter the one or the other. In evolutionary biology, where one is concerned with past events— the mutations and the selections—that have led to the existence of a certain contemporary pattern in the DNA of a particular species, one is likewise dealing with uniqueness, the particularity of history.

Indeterminacy in biology is an outcome of the unpredictability of unique events. Predictability rests upon the statistical behavior, according to the laws of probability, of sufficiently large numbers of individuals. We may illustrate this principle very appropriately from the field of genetics, the branch of biology that is most advanced theoretically and most mathematical in its treatment of phenomena. In a particular kind of mating—let us say, one between a purebred spotted dog (such as a Dalmatian) and a purebred non-spotted dog—experiment and observation tell us to expect only offspring that are spotted. This results from the fact that all gametes from the one parent carry a gene for spotting, all gametes from the other carry a gene for non-spotting, and every fertilized egg will therefore carry a gene of each sort and be heterozygous. This rule predicts that the progeny will all be alike; only by observation can we discover that spotting is dominant over non-spotting in dogs, and that the character of the progeny will all be spotted rather than all non-spotted. But predictability here, given such initial observations, is virtually perfect. Now let us cross the heterozygous spotted dogs together. Each dog produces half of its gametes carrying the one gene, the other half the alternative gene, or allele, as such a gene is called. Random fertilization between two kinds of sperms and two kinds of eggs, existing in equal numbers, leads one to expect one-fourth of the progeny to be pure spotted, half to be heterozygous (and spotted), and one-fourth to be pure non-spotted. If one makes a sufficiently large number of matings of this type, and produces litters totaling a hundred dogs or more, it is evident that this prediction is realized. Nevertheless, the prediction is a statistical one. Any single litter may deviate rather widely from the predicted proportions. The chance that a pup in such a litter will be spotted rather than non-spotted is 3:1, but the individual, particular event that produces a particular genotype in a particular dog cannot be predicted except as a probability.

The dog has many pairs of chromosomes, and the maternally and paternally derived members of each pair assort independently of those of every other pair in the special cell divisions leading up to the formation of mature germ cells. Thus, if we symbolize by A and A' one pair of chromosomes, B and B' a second pair of chromosomes, etc., a heterozygous individual that is $AA';BB'$ will form four kinds of gametes: $A;B + A;B' + A';B + A';B'$. In mathematical terms, the number of kinds of gametes that can be produced is 2^n, where n is the number of pairs of elements assorting independently. The number of kinds of fertilized eggs that can be produced when two doubly heterozygous individuals mate is then $(2^n)^2$. If n exceeds 20, these expressions become exceedingly large. For the dog, $2^n = 2^{39}$ = nearly 550 billion; for humans, $2^n = 2^{23} = 8,388,608$. The squares of these numbers are so large that it is evident that the potential number of kinds of offspring producible from one sexual union are so vast that all the past, present, and future members of the species are not likely to approach it. The variety producible by recombination of the pairs of chromosomes is further increased by a process called crossing over, which permits pairs of genes that are linked, that is, are carried within the same pair of chromosomes, also to recombine. This is mathematically equivalent to saying that in the expression 2^n, n actually signifies the number of heterozygous pairs of genes which are present in each of the mates. This number may be very much larger than the number of pairs of chromosomes. Genetic variation is therefore almost infinite in any sexually reproducing population that is not strictly inbred. The genotype of each individual in such case becomes unique. Only by limiting attention to a relatively few pairs of genes can we achieve predictability.

The uniqueness of the individual is to be seen in biology not only at the molecular level of the DNA which constitutes the genotype. It also prevails at every other level. It is solely by abstracting from the infinitely varied individuals those elements and characteristics which they possess in common that the biologist establishes categories and species. As Mayr [8] very well expresses it:

> the individuality . . . so characteristic of the organic world, where all individuals are unique; all stages in the life cycle are unique; all populations are unique; all species and higher categories are unique; all interindividual contacts are unique; all natural associations of species are unique; and all evolutionary events are unique (p. 1505).

Uniqueness, as we have said, does not preclude prediction of a statistical sort, provided the populations and samples are sufficiently large. In fact, all scientific predictability is ultimately of this sort. But we come now to the final issue.

In the physical sciences, except at the level of quantum indeterminacy, one deals always with populations of enormous numbers of molecules or other units, and the statistical laws predict with high accuracy. In astronomy, one deals with large numbers of orbital revolutions of a planet or satellite, or with a large and theoretically infinite number of observations of a radiation-emitting body. In biology, however, one deals with finite, and often very small, numbers of cases which, moreover, represent a history derived from previous finite and often very small populations of events. First of all, evolution is based upon the occurrence of mutations. These are exceedingly rare accidental alterations of the DNA, which thereafter are perpetuated. In a large population of organisms, every potential sort of mutation may occur, perhaps a number of times, in each generation. But in a small population a given type of mutation will occur, on the average, only once in many generations, and just when it will in fact occur remains unpredictable, this event being purely of the nature of a statistical accident. It follows that the fortunate mutations, in terms of the fitness and reproductive survival of a population subjected to new environmental conditions, may or may not, quite by accident, occur just at a time of selective crisis. The further fate of this population is thus determined by the random occurrence of an unpredictable event. We are forced to conclude that the evolutionary process is a causal chain of events the individual members of which are often—though not always—unpredictable, and which in turn delimit the possible situations existing in the next period of time. Like the flow of human history, which also contains a similar element of uniqueness of events, with the past limiting the character of the present and the future, there is limited usefulness of the evolutionary past for prediction. The probability mathematics of small numbers and unique events is simply not the same as the probability mathematics of large samples and large populations. This is the reason why the "explanations" of biology can in some respects not be reduced to the laws of physical science. Biological systems have a particular evolutionary history that conditions their present and their future.

I have discussed two of the four reasons Mayr [8] gives for the existence of indeterminacy in biology, namely, the "randomness of an event with respect to the significance of the event," as in the case of mutations, and the "uniqueness of all entities at the higher levels of biological integration." I am not so impressed with the validity of his two other reasons, which are the "extreme complexity" of living systems, and the "emergence of new qualities at higher levels of integration." It seems to me that these reasons are akin to those that have previously been advanced and found wanting. If the arguments advanced in the discussion of the borderline between life and the nonliving are sound, then one might expect that eventually, and in theory, the laws of the physical sciences could be extended to explain systems of the utmost complexity. The emergence of new qualities is also not limited to living organisms. There is "emergence" in this sense when three kinds of elementary particles—neutrons, protons, and electrons—unite to produce an atom with new and unpredictable properties; or when atoms of hydrogen and oxygen unite to produce a molecule with the unpredictable properties of water.

But the uniqueness of the particular event, embedded in the history and evolution of life, seems an unanswerable argument for the impossibility of explaining all aspects of life in terms of the laws of physical science which are demonstrable in nonliving systems. Finally, the randomness of behavior at distinct levels of organization leads to statistical laws based on probabilities that are applicable strictly to the entities that are exhibiting the random behavior. These statistical laws are explications as final at one level as at another. They relate to the nature of what we mean by "randomness," by "chance," and by "probability," rather than to the physical and chemical nature of material systems and measurable forces upon which our classical ideas of causation and determinism are founded. They find their unity in mathematics. They express the ultimate uncertainties of particular events in the real world where the laws of science deal only with the average outcomes.

References

1. E. Nagel, *The Structure of Science,* Harcourt, Brace and World, New York, 1961.
2. B. Commoner, "In Defence of Biology," *Science,* **133,** 1745–1748 (1961).
3. E. S. Russell, *The Interpretation of Development and Heredity,* Oxford University Press, Oxford, 1930.
4. N. W. Pirie, "The Meaninglessness of the Terms 'Life' and 'Living,'" in J. Needham and D. E. Green, Eds., *Perspectives in Biochemistry,* Cambridge, at the University Press, 1939, pp. 11–22.
5. I. Asimov, *The Intelligent Man's Guide to Modern Science,* Vol. 2 (The Biological Sciences), Basic Books, New York, 1960.
6. A. Kornberg, "Pathways of Enzymatic Synthesis of Nucleotides and Polynucleotides," in W. D. McElroy and B. Glass, Eds., *The Chemical Basis of Heredity,* Johns Hopkins Press, Baltimore, 1957, pp. 579–608.
7. J. B. S. Haldane, "The Origin of Life," *Rationalist Annual,* **1928,** 148–153. A. I. Oparin, *The Origin of Life on the Earth,* 3rd ed., trans. by Ann Synge, Academic Press, New York, 1957.

8. E. Mayr, "Cause and Effect in Biology," *Science*, **134**, 1501–1506 (1961).
9. H. Bergson, *Creative Evolution*, trans. by Arthur Mitchell, Modern Library, New York, 1911.
10. R. B. Braithwaite, *Scientific Explanation*, Cambridge, at the University Press, 1955.
11. M. Bunge, *Causality*, Harvard University Press, Cambridge, Mass., 1959.
12. M. Scriven, "Explanation and Prediction in Evolutionary Theory," *Science*, **130**, 477–482 (1959).
13. M. Bunge, "Causality, Chance, and Law," *American Scientist*, **49**, 432–448 (1961).

Discussion

W. Busse (*du Pont; University of Delaware*): I am just wondering if you have not wound up explaining the non-explainability on the basis of physical and chemical laws?

B. Glass: Yes, that is my conclusion; that there are certain unique aspects to which the laws of physics and chemistry cannot ever be extended because they deal with particular events that happened in the past and their consequences, rather than with the statistical probability which is the basis of scientific law.

Dr. Busse: Would you care to go into the requirements that make an event unique? I am not sure but what everything in physics could be considered unique, and yet, it doesn't always work out that way. I mean, we can ignore that factor in many cases; yet, under certain circumstances, we recognize it as an unique event to which this uncertainty applies. Now, such is the case of very small objects, such as the particle, but there is also a uniqueness in the larger events, such as beams of larger groups. How much of that uniqueness is a function of our awareness?

Professor Glass: How much is there really a distinction between the uniqueness in the biological system and the physical system as we commonly deal with it? What I mean by uniqueness is simply the actual occurrence of one among many possibilities which are equally probable on the basis of predictability and which, by its occurrence, excludes any other possibility among those alternatives. In other words, among the more than 17 billion possibilities arising from the union of the gametes of a particular human male parent and a particular female parent, just one is actually realized in the fertilization of an egg. Once this has become an event, all the other millions of possibilities are excluded. In a way, this is something like playing with cards and considering how many different kinds of hands can be dealt. The number is staggeringly large, but the dealer starts. He is not troubled by the fact that he has to make a selection from an infinite variety of hands. He lets chance take care of that. And by random and unpredictable events, one particular hand is dealt. Now, the nature of the game that will follow depends on the particular hand that is dealt. Looking at the matter in advance, one could predict only that one of certain innumerable possibilities would actually be realized but one has no way of predicting what particular hand will be dealt and, therefore, no way of predicting what particular kind of game will follow. The evolutionary character of life is like that. And, unless I am mistaken, the laws of physics and chemistry will not and cannot explain this sequential type of happening.

M. Primack (*Lincoln University*): As I understand it, the arguments that are usually advanced in biology that are not in terms of physics, i.e., the laws of physics and chemistry, are part of an argument for the autonomy of biology; but it seems here that, as I understand it, yours is not, because the events which are not explainable in terms of the laws of biology and chemistry are not to be explainable at all.

Professor Glass: I wouldn't say that they are not explainable at all. They are explainable *in principle*. You can explain the game of bridge according to certain rules which will apply to any of the infinite variety of hands that may be dealt. The particular hands that are dealt have nothing to do, really, with the rules of the game, and so it is that in the evolutionary history of life, we can say what the rules of the game are. This is what Scriven means by the distinction that in biology, evolutionary theory shows that one can explain without being able to predict. We can explain the rules but we cannot predict what the course of evolution is ever going to be because it depends at each point upon the selection from a vast possibility of equally probable occurrences of just one, at the right time and the right place.

Professor Primack: Can you explain the selection? It seems to me that the events which you say are unexplainable in terms of physical and chemical laws are the selection of combinations. Now, the question is: Is this explainable at all?

Professor Glass: No, I said also the mutations, because the mutations are predictable in a statistical sense. If you have a large enough population, you can be sure that you will get a certain number of mutations from $A_1, \cdots, A_n$, but what you can't predict is just when and where those will occur, in what particular individuals, in what particular cells because that actual mutational event is of the nature of an accident. In a small population, this kind of particular mutation may not occur for many, many generations—only once in many generations—because of the small number of genes of this kind to undergo this possibility of accident. So, the actual occurrence of this event may come about in a time and situation when it has no importance whatsoever. It is simply wiped out. Or it may happen to fit into an environment, or the environment may change, so that this mutation is just what's needed to enable the population to adapt to the new conditions.

Professor Primack: Do you think that you have given any arguments for the autonomy of biology from theoretical physics?

Professor Glass: I think that what I have done is to point out that in certain respects, biology is history, an evolutionary history which is based upon the occurrence of particular, unique and unpredictable events that condition the future. To the extent that it is like that, it isn't simply physics and chemistry.

B. Baumrin (*University of Delaware*): If someone characterized modern or contemporary physics and chemistry as statistical and indeterministic in the quantum-mechanical sense, would it be the case that you would not characterize your historical indeterminism in biology as something more like the mechanistic model that previously prevailed in the physical sciences; namely, a model which entails that processes are irreversible and that the past history of the material under consideration determines *in toto,* within the environment, the future of the material?

Professor Glass: In my mind, there is a rather sharp distinction between those aspects of biology which we nowadays call molecular biology, which so far as I can see is strictly physical and chemical and which deals with the current ways, the molecular and physical ways, in which the hereditary material works out its consequences; and on the other side, this historical evolutionary aspect of biology, which deals with the way in which the DNA has come to be what it is at the present time. This is the aspect that so often makes people think of living systems as having something purposeful or purposive within them, because of the remarkable way in which these patterns fit the organism for the conditions of life. But we can explain evolution without predicting the course of evolution, just as historically you can look back at the events in the history of human society and say "Yes, well it happened this way because . . . ," but you can't look forward and use the same principles to predict what will happen tomorrow, for the simple reason there are too many of these accidental unique events that determine the course of affairs. I would say that in biology of this sort, there is something analogous to the indeterminacy of quantum mechanics but it isn't based on quantum mechanics. And you can't use quantum mechanics, so far as I can see, in any way to explain organic evolution. But the laws of biology are also often statistical and indeterministic. Such laws reduce to the nature of random behavior and of chance. They reduce to the mathematics of probability rather than to physical or chemical laws.

T. Bynum (*University of Delaware*): Isn't it true that the development of human intelligence, then, in an evolutionary manner, involves a feedback mechanism of the type that will arrange that in the future, evolution won't be a blind process but will be directed with a purpose? So, we may argue that the purposefulness in evolution up to now has been pointless, but from this point on, having reached this stage, we direct and control in a purposeful way subsequent evolution.

Professor Glass: Is the question whether the evolution of human intelligence has reached a point where we might do away with this accidental, unique aspect in evolution and bring it under guidance and control? The doubt that always troubles me here is not whether human beings have sufficient power to do this but whether they have sufficient wisdom. Can men even agree on any direction or goal in their control of human evolution itself?

Mr. Bynum: It seems to me that this distinction you make between the biological sciences and the physical sciences, the historical distinction, might break down if you change the scale, the way you look at things, and consider the possibility that a chemical reaction has a history as well, though a very small one, and the individual components of this history are unpredictable in the same sense that our biological events are.

Professor Glass: Yes, that is precisely my point. If in chemistry one dealt not with chemical reactions involving billions of molecules of the same kind, but with one atom or pair of atoms undergoing a reaction, then this would be certainly a unique kind of event and perhaps also unpredictable in its consequences. What we get by lumping many millions and billions of events together is a statistical probability from which we can make predictions.

A. M. Clark (*University of Delaware*): It would seem that you could still bring physics and biology into a single system. If you handled both of them statistically, then you have predictability in both cases, but if you get back to the single atom, where you have a combination of carbon and hydrogen, then you are up against identical difficulties.

Professor Glass: That is a good question. I think it shows that I haven't made my point with sufficient clarity. I am not saying that the systems which exist in biology and in the physical sciences are necessarily different. That wasn't the question I posed. The question was: Can the laws of physical science which are demonstrable in nonliving systems be expected ultimately to explain all the laws of living systems? Now, I think that if you ever develop a chemistry and physics of single quanta, of a single ultimate particle, then you would have something analogous to those biological problems where unique events occur and determine the direction of affairs. But in between these levels of organization, there exists our multimolecular, multidimensional world; and I do not see, at least at the present time, how the development of quantum mechanics, which like these aspects of biology I have been discussing deals with unique events, in any way jumps that gap and explains the processes of evolution. I conclude, therefore, that you cannot derive the historical course of evolution from quantum mechanics. To me that is too big a jump.

Professor Clark: Supposing you formed an artificial ecological system where each population in the system was so large that at any one time you had a number of all the possible mutations, don't you think that in such a system that you could, at least for a time, have a chance of predicting the course of evolution?

Professor Glass: Certainly. That suggestion brings out precisely the point that in the actual world, in the actual course of affairs, you most often did not have such conditions, and the uniqueness of events then determined an unpredictable course that seems to be continuing. Of course, you can imagine a kind of universe in which all biological populations were statistically sufficiently large that every possibility would be realized—even the square of 550 billion kinds of offspring of one pair of dogs—but you would have to have dogs that could live forever and reproduce in a more prolific way than at present, and you would have to have more standing room in the universe for all these dogs before you could realize all these possibilities.

Professor Clark: But if the system contained very simple organisms, you were speaking of fewer numbers of possibilities, couldn't one actually do the job?

Professor Glass: Well, as simple a kind of species as we know is the bacterium. Yet a single bacterium has thousands of genes, each capable of varying independently of the others, and undergoing combinations with all the variants of the others so that there is an almost infinite potentiality for variation within a population of bacteria. You can't produce under any realistic conditions a population of bacteria that would realize even a tiny fraction of one per cent of the potential variability of the population. This is the limiting problem, you see—real conditions limit.

D. W. Oplinger (*du Pont*): Are we approaching a condition where we might predict that if we invent a new poison to attempt to control the Japanese beetle or the mosquito, or something like that, that within some short term, there will be a mutant species that will be immune to this poison?

Professor Glass: On the basis of our past experience, we can predict in a very general way that what has happened already more than once is likely to happen again—that the Japanese beetle, or the house fly, or the mosquito will undergo a mutation that will make it resistant to the agent. One of the very interesting genetic systems that has been recently analyzed in these terms is the relationship between the genotypes of corn and of the corn rust, which is a fungus that attacks the corn leaves. There are a number of genes in maize that confer resistance to the attacks of the rust in various ways so that the attack is less virulent and the corn plant can survive. And there are a number of genes in the rust that vary its virulence and these fit together in a very neat way. There is a continual shifting interplay between these two sets of genes, the one set in the corn, the other in the parasite. Every time the corn has a mutation that makes it a little more resistant, or a little less resistant to the rust, some corresponding mutation, having occurred in the rust, will be selected and will produce a combination so that these two things will go on living together, one at the expense of the other, but without the parasite's putting the host out of business altogether.

J. Thomas (*University of Delaware*): You say that there is emergence in the biological realm but with unpredictable properties, but when you make a new element that hasn't been made by man before, you can predict the properties and then make it, and then find that the properties are as predicted. In other words, certain elements were predicted to be able to exist and have certain properties, then the existing elements were varied by different techniques and found to closely agree with the predicted properties.

Professor Glass: I don't mean to say there is no possibility of predicting the properties of newly discovered elements or compounds in advance; but to the degree to which the properties of a molecule are unpredictable from the knowledge, pure and simple, of the component atoms and their ways of combination, I think that the emergence of new properties is analogous to the emergence of properties in the cell. I don't see anything different in the two types of emergence. I think the argument that emergent qualities in the realm of living organisms sets them apart, doesn't really set them apart very much, if at all. If we take seriously the current theory of the origin of the first living systems on earth from the nonliving, then there must have been an emergence of new qualities and new properties when the DNA first became incorporated into the first coacervates. If it had never happened before, even if there had been a scientist around, he would not have been able to predict what the result would be.

W. Balcavage (*University of Delaware*): How could these accidental and unique events take place? Couldn't we inquire what conditions must have existed previous to an event which would have been sufficient to predict it?

Professor Glass: What you are suggesting is really that there is no such thing as chance—that if you analyze any situation sufficiently, you can always determine a number of physical and chemical factors in the situation that made it turn out exactly as it did. That is an arguable point which would take us a great deal of time to discuss, and I don't know that I have a satisfactory answer; but I am quite sure that chance, in the sense of at least the determination of events by a multiplicity of such minor causes that for all practical purposes they can never be isolated and identified, does exist.

Mr. Balcavage: Isn't the indeterminism view that you profess one which refers merely to the large number of things that have to be observed?

Professor Glass: No, the large number of possibilities compared to the few that become actual. Suppose there are eight million different possible kinds of sperms produced by the male parent and eight million possible kinds of eggs produced by the female parent. There are then 64 trillion (64×10^{12}) possibilities of the combination of the kinds of sperms with the kinds of eggs. A baby represents a single one of these possibilities. Now why this particular baby? A multiplicity of minor causes which render unpredictable what particular event will be realized! We call this chance. It does not mean that no physical and chemical causes were involved. It means simply that each other possibility was just as probable as the one that was realized. The statistical laws deal with these probabilities, not with physical and chemical causes.

PART V

Philosophical Aspects of the Social Sciences

Are the Social Sciences
Really Historical?

Alan Donagan, *Indiana University*

The title of this paper is, as no doubt you expected, fraudulent. Although I have opinions about the nature of the
social sciences which I shall not conceal, I do not delude
myself that, even were those opinions true, I could demonstrate their truth in a single lecture. My title is fraudulent
in another way. It might lead the unwary to expect from me
not only comprehensive knowledge of the various social
sciences and of history, but a thoroughly sifted philosophical
interpretation of their methods and results. Well, if such
were your expectations, I apologize. I know some history, a
very little psychology, anthropology, economics, and sociology, and I am a professional philosopher. My only excuse
for discussing the topic I have proposed is that it is important; that very few do discuss it; and that the few that have
done so, for better or worse, have neither asked some questions which puzzle me, nor been afflicted with some of my
doubts. My questions and doubts, not to speak of my conclusions, may be foolish as well as false. Any man is likely
to make a fool of himself in discussing subjects in which he
is not a specialist. But has any man since Max Weber mas-
tered all the requisite special sciences? The work must be
done, even if the workmen are bad.

At the present time, at least three different general accounts of the nature of the social sciences have found advocates among competent students. The latest, which has some
claim to be also the oldest, is that the social sciences are
really philosophical. It has been persuasively argued by
Peter Winch, in his book *The Idea of a Social Science*. How-

ever, despite my debt to Winch's book, I cannot accept its principal thesis. I have therefore chosen to discuss the two remaining accounts, which were anticipated by Wilhelm Windelband in his celebrated Rectorial address at Strasbourg in 1894, *Geschichte und Naturwissenschaft*. Windelband argued that there are two kinds of science, *nomothetic* sciences, which are concerned with the establishment of general laws, and *idiographic* sciences, which are concerned with the exploration of individual facts. The physical sciences Windelband took to be specimens of the former; history, of the latter.

Although nobody today would accept Windelband's distinction in the form he gave it, and although he used it to separate history from the natural sciences rather than to throw light on the nature of the social sciences, its influence is still with us. Most social scientists, whether they know it or not, tend to think of their sciences either as something like what Windelband called "nomothetic" or as something like what he called "idiographic." Sometimes, however, they confound the two. In this lecture I shall try: first, to state, as clearly as I can, what the two conceptions are which Windelband began to analyze; and secondly, by examining an example of an economic law, Gresham's Law, to argue that it does not satisfy the nomothetic conception.

1. The Social Sciences as Nomothetic

The conception of the social sciences as nomothetic, as fundamentally like the natural sciences in their aims and methods, has been brought to a high degree of sophistication by such men as Carl G. Hempel and Ernest Nagel in this country, and Karl Popper in Britain.

In outline, the conception of natural science that these men have developed is this. The natural sciences are concerned with explaining natural events; and they do so by showing that, given other natural events (the initial conditions) the events to be explained necessarily followed according to laws of nature. (For simplicity, I ignore explaining probabilities by probabilistic laws.) Laws are universal truths, which are both falsifiable (that is, they *logically could* be in conflict with empirical evidence) and well corroborated (that is, they *in fact do not* conflict with any evidence which has been discovered, after a methodical attempt to find such evidence). If two equally falsifiable but incompatible hypotheses both accord with all known evidence, neither is regarded as corroborated; it is necessary to find evidence which will decide between them. And, since any hypothesis can be squared with any evidence by *ad hoc* hypotheses, it is laid down that *ad hoc* hypotheses must not be invoked merely to save an hypothesis, and that no hypothesis will be considered as an alternative to another unfalsified hypothesis unless it is equally falsifiable.

The laws of nomothetic science simply assert universal and physically necessary connections. It is pointless to ask why a law of nature holds, unless you mean only, "Is it derivable from some other law or laws?" Whether laws fulfill any purpose, divine or other, nomothetic science neither does nor can tell us. It contains no vestige of anthropomorphism.

Many competent students maintain that both psychology and the social sciences proper are nomothetic in this sense. Let me begin with psychology; for, although I have little to say about it, I hope that that little may throw light on the social sciences proper. Psychology conceived as a natural science is behaviorist in method; and what from the beginning distinguished the behaviorist approach was its rejection of introspection, and its determination to confine whatever in human life it tried to explain to that which is "intersubjectively observable." Although some behaviorists also confine the variables which they employ in their hypotheses to such as are intersubjectively observable, so to define behaviorism would be eccentric. Like any other scientists, behaviorists may postulate theoretical entities whenever they have reason.

Behaviorism may be as prodigal in theoretical entities as

any scientific theory. What is remarkable about it is its self-denying ordinance respecting what it tries to explain. Here, unfortunately, one of the best philosophers of our time, Professor Gilbert Ryle, has unwittingly caused much confusion. In *The Concept of Mind,* you may remember, Ryle praised behaviorism for showing how "bloodless and spineless" Descartes' introspectible operations of *res cogitans* are; and set about showing that most operations of mind, far from being "private" episodes to which their agent has "privileged access," are as "public" as can be. Since it is true that the Cartesian "private episodes" which Ryle rejects (in some cases, I think, wrongly) include at least some of the introspectible feelings, ideas, etc., which behaviorists methodically ignore, it is almost irresistibly tempting to identify Ryle's public activities with the behaviorists' "intersubjectively observable" specimens of behavior. Moreover, anybody who yields to that temptation can claim Ryle's own sanction for doing so.

Yet the difference between Ryle's position and any strict form of behaviorism becomes manifest as soon as you consider what each implies about human speech. To behaviorists, speech admits of scientific investigation only in a measure as it is "intersubjectively observable"; and all strict behaviorists interpret this as excluding any reference to what is commonly thought of as the speaker's meaning, because to speak of a man as saying and meaning something is to attribute to him what, in their terminology, is an "introspectible" thought. Hence, behaviorists investigate speech as though it were a physical process. They occupy themselves with the causes and effects of uttered noises and scribbles; and, if they speak of "meaning" at all, they use it to refer only to the causal relations in which this or that uttered noise or scribble stands to other events, including other utterances.

Some philosophers—for example, Ernest Nagel in *The Structure of Science* (see pp. 477–8, 554 n.)—have pointed out that "the term 'behaviorism' does not have a precise doctrinal connotation," and that some professed behaviorists interpret the requirement of intersubjective observability liberally if not licentiously. Nagel's own view that what he calls "reason analysis," the application in sociology of certain well-established historical techniques, "provides . . . support for the general position . . . that human dispositions and intentions can be successfully investigated by behavioristic methods" (*op. cit.*, p. 554 *n.*), extends the sense of *behavioristic* in such a way. I am not concerned to deny that you can also obliterate Windelband's distinction between the nomothetic and the idiographic approaches to the social sciences by extending the sense of *nomothetic*. But if *nomothetic* and *behavioristic* are to be useful in methodology, they must be used strictly.

But why insist that all strict behaviorists interpret intersubjective observability as excluding any reference to meaning in the ordinary sense? Consider one of Nagel's remarks: "Professed behaviorists today generally accept introspective *reports* by experimental subjects, not as statements about private psychic states of the subjects, but as observable verbal *responses* the subjects make under given conditions" (*op. cit.*, p. 477). What Nagel says, of course, is true: true, but ambiguous. For in what sense is a "verbal *response*" observable? That the subject makes a certain noise is undoubtedly observable. The strictest of behaviorists must take account of that. But what if the noise is interpreted as a *linguistic* utterance? A behaviorist can so interpret it if and only if he can give a behavioristic sense to the terms he must use in so interpreting it. Suppose the subject says, "That tickles." A behaviorist can say, "The subject reported that he felt a tickle," if and only if he has a behavioristic theory according to which when that subject uttered the noise "That tickles," he meant that he felt a tickle. For a behaviorist to offer such an interpretation, without any theory to justify it, would be as though a physicist, in the absence of any physical theory about a divine language, were to say that when it thunders, God is expressing anger. The objection, "But no physicist would claim God as a *physical* entity," has no weight at all. No behaviorist has a right to claim that a subject who can mean things by his utterances is a *behavioristic* entity, unless he can elucidate the expression "to mean something by an utterance," in behavioristic terms. It is notorious that no behavioristic elucidation has been provided in terms of which even the verbal responses of subjects in experimental situations can be interpreted.

Ryle is not only not committed to the behaviorist program, but again and again he tacitly implies that it is false. *The Concept of Mind* contains no theory of meaning whatever (the omission of an entry "Meaning" from its index is not accidental); and although Ryle has attacked certain theories of meaning as false, e.g., the theory that the meaning of a word is an image or something of the kind, he has never countenanced the restricted technical sense of "meaning" in behaviorist psychology as philosophically adequate. Even more important, when Ryle attacks what he calls the myth of "the ghost in the machine," and argues that the operations of minds are normally public, he takes it for granted that the significance of significant gestures and significant speech is public.

I have digressed on the difference between behaviorism and Ryle's position in order to forestall a serious objection to what I shall go on to say. It may appear to some readers either that to reject a Cartesian conception of mind entails accepting a behavioristic one, or that to reject behaviorism as a philosophical theory entails accepting a Cartesian conception of mind. Neither entailment holds. Even if Ryle was right in rejecting all Cartesian privileged access, his analyses contain an element which strict behaviorism cannot tolerate: namely, reference to speech and gestures as having meaning in the ordinary sense. Nobody who upholds Ryle's analyses of the various intellectual activities can be a philosophical behaviorist, but neither can he be a Cartesian.

The doctrine that the social sciences are at present natural sciences does not presuppose that they are reducible to behaviorist psychology. Rather, it asserts that the social sciences, at least insofar as they have been successful, have adopted the methods of natural science in their own way. They ignore whatever in social processes is not intersubjectively observable; and they seek to explain social processes by means of laws which employ no concepts except those whose application is intersubjectively observable, either directly (if they are nontheoretical) or indirectly (if they are theoretical). As Durkheim laid down: A natural scientist of social processes must "consider social facts as things." What I have shown to hold for behaviorist psychology holds of any strictly nomothetic social science. It cannot employ any concepts which presuppose the ordinary common-sense notion of what a man *means* when he says or does something significant. From now on, adapting a term made familiar by Brentano, I shall call such concepts "intentional" concepts. A strictly nomothetic social science, then, must develop a set of non-intentional concepts applicable to social processes. Now, advocates of the conception of the social sciences as natural sciences protest that sciences like economics and sociology have done no less than that. There can be no doubt that typical concepts of economics, whether wholly or partly taken from those applicable to ordinary human intercourse, like *effective demand* or *liquidity preference,* or not, like *balance of payments* or *inflation,* on the face of it do not stand for significant actions. They appear to be neutral descriptive terms, introduced by objective social scientists, to describe social processes which go on no matter what the individuals caught up in them hope or fear their individual actions will bring about.

It is not at all absurd to hold that some of the social sciences, particularly economics and sociology, have discovered laws of social processes which do not employ what I have called intentional concepts; and it is certain that strict behaviorist psychologists have been trying to dispense with intentional concepts in studying human behavior, both individual and social. However, as Nagel has candidly acknowledged, neither behaviorist psychology nor nomothetic social science has developed theories "known to be adequate for explaining the entire range of human conduct" (*op. cit.,* p. 477). Before speculating about the future of such sciences, let us turn to the second of Windelband's kinds of science: the idiographic.

2. The Social Sciences as Idiographic

My exposition of the "idiographic" conception, like my earlier exposition of the "nomothetic" one, does not agree with that of every advocate of that conception. Indeed, it could not. It is largely derived from R. G. Collingwood's *The Idea of History.* In Collingwood's view, all social processes are ultimately describable in terms of the actions and inter- actions of human beings, and those actions and interactions themselves must be described—what Brutus did in stabbing Caesar, what his action was—until you have stated why he did so, or, as Collingwood put it, "what Brutus thought which made him stab Caesar." An established idiographic explanation of an action resembles one in natural science in three respects: the event to be explained is deduced from its *explanans* (or its deducibility from it is made plain); the *explanans* contains a statement of the initial conditions from which the event to be explained sprang; and the explanation is falsifiable but well corroborated. The difference between an idiographic and a nomothetic explanation is that the statement of the initial conditions is connected with the statement of the event to be explained, not by a law or uni- versal hypothesis, but by a statement of what, at the mo- ment of acting, the agent thought. An agent's thoughts may be divided into the purposes and principles on which he was resolved, his appreciation of his situation, and his calcula- tions; and any or all of these may have been reasonable or unreasonable, sound or unsound. Since statements about a man's thoughts can only be made in the traditional "mental- istic" vocabulary, or another of the same kind, idiographic explanations inevitably employ intentional concepts.

Nobody has ever offered a serious reason for doubting

that at least some historical explanations purport to be idiographic in the sense I have described. But it has been doubted whether any such explanation has been or can be scientifically corroborated, on the ground that you cannot scientifically corroborate any statement about what anybody thinks. Every man knows his own conscious thoughts immediately, without corroboration; but whatever thoughts you may attribute to others, you cannot know, either immediately or by scientific reasoning, that they in fact have them.

Perhaps you have now divined why I insisted on boring you with a digression on the difference between philosophical behaviorism and the position of Ryle's *The Concept of Mind*. An idiographic science is only possible if neither Cartesianism (which asserts that thoughts, in the ordinary sense, may be known immediately but not scientifically) nor philosophical behaviorism (which denies that thoughts, in the ordinary sense, exist at all) is true. Not the least important of Ryle's achievements in *The Concept of Mind* was to show that a philosophy of mind which is neither Cartesian nor behaviorist is possible. Wittgenstein's *Philosophical Investigations*, written before Ryle's book, but published after it, points in the same direction; and, better on the subject of acts of thought than either Ryle's or Wittgenstein's books, there is P. T. Geach's *Mental Acts*. If you ask me why I think that hypotheses about the thoughts of others can be scientifically corroborated, I shall refer you to the writings of good historians, e.g., to J. E. Neale's convincing demonstration, in his *Elizabeth I and Her Parliaments*, of a series of hypotheses about Queen Elizabeth I's plans during the preparation of the Uniformity Bills of 1559. If you ask me how such demonstrations are philosophically possible, I shall refer you to Geach's *Mental Acts*.

3. Can Social Processes Be Explained Both Nomothetically and Idiographically?

Confronted with the question, "Are the social sciences nomothetic or idiographic?" some philosophers answer as follows: "That depends on which social scientist you have in mind. Some approach their subject nomothetically, others idiographically. But that does not matter; for the two approaches differ categorically. Human actions and social processes can be investigated in both ways: as 'intersubjectively observable' in the sense in which all natural processes are, they can be explained in terms of the non-intentional concepts of natural science; as expressions of thought they can be explained idiographically. There can be no conflict between these kinds of explanation, because both they and what they explain belong to different categories." This position has not only been endorsed by Ryle, in *The Concept of Mind*, in which he roundly declared that "there is no contradiction in saying that one and the same process . . . is in accordance with two principles of completely different types and such that neither is 'reducible' to the other, though one of them (the idiographic) presupposes the other (the nomothetic)," but it was earlier affirmed by Collingwood himself, in *The New Leviathan*.

There was a time when I was content with Ryle's and Collingwood's view; and I do not wish to prolong this lecture by explaining my recent qualms about it. However, I do wish to point out that while it is true, as Ryle says, that there are *some* pairs of principles of completely different types such that one and the same process accords with both, it does not follow that *all* pairs of principles of completely different types are of this kind. Nor is it at all clear that idiographic explanations of human actions presuppose nomothetic explanations of the physical side *of those actions*. It is indeed true that the various bodily functions can be nomothetically explained, and that human actions only take place in reasonably well-functioning bodies; but it does not follow that if a given human act can be idiographically explained, then the individual physical movements involved in that act, as well as the general functioning of the body which makes those movements possible, can be nomothetically explained. If you punch somebody on the nose because he has insulted you, I can explain your act idiographically; but it does not follow that any nomothetic explanation of movements of your body involved in that punch can be given, whether in behavioristic psychology or neurophysiology. Certainly no such explanation can be given in the present state of those sciences.

This result, however, is purely negative. It may be that human actions and social processes can be explained idiographically but not nomothetically; or it may be that they can be explained in both ways. All I have shown is that it is not necessary to hold, with Collingwood and Ryle, that they can be explained in both ways. I should not have said anything about the matter at all did not many of our contemporaries think that Collingwood's and Ryle's view is not only true but, when stated, obviously true. The latter it certainly is not.

4. Analysis of an Apparently Nomothetic Explanation

Since it is plainly impossible in this lecture to establish any conclusion about *all* explanations in the social sciences, I shall conclude by arguing that some such explanations, which are commonly received as nomothetic, are in fact covertly idiographic. Whether this is so of all such explanations, I shall not attempt to argue. However, if you are tempted to jump to that conclusion, you will find yourself holding that the social sciences are really historical; for, as I think I have shown, idiographic explanations are typically historical. That is as close as I shall come to answering the question which is the announced title of my lecture.

One of the oldest and best established laws of economics is the proposition in monetary theory known as Gresham's Law. According to the *Encyclopaedia Britannica* (11th ed.) it was stated, before Gresham, by Oresme in the late Middle Ages, and in 1526 by the great astronomer, Copernicus, in his *De monetae curendae ratione*. Macaulay has pointed out that the phenomenon is noticed, but not stated as a law, in a comedy of Aristophanes. The common formula of this law is: *Bad money drives out good.* Its more technical formulation, given by H. D. Macleod in 1857, is: The worst form of currency in circulation regulates the value of the whole currency and drives all other forms of currency out of circulation.

On the face of it, this law connects two kinds of social process, neither of which is necessarily brought about by human design: the circulation of an inferior alongside a superior form of currency, and the gradual disappearance from circulation of the superior form. The law is well corroborated. It has been confirmed in a variety of circumstances: where there is underweight or debased coin in circulation with full-weight or pure coin of the same metal; where there are two metals in circulation, and one is undervalued as compared with the other; and where less convertible paper money is put into circulation with a more convertible paper money or with a metallic currency. There are societies to which it does not apply, either because they lack a monetary system, or because their currency is uniform; but if there is any case to which it applies which has falsified it, I at least do not know of it. It is employed in historical explanations; and it has been invoked in making true predictions. Need we say more? Here is one social science, economics, which at least in part is nomothetic.

One slight doubt remains. As Popper has taught us, a scientific hypothesis is corroborated, not by accumulating favorable evidence, but by seeking *and failing to find* unfavorable evidence. Have we truly sought evidence against Gresham's Law? Where might we expect to find it?

Suppose there were a society which had a monetary system, but in which there was little money because each man provided his family's food and shelter by his own labor on his own land; suppose, furthermore, that coins of varying quality circulated side by side, that tendering money was a recognized occasion for display, and that anybody who tendered inferior money was scorned and derided. Anthropologists have encountered societies with practices far more remote from ours than these. What economist would predict that Gresham's Law would be found to hold in such a society?

At this point an objection may be entered. A society such as you have described, it may be protested, does not have a pure monetary system; the tendering of money for goods normally has an object other than to obtain its maximum value in goods, namely, to display the quality of the coins tendered. Now if Gresham's Law is taken to apply only to societies with a pure monetary system, the existence of a society such as I have described cannot falsify it.

Such rejoinder would save Gresham's Law at the price of making it logically unfalsifiable. For let a pure monetary system be one in which money is normally tendered in order to obtain its maximum value in goods, then it *logically* follows that Gresham's Law obtains in it. The nineteenth century historian Lord Macaulay has explained this so lucidly, that I hope you will bear with a quotation. He is writing of the state of the English coinage in 1695, and this is what he says:

> Yet any man of plain understanding might have known that, when the State treats perfect coin and light coin as of equal value, the perfect coin will not drive the light coin out of circulation, but will itself be driven out. A clipped crown, on English ground, went as far in the payment of a tax or a debt as a milled crown. But the milled crown, as soon as it had been flung into the crucible or carried across the Channel, became much more valuable than the clipped crown. It might therefore have been predicted, as confidently as any thing can be predicted which depends on the human will, that the inferior pieces would remain in the only market in which they could fetch the same price as the superior pieces, and that the superior pieces would take some form or fly to some place in which some advantage could be derived from their superiority. (*History of England,* Chap. 21)

You will notice that Macaulay takes it for granted that the only normal point of tendering money is to obtain as much for it as you can.

That Gresham's Law obtains in a "pure" monetary economy is therefore logically unfalsifiable. Does that dispose of its claim to be a law? There is no doubt that it disposes of its claim to be a law in the sense defined by such theorists of nomothetic science as Hempel and Popper, which requires that laws be empirically falsifiable. But neither Popper nor Hempel is infallible. After all, do physicists consider Newton's Laws of Motion to be empirically falsifiable?

In mechanics, Newton's Laws of Motion have a special place; indeed, if they were abandoned, it would be as reasonable to say that mechanics itself had been abandoned as that it had been revised. And in view of that vast body of knowledge which presupposes mechanics, it is plain that no odd or unexplained phenomenon would tempt any scientist to question the fundamental laws of mechanics itself.

Does it follow that the fundamental laws of mechanics are not falsifiable? Not at all. It only follows that they are very well established; and that it is difficult to give a coherent scientific description of a possible world in which they do not hold—difficult, because so much depends on them that, should you suppose them to be false, you would be compelled to suppose that the physical world is different from what we perceive it to be in almost every respect.

The comparative immunity of the Newton's Laws of Motion to empirical falsification is altogether different in character from the logical immunity of Gresham's Law to falsification in a pure monetary system. It would manifestly be trifling to argue that Newton's Laws must hold in any pure mechanical system, if you define a mechanical system in part as one in which Newton's Laws hold. Newton's Laws are laws because it is possible to specify the phenomena for which they hold, *without* defining those phenomena either in terms of those laws themselves, or in terms of more ultimate laws from which they can be deduced. But it is not possible, so I contend, to specify the phenomena for which Gresham's Law holds, without defining those phenomena in terms of economic laws from which Gresham's Law is deducible. Moreover, I know of no economic law which can be shown to hold of any set of phenomena, unless those phenomena are specified as falling within an economic system which is defined either in terms of that law, or in terms of other laws from which that law is deducible.

Having shown that Gresham's Law does not satisfy the nomothetic conception, I must now exhibit its connection with the idiographic one. That a given society has a given economic system is a fact about what the members of that society normally try to accomplish in producing and distributing goods; in short, it is an historical fact about the purposes which members of a given society normally have in mind in certain situations. Such historical facts have not as yet been explained nomothetically, whether in economics or in sociology. Marx's attempt so to explain the existence of capitalism was a brilliant but unmistakable failure. The only explanations we have of such facts, and we do not have many, are historical, i.e., idiographic.

There is a lesson in this. In all societies there are certain departments of life in which most of their members normally seek certain ends and refuse to sanction certain means of attaining them. From such information it is often possible to deduce certain general truths about those societies; or even, as in the case of Gresham's Law, certain general truths about a whole class of similar societies. These general truths may also be discovered empirically, as Aristophanes discovered Gresham's Law to obtain in Athenian economy. But if the fact that such general truths hold good in a given society or class of societies is derivable from historical facts about the ways in which members of those societies normally think, and if those historical facts cannot themselves be explained nomothetically, then the social sciences which treat of such truths are not genuinely nomothetic. If economics is a nomothetic science, it is nomothetic all through. To the extent that what I have said of Gresham's Law is true of other economic and sociological laws, economics and sociology are not nomothetic, but fundamentally idiographic, or, if you prefer, historical. To *what* extent that is so, you must decide for yourselves.

Discussion

D. Pruitt (*University of Delaware*): I don't see why you can't take these intentional concepts and treat them as intervening variables in the way we usually do in psychology. I can think of an experiment to test your revision of Gresham's Law, an experiment in which I will manipulate observables and predict observables. We have to manipulate the meanings, but I can think of contingent conditions for manipulating these meanings: for example, rewarding a person if he puts some sort of stated meaning on money, or punishing him if he puts some other meaning on it. Now we have an experimental situation in which you have an experimentally created community with two currencies.

A. Donagan: As I understand it, you say that you could give a nomothetic explanation of the existence of a certain kind of society in which Gresham's Law would hold, that is, a society in which people were conditioned by reward and punishment to use money as money only, and not as something else. I am not myself sure of that, if only because, even in the Big Brother kind of society, it is difficult to ensure effective conditioning. It is *a priori* possible that the result of such conditioning would be a revulsion against the whole institution of money. In a laboratory situation, where you have people in Skinner boxes, you might do it, but not in an ordinary life. However, I do agree with you that it is logically possible that some kind of conditioning would do the trick.

Professor Pruitt: Most behavioral psychologists allow a stimulus to be connected with a response by way of an intervening variable, which may be defined in terms of intentional concepts. Hull, in fact, introduced intentional concepts into behavioral theory.

Professor Donagan: Did Hull do so in the sense I have specified? I introduced the notion of an intentional concept by reference to "ordinary" meaning. Now, when someone utters a noise that means so and so, doesn't Hull analyze this in something like cause–effect terms, and not in terms of the "meaning" in the ordinary sense?

Professor Pruitt: I would think of the implicit response which can be thought of as representing the go-box to the rat, and which determines the rat's behavior when he starts to feed. The rat grasps the notion of the meaning of "go."

Professor Donagan: A rat doesn't grasp what I mean by the meaning of "go." You can describe what a rat does, and some things in human behavior, without employing any intentional concept whatever. Take my statement: "When the subject Joe uses the word *cat*, he means a furry quadruped of a certain kind." If you viewed this as Hull does, you would interpret it as follows: "When a furry animal of a certain kind is presented to the subject Joe, he will produce the noise 'cat' or the scribble 'c-a-t'; when the subject Joe, showing signs of disturbance, says a word like 'cat,' and you give him a dog, he stays disturbed; but when you give him a cat, he becomes quiet." This is a crude behaviorist analysis of what, in a very simple language, saying and meaning "cat" might be. Now, in the sense in which I use "intentional," there is no intentional concept in this analysis at all. The fact that Joe "responds" in these ways does not show him to mean (in the ordinary sense) anything at all when he says "cat." He would do so only if it would make sense to speak of him as making a mistake or being deceitful. A simple case would be a man who could say "cat" when there wasn't a cat, or who could say "cat" and be satisfied when you gave him a dog, either because he had made a mistake about what he saw or wanted, or because he intended to deceive somebody. This would be intentional because in analyzing it you must refer both to what the word *cat* means, and to the difference between what the man thought and what he said. To do the latter, you must specify other words, e.g., *dog* and treat them, too, as having meanings in the ordinary sense. The behaviorist analysis I have outlined cannot deal with such cases.

D. W. Oplinger (*du Pont*): Do you mean to ask, "Are the social sciences really sciences?" on the basis of your conclusion that they are idiographic? Isn't it a matter of taste whether you call them sciences or not, if they are really idiographic?

Professor Donagan: I think Windelband is right. There are two kinds of science, not two senses of the word *science*. I would say that history is a science in the following three crucial respects. First, it gives explanations which really explain. Second, it gives explanations which can be falsified. Third, it can demonstrate some of its explanations. Any mode of inquiry which does those three things qualifies as a science. Of course, if you choose to use the word *science* so that it means what I call nomothetic science, then I agree that in your sense idiographic sciences would not really be sciences. But that would be trivial. I predict that a hundred years from now, the social sciences will have found enormously more about patterns of behavior which historians have, on the whole, ignored; but I also predict that those patterns will not be found to rest on underpinning general laws, as patterns in physical nature do, but on the kind of foundation with which the idiographic sciences deal. Now that is a prediction. No amount of philosophical *a priori* speculation can determine what the future of any empirical science will be.

M. Primack (*Lincoln University*): I would like to ask what connection there is between your notion of an idiographic explanation which involves intentional concepts and Dilthey's notion of the operation called *verstehen;* and also how you would answer the sort of objections that Hempel raises to such notions?

Professor Donagan: There is indeed a connection between my views and Dilthey's. I haven't read much of Dilthey; but in what I have read, I have been impressed with the amount of insight he showed and the amount of truth he managed to get over. As for Hempel, what he says about *verstehen* as a means of verification is completely correct. Hempel interprets the theory of *verstehen* as the notion that, in the idiographic sciences, you arrive at your explanations by looking at the evidence "empathetically," and waiting for an explanation to pop into your head. Hempel's objection to this is that even if that were how an historian arrives at his explanations, it would not help him to corroborate them. *Verstehen* might be a way of getting hypotheses, but it is not a way of proving or corroborating them. However, I disagree with Hempel's view that if you abandon nomothetic science then *verstehen* is the only means of verification you have left. Suppose you want to establish the proposition "Donagan predicts that in the next century the social sciences are going to move in the direction of the idiographic conception rather than the nomothetic one." How do you know that I think that? Well, I did say it. But that evidence admits of two interpretations, or three. One is that I am not in control of my speech. Another is that I am lying. A third is that I am telling the truth; that is, telling the truth about what I think. It's up to you to decide whether I have lost control of my speech; but, no matter how foolish what I have said may be, I do not think it to be incoherent in that sense. So exclude the first explanation. Take the other two, the idiographic ones: Am I lying, or am I not? There could be reasons for my lying. But what on earth would make me lie about this subject in this situation? Unless you can suggest evidence for hypotheses that would entail that I am lying, to say, "He is lying because he could have a reason for lying," would violate a standard rule of science: the rule against using *ad hoc* hypotheses. A natural explanation of why I said what I did is that I thought it. By a "natural explanation," I mean one that fits all the facts, and involves no *ad hoc* hypothesis. The explanation that I am lying involves an *ad hoc* hypothesis. *Verstehen* or intuition cannot prove any statement about someone else's thought. At best, it can suggest hypotheses. To prove an hypothesis, whether suggested by *verstehen* or not, you must show that it alone survives all the tests you can imagine, without forcing you to appeal to any *ad hoc* hypothesis.

Professor Primack: It would seem that you are presupposing some knowledge of the connection between purpose and activity, or some knowledge of the interconnection between purposes, and this seems to be a presupposition of idiographic explanation. How do you get such a knowledge?

Professor Donagan: Take the compound proposition, "Donagan wants to communicate the proposition P to an audience; he does not have any other end in view which conflicts with communicating P to that audience; he can communicate it now; and he hasn't done so yet." It seems to me to follow from all this that Donagan *does* utter the proposition P. You don't need any further hypothesis at all. It is built into the notion of a purpose on which you are resolved, that if you have no incompatible purpose, don't change your mind, and recognize the occasion as appropriate, then you will carry out your purpose. This is as much built into the concept of purpose, as being male is logically built into the concept of being a brother.

Professor Primack: It would seem that such an explanation was tautological.

Professor Donagan. No. It is not a tautology that I want to communicate the proposition P.

Professor Primack: But if you do . . .

Professor Donagan: Yes, if I do, that is a tautology. But the explanation I gave was not hypothetical.

Professor Primack: All such explanations lead to tautologies?

Professor Donagan: The explanation won't be, but the connection between the explanation and what it explains will be. That is a virtue and not a vice. It holds for the connection between any good explanation and what it explains.

N. Axelrod (*University of Delaware*): It seems to me that you are running into a paradox. You are trying to explain, that is, to give a rational account of whether you are lying or whether you are telling the truth. If we take these as two hypotheses, and that we are trying to decide which of them is true, then are you not trying to explain your utterance in a nomothetic sense? Are you not trying to prove that one of these is right?

Professor Donagan: Why do you say that that is nomothetic?

Professor Axelrod: Because you must use some method of defining what is truth in this case. What are you going to use as your criterion of truth? How am I going to be able in any idiographic sense to say what is truth?

Professor Donagan: My criterion for truth in idiographic science is the same as my criterion in nomothetic science: namely, "Is this the only one of a set of equally falsifiable hypotheses, which squares with the known facts without *ad hoc* hypotheses?"

Professor Axelrod: In that case, I should come to the conclusion that in principle you were lying, because earlier you said that a scientist who is presented with two propositions, equally falsifiable, but neither of which are unfalsified, will accept the riskier of the two propositions.

Professor Donagan: Oh, no. I did say that indeed, but in my account of falsifying a proposition I laid it down that no *ad hoc* hypothesis must be involved. I said *P*, which, as far as it goes, is evidence that I think *P*. It favors the hypothesis that I think *P*. It does not favor the hypothesis that I think not-*P*. You can, it is true, square it with the hypothesis that I think not-*P*, by supposing that I have some motive or other for lying. But the statement that I have some unspecified motive for lying has no support whatever. It is *ad hoc*, i.e., it is brought in solely to square the hypothesis that I am lying with a piece of evidence which conflicts with it.

Professor Axelrod: Doesn't this depend on some intuition that you are telling the truth?

Professor Donagan: No. If you had been talking with me outside and I had said "I am going to go in and lie about my views because I have made a bet, and will make $1000 by doing it," and had shown you an entry in a betting book, then you would have evidence that I really was lying and would be making, not an *ad hoc* hypothesis, but a well-supported one. You can carry this as far as you like. Perhaps the real bet was to show you a spurious betting book to see whether you would rise in triumph in the course of discussion. The point is that if you at any stage make an hypothesis against some evidence without either having or thinking you can find other evidence to back it up, your method is bad. It isn't intuition to go from "He says this" to "He believes it." Why else do you say a thing except that you believe it? In exceptional cases, you may have some reason for lying. But to allege that a man is lying is a bad method unless you can suggest a reason why he might do so, a reason for which you have or think you can find evidence.

The Structure of Malthus' Population Theory *

A. G. N. Flew, *University of Keele*

I

The philosophical object of the present exercise is to take Malthus' population theory as a comparatively simple yet extremely important example of a theory in social science, and to consider its structure, nature, and functions. To do this it is necessary first to sort out a confusion of sources, and then to give an account of what Malthus' theoretical framework in fact was. Only after that, in Part III, is it possible to attempt some reconstructive criticism. The philosophy of science, in the narrowest sense, comes at the end, in Part IV. But though the first two Parts, and even the third, are from this narrow point of view merely propaedeutic, a little straightforward interpretation of the essence of Malthus is surely no bad thing in itself. For misconceptions of his views are widespread and gross, and they help to confuse religious and political controversies about practical population problems. And these are problems which, as Malthus saw, must have a primary interest to anyone concerned for the relief of man's estate.

The main sources for all Malthus' views on population are four. The first is the first edition of the essay, *An Essay on*

* The present paper is a revised version of an article published some six years ago in the *Australasian Journal of Philosophy*. My excuse for contributing a mere revision rather than an entirely fresh article is that my invitation to join the Seminar at the University of Delaware came rather late in the day. I should like here to thank the Editors both of the *AJP* and of the present volume for so willingly consenting to this arrangement.

the Principle of Population as it Effects the Future Improvement of Society, with Remarks on the Speculations of Mr. Godwin, M. Condorcet, and other Writers. This appeared in 1798, and was reissued in facsimile by Macmillan (London) in 1926. As its full title suggests, it was an occasional polemic directed particularly at various currently fashionable utopian writers. We refer to this, in the facsimile edition, as the *First Essay.* The University of Michigan Press produced a paperback edition of this *First Essay* in 1959, with a foreword by K. E. Boulding.

The second source is the second edition of the essay, significantly retitled *An Essay on the Principle of Population; or, a View of its Past and Present Effects on Human Happiness; with an Inquiry into our Prospects respecting the Future Removal or Mitigation of the Evils which it occasions.* This appeared in 1803, and, as the author himself said in the Preface, "In its present shape it may be considered as a new work . . ." (Sixth edition, Vol. I, pp. v–vi). We shall refer to this, always in the pagination of the more accessible, and in the main text substantially unaltered, sixth edition of 1826, as the *Second Essay.* This is no occasional polemic but a laborious treatise offered as the author's definitive contribution to the subject. A great deal of confusion has been, and continues to be, caused by failure to appreciate the differences between the *First Essay* and the *Second Essay.* The most convenient modern edition of the *Second Essay* is probably that in the Everyman Library. This has recently been reissued with an Introduction by a Roman Catholic, Professor M. P. Fogarty, who insists usefully that Malthus himself was strongly opposed to contraception, and that perhaps the best example of an authentically Malthusian response to a population problem is to be found in the Republic of (Southern) Ireland. (It is one of the little paradoxes of the history of ideas that the name of Malthus should have been stolen for the "Malthusian drill" of Mr. Aldous Huxley's *Brave New World.* But then, and similarly, the author of *The Republic* could scarcely be construed as an unqualified advocate of "Platonic love"!)

The third source comprises the appendixes to the third and fifth editions of 1806 and 1817, also published separately in the same years, in which Malthus "wished to correct some of the misrepresentations which have gone abroad respecting two or three of the most important points of the Essay" (*Ibid.*, Vol. II, p. 443). We refer to these as the *1806 Appendix* and *1817 Appendix,* again using the pagination of the sixth edition.

The fourth and final main source is *A Summary View of the Principle of Population.* This consists of the greater part of Malthus' article on "Population" for the 1824 Supplement of the *Encyclopaedia Britannica.* This summary appeared in 1830, four years before his death in 1834, and is thus his own last published statement of his theory. It has recently been conveniently reprinted in *Introduction to Malthus,* edited by D. V. Glass.* We refer to this edition. These four are not quite all the original sources. But they are all the main ones, and they are for present purposes sufficient.

II

A. The foundation of the whole structure is in every successive treatment substantially the same, but it is presented most powerfully in the *Summary.* "In taking a view of animated nature, we cannot fail to be struck with a prodigious power of increase in plants and animals" (p. 119). "Elevated as man is above all other animals by his intellectual faculties, it is not to be supposed that the physical laws to which he is subjected should be essentially different from those which are observed to prevail in other parts of animated nature" (*Ibid.*, pp. 121–122). ". . . all animals, according to the known laws by which they are produced, must have a capacity of increasing in a geometrical progression" (*Ibid.,* p. 123).

* C. A. Watts, London, 1953.

This contention as far as the human animal is concerned is then supported and made more precise by examining what has in fact happened with practically isolated human populations in peculiarly favorable, although not of course ideal, conditions. So "It may be safely asserted, . . . that population, when unchecked, increases in geometrical progression of such a nature as to double itself every twenty-five years" (*Ibid.*, p. 138).

B. At this stage in every statement of his theory Malthus argues for the conclusion that: ". . . the means of subsistence, under circumstances the most favourable to human industry, could not possibly be made to increase faster than in an arithmetical ratio" (*Second Essay*, Vol. I, p. 10); that "by the laws of nature in respect to the powers of a limited territory, the additions which can be made in equal periods to the food which it produces must, after a short time, either be constantly decreasing, which is what would really take place; or, at the very most, must remain stationary, so as to increase the means of subsistence only in arithmetical progression" (*Summary*, p. 143).

C. He next compares these two powers, of reproduction and production, noticing the utter disproportion between the geometrical progression of the one (1, 2, 4, 8, 16, 32 . . .) and the arithmetical progression of the other (1, 2, 3, 4, 5, 6 . . .). In every statement of his position it is with the help of the observation of this disproportion that he tries to derive the conclusion that there must always be some check or checks operating against the power of reproduction. "By that law of our nature which makes food necessary for the life of man, the effects of these two unequal powers must be kept equal. This implies a strong and constantly operating check on population from the difficulty of subsistence" (*First Essay*, p. 14). So ". . . the power of population being in every period so much superior, the increase of the human species can only be kept down to the level of the means of subsistence by the constant operation of the strong law of necessity, acting as a check upon the greater power" (*Second Essay*, Vol. I, p. 11). But in the *Summary* he is much more cautious: "it follows necessarily that the average rate of the *actual* increase of population over the greatest part of the globe . . . must be totally of a different character from the rate at which it would increase, if *unchecked*" (p. 143; italics original).

D. "The great question, which remains to be considered, is the manner in which this constant and necessary check on population practically operates" (*Summary*, p. 143). "The natural tendency to increase is everywhere so great that it will generally be easy to account for the height at which the population is found in any country. The more difficult, as well as the more interesting, part of the inquiry is, to trace the immediate causes which stop its further progress. . . . What becomes of this mighty power . . . what are the kinds of restraint, and the forms of premature death, which keep the population down to the level of the means of subsistence?" (*Second Essay*, Vol. I, p. 218). Elsewhere Malthus quotes the question Captain Cook asked of New Holland in his *First Voyage,* "By what means are the inhabitants of this country reduced to such a number as it can subsist?"; remarking that "applied generally" it may "lead to the elucidation of some of the most obscure, yet important, points in the history of human society. I cannot so clearly and concisely describe the precise aim of the first part of the present work as by saying that it is an endeavour to answer this question so applied" (*Ibid.,* Vol. I, p. 67).

But, of course, in addition to this speculative and academic interest in discovering what the checks are and how they have operated, Malthus always had a practical concern to find out and advocate what they ought to be and how they ought to operate. It is this concern which directs the whole of the *First Essay* and the second two Books of the *Second Essay,* and which shows itself repeatedly, not always fortunately, elsewhere. There is no suitably short passage to quote from the former. (Compare, however, pp. 346 ff.) But at the beginning of the fourth book of the

Second Essay, Malthus wrote that taking the operation of some great check as "an inevitable law of nature; . . . the only inquiry that remains is, how it may take place with the least possible prejudice to the virtue and happiness of human society" (Vol. II, p. 255).

E. In the next stage of his argument, Malthus' second thoughts were importantly different from his first. But in both cases the duality of his interests leads him to mix two quite different systems of classification.

(i) In the *First Essay* the categories "preventive check" and "positive check" are presented as the most important, but not as together exhaustive: "a foresight of the difficulties attending the rearing of a family acts as a preventive check; and the actual distresses of some of the lower classes, by which they are disabled from giving the proper food and attention to their children, acts as a positive check" (pp. 62–63); but "to these two great checks to population . . . may be added, vicious customs with respect to women, great cities, unwholesome manufactures, luxury, pestilence, and war" (pp. 99–100). In the *Second Essay,* and thereafter, "positive checks" and "preventive checks" are the labels of two categories which are supposed to be mutually exclusive and together exhaustive. The former "include every cause [e.g., wars, pestilences, and famines] . . . which in any degree contributes to shorten the natural duration of human life" (Vol. I, p. 15). The latter, though the outlines are blurred both by the author's delicacy of expression and by his moral commitments, is complementary. It includes all checks to the birth rate: from "the restraint from marriage which is not followed by irregular gratifications"; through "promiscuous intercourse, unnatural passions" and "violations of the marriage bed"; to "improper arts to conceal the consequences of irregular connections" (Vol. I, p. 16). Elsewhere after "promiscuous concubinage" he brings himself to mention enigmatically "something else as unnatural" (Vol. II, p. 8); that is, of course, contraception.

(ii) But in addition to this method of division he employs a second, cutting right across the first, which is also offered as exclusive and exhaustive, and which is obviously not at all value-neutral. Thus in the *First Essay*, as the sentence immediately following the last passage quoted from this source, he writes: "All these checks may be fairly resolved into misery and vice" (p. 100). And, a little later, "In short it is difficult to conceive any check to population, which does not come under the description of some species of misery or vice" (p. 108). However in the *Second Essay*, as he is at pains to point out in his Preface, he "so far differed in principle from the former, as to suppose the action of another check to population which does not come under the head of either vice or misery; and, in the latter part I have endeavoured to soften some of the harshest conclusions of the first Essay" (Vol. I, pp. vii–viii). The new third category in this trinity is "moral restraint," one of "the preventive checks, the restraint from marriage which is not followed by irregular gratifications" (Vol. I, p. 15). With this vitally important modification, the old claim to exhaustiveness is repeated: "the checks which repress the superior power of population . . . are all resolvable into moral restraint, vice, and misery" (Vol. I, p. 24).

F. Finally, Malthus makes the point that the values of the various possible checks do not vary entirely independently: "The sum of all the positive and preventive checks, taken together, forms undoubtedly the immediate cause which represses population . . . we can certainly draw no safe conclusion from the contemplation of two or three of these checks taken by themselves, because it so frequently happens that the excess of one check is balanced by the defect of some other" (Vol. I, p. 256). Although his general statements about the relations between the various checks considered as variables are usually, like this one, curiously weak, his particular arguments again and again depend on the subsistence of far stronger connections. Thus in the *First Essay* he remarks that Price's failure, after supposing that all the checks other than famine were removed, to draw "the obvious and necessary inference that an unchecked population would increase beyond comparison, faster than the earth, by the best directed exertions of man, could produce food for its support" was "as astonishing, as if he had resisted the conclusion of one of the plainest propositions of Euclid" (pp. 340–341). Again, in the *Second Essay*, he quotes with approval the remark of a Jesuit missionary that "if famine did not, from time to time, thin the immense number of inhabitants which China contains, it would be impossible for her to live in peace" (Vol. I, p. 226). Furthermore, the whole force of his argument for his proposals for encouraging Moral Restraint lies in the contention that this check might by these means be substituted for those others which he classed as species of Vice or Misery to a greater extent than in modern Europe it had already been.

III

This was the theoretical framework with which Malthus organized his empirical investigations and on which he based his policy proposals. We proceed to examine it.

A. The foundation of the whole theory consists simply in the proposition that human populations, like those of other living creatures, have the power to multiply themselves by reproduction; on a conservative estimate, once every 25 years. (See Sec. II.A, above.) We have four comments on this basic proposition.

(i) Malthus, in drawing attention to this power, was not, of course, thereby maintaining that human populations always, or usually, or even ever at all, in fact increase at this rate; though part of his supporting evidence was that for limited periods, under conditions which were temporarily almost but never quite ideal, and which he was himself most concerned to argue must be exceptional, this has indeed actually happened. He states categorically that "in no state that we have yet known has the power of population been left to exert itself with perfect freedom" (Vol. I,

p. 4). What he was maintaining was the crucially different thesis that human, like animal, populations would multiply at some such rate if they were not held in check by counteracting forces. It is precisely with these checks that by far the greater part of Malthus' writings are concerned.

It is necessary to labor this point since many of his critics, including some who have read him, have failed fully to grasp it. Thus, Kenneth Smith in his elaborate polemic, *The Malthusian Controversy*,* remarks that Place's "advocacy of birth control was the beginning of a movement which can completely nullify the geometrical or any other ratio" (p. 325). Later he says that "Malthus opposed birth control, yet it has become so widespread that where it is practiced the notion of a geometrical ratio can have no validity at all" (p. 329). Yet, obviously, the spread of birth control has not the slightest tendency to invalidate Malthus' basic principle. Quite the contrary. It is only and precisely to put some check on this power to multiply that contraception is required!

(ii) Malthus throughout and explicitly makes the reasonable, but not unquestionable, assumption that sexual desire and the capacities to fertilize and to conceive are constants. Thus, in the *First Essay*, he denies that there has been "a decay of the passion between the sexes. We have sufficient reason to think that this natural propensity exists still in undiminished vigour" (p. 62). In the *1817 Appendix* he still insists "that neither theory nor experience will justify us in believing either that the passion between the sexes, or the natural prolificness of women, diminishes in the progress of society" (Vol. II, p. 483). The (British) Royal Commission on Population in its *Report* † found in much the same sense: "It is just possible that there has been some decline in reproductive capacity, though there is no positive evidence to this effect; and indeed so far as we know reproductive capacity may well have risen" (p. 34).

* Routledge and Kegan Paul, London, 1951.
† Her Majesty's Stationery Office, London, 1949.

(iii) Malthus, in defending his basic proposition that human, like animal, populations possess the power to multiply, and in estimating the rate at which this multiplication would occur if it were not checked, neglected the possible effects of differences in age and sex distribution within these populations. He also neglected individual variations in potential fertility. Yet, to take the extreme case, a population entirely of the same sex would possess no power at all to multiply by reproduction. Or again you might have a population equally divided between the sexes but containing such a very small proportion of women of child-bearing age and such a very high proportion of old people that it would be biologically impossible for total numbers to begin to increase until after a period in which they were lower than when they began. Furthermore, to take a case which is not fanciful or far-fetched, a population in which young people predominate will possess a greater power of multiplication than an otherwise identical population in which most of the women are beyond the age of child bearing. So Malthus' basic principle needs to be qualified to refer only to human populations in which the age and sex distribution is not freakish. Henceforward we will take this qualification as read.

This is very rough and ready. But since a rough and ready formulation is all that Malthus himself was attempting to offer, this is all that it is appropriate for us here to attempt. His estimate of the measure of this multiplicative power is similarly approximate; and it was presented as, what it surely is, a minimum. To produce a precise estimate we should need to stipulate precise conditions about the constitution of the populations concerned, and about their marital practices, and perhaps about other things too. It is perhaps worth noticing in passing that Malthus always assumed strict monogamy as the norm; although this must "waste" some reproductive power, as when a (potentially) fertile woman is married to a sterile husband. Because Malthus only needed and offered an avowedly conservative estimate, he was not inconsistent in suggesting a rate lower than that which he believed some of his evidence indicated had actually at times been reached, while insisting at the same time that the power never does operate unchecked.

(iv) Though we have been talking of "populations," Malthus himself usually talked of "population," and assumed that what applied to the total world population applied to sections of it and the other way about. He met the difficulties to which this practice gave rise by inserting such qualifications as "in the long run." He thus neglected, among other things, the refinements mentioned in the previous paragraph.

B. The second stage in the construction of the theory is the attempt to establish an upper limit to the possibilities of expanding food production. (See Sec. II.B.)

This attempt to define such a limit by a particular arithmetical progression has often and with reason been attacked as unfounded and arbitrary. The power to multiply is a manifest biological fact; and the estimate of the possible unchecked rate of multiplication as a particular geometrical progression was based on an examination—no doubt not faultless—of population statistics. But this estimate of the limiting rate of increase of food production is supported not by any numerical evidence but rather by an appeal to what "we can imagine that any possible exertions of mankind could make it" (*Second Essay*, Vol. I, p. 10) in the light of the (then) state of "the science of agriculture . . . in England and Scotland" (Vol. I, p. 8). So, of the two famous ratios, the arithmetical certainly is arbitrary in a way in which the geometrical is not.

Nevertheless, it is proper to emphasize, what Malthus' hostile critics seem rarely to have noticed, that from the first the arithmetical ratio was presented not as a discovery but as a reasonable maximum supposition. In the *First Essay*, Malthus writes: "If I allow . . . I think it will be allowing as much as any person can well demand" (p. 21); and "Let us then take this for our rule, though certainly far beyond the truth . . ." (p. 22). In the *Second Essay* he urges: "If this supposition be applied . . . and if it be allowed . . . this will be supposing a rate of increase much greater than we can imagine that any possible exertions of mankind could make it" (Vol. I, p. 10). Finally in the *Summary:* "it must be allowable, if it throws light on the subject, to make a supposition . . . which, without pretending to accuracy, is clearly more favourable . . . than any experience we have . . . will warrant" (p. 140).

C. The third stage is to compare these powers of production with those of reproduction and, with the help of "that law of our nature which makes food necessary for the life of man" (*First Essay*, p. 14), to infer that the latter must always somehow be checked by the former. (See Sec. II.C.)

This conclusion cannot validly be inferred from these premises alone. There are three reasons. First, because in supposing that arithmetical limit, Malthus seems—though unfortunately he is not nearly as clear and definite as we could wish—to be offering it as an *average:* "considering the present average state of the earth, the means of subsistence, under circumstances the most favourable to human industry . . ." (*Second Essay,* Vol. I, p. 10). But from the permanent subsistence of such a general average limit you cannot deduce that the same limit will be effective all the time in every particular case. Second, because even granting that from these premises you might infer that the power of reproduction *would* always be checked, in the long run, by the limitations of the power of production, if it were not checked by anything else, you certainly cannot infer from them that it *is* or *will* always be so checked. Not, that is, unless you *also* know that it never is or will be checked by anything else. But Malthus, in the *Second Essay,* on the very next page after he has tried to draw the stronger conclusion, admits the existence of other checks, "causes, independent of this scarcity, . . . which tend prematurely to weaken and destroy the human frame" (Vol. I, p. 12). There is also the realized possibility, which he nowhere seems to recognize, that married couples may restrain their reproductive power for reasons which are not financial at all. Third, because the two progressions are in step for the first two stages and only begin to diverge at the third. (Compare 1, 2, 4, 8 ··· with 1, 2, 3, 4 ····.) Thus whenever you suppose them to begin to operate, so long as they begin together, there is bound to be an initial period in which the productive is *not* checking the reproductive power.

By the time he came to write the *Summary*, Malthus seems to have begun to realize that his premises here were insufficient to bear conclusions as strong as those which he originally attempted to derive from them. His conclusion there is only "that the *average* rate of the actual increase of population over the greatest part of the globe . . . must be totally of a different character from the rate at which it would increase, if unchecked" (p. 143; italics mine).

Perhaps this slowness to recognize and rectify the formal inadequacies of his argument can be partly attributed to the fact that Malthus held that "the history of every people that have ever existed will abundantly prove . . . that population does invariably increase, where there are the means of subsistence . . ." (*First Essay*, p. 37). Later he claimed that "If every man were sure of a comfortable provision for a family almost every man would have one . . ." (*Second Essay*, Vol. II, p. 6), and that "there is no reason whatever to suppose that anything besides the difficulty of procuring in adequate plenty the necessaries of life, should either indispose . . . persons to marry early, or disable them from rearing in health the largest families" (*Summary*, p. 144). However, while the failure to recognize the fallacies in this argument may be partly attributed to the fact that Malthus held certain propositions, it is presumably also true that he held these partly because they were suggested by his fallacious argument. Guiding ideas may also misguide.

D. The fourth stage consists in raising the question of how and in what forms "this constant and necessary check on population practically operates" (*Summary*, p. 143), and how we ought to adjust to the unchangeable fact that in some form it always will operate. (See Sec. II.D.)

(i) We have argued in the previous section (Sec. III.C, above) that the conclusions which Malthus pretends to derive from a comparison of his two ratios do not follow from his premises as stated. Fortunately, to generate his master speculative question, this argument is not required. So there is no need for this reason to try to patch it up by adding as further premises any questionable generalizations about populations always multiplying up to the limits of available subsistence, or about almost everyone wanting to have as many children as they can afford. We do not even need to make any controversial supposition about the limits of the possibilities of food production. By simply comparing the natural power to multiply at a rate of the order estimated by Malthus with the undisputed facts that actual human populations often rise, sometimes remain stationary, and occasionally fall, but scarcely ever multiply at anything like such a rate; we can infer that some check or checks are usually operating against this power. If we then notice that even in the exceptional populations in the exceptional periods, some people die without exhausting their procreative possibilities, we can conclude not merely that checks are usually operating but that they are operating always. This conclusion can generate the necessary master speculative question; and it is a conclusion which can be derived without recourse to any controversial suppositions or questionable assertions.

(ii) Besides the speculative, academic interest, there is in Malthus always—and creditably—a strong practical concern. The comparison of the ratios is intended to establish not only that always and everywhere there have in fact been checks on the power of multiplication "from the difficulty of subsistence," but also that the operation of checks is a matter of unalterable and universal natural necessity, to which we must adjust all our political hopes and social policies. Unfortunately—or fortunately—his premises here are inadequate to yield even the second part of this conclusion.

Furthermore, it is a conclusion which is in any case very likely untrue. For surely there have been, or at any rate could be, populations which, thanks to the unexploited richness of the territory and the technical possibilities available to them, could multiply at the full biologically possible rate for several generations without feeling any shortage of the means of subsistence; and this even if that rate is in fact considerably larger than Malthus estimated? So it would probably be wise, if we want to establish some general conclusion applying to the whole population of the world, to be considerably more modest.

One could, for instance, make calculations such as those made in 1956 by W. A. Lewis. These showed that if the present world population were to double itself every 25 years it "would reach 173,500, thousand million by the year A.D. 2330, at which time there would be standing room only, since this is the number of square yards on the land surface of the earth." * As Malthus himself remarked, in another connection: "Though I may not be able, in the present instance, to mark the limit, at which further improvement will stop, I can very easily mention a point at which it will not arrive" (*First Essay*, p. 164).

Alternatively, or additionally, it is possible to make calculations for one or several particular populations. In such cases it becomes practicable to improve on Malthus' rough but conservative estimate of the multiplicative power of the human animal, by taking into account the actual age and sex distribution of the particular populations in question. In such cases, too, it becomes not merely practicable but essential to replace Malthus' general supposition of the arithmetical ratio by an estimate based on the material and human resources and the technological possibilities presently available to these actual populations.

It may be impossible to establish that there is an irremovable universal general limit on the possibilities of expanding

* *Duke of Edinburgh's Study Conference: Background Papers,* Vol. II, Oxford University Press, London, 1957, p. 94.

food production, which is and must be always and everywhere operative as a check on the growth of any human population. But it is easy to support the weaker, qualified conclusions that world population could not possibly multiply unchecked for very long and that even lesser populations in peculiarly favorable circumstances could not do so indefinitely.

(iii) J. S. Mill, an extremely sympathetic critic, writes of "a passing remark of Mr. Malthus, hazarded chiefly by way of illustration, that the increase of food may perhaps be assumed to take place in an arithmetical ratio, while the population increases in a geometrical," and claims that "every candid reader knows that Mr. Malthus laid no stress on this unlucky attempt to give numerical precision to things which do not admit of it, and every person capable of reasoning must see that it is wholly superfluous to his argument" (*Principles of Political Economy*, 1909 edition, p. 359).

This is far too generous. For the comparison of the two ratios appears prominently in both *Essays* and the *Summary*, and the immediate popular impact of Malthus' ideas on population must be largely attributed to the appearance of "mathematical certainty" which it lent to some of his main theses. Nor is it by any means superfluous to his argument, if this is to say that the conclusions which he tries to derive in this way are themselves inessential or peripheral. But in another way Mill is not quite generous enough. For it was not for nothing that Malthus had been trained as a mathematician at Cambridge. The supposition of the arithmetical ratio may indeed have been an unfortunate excess of mathematical-mindedness. But there was nothing either unfortunate or excessive about expressing our human animal power of multiplication as a geometrical ratio, nor yet about Malthus' concern to extend the sway of numerical precision within his chosen field of population studies and population policies.

E. The fifth stage consists in classifying possible checks on the multiplicative power of populations. Two quite independent sets of categories are employed. (See Sec. II.E.)

(i) The first of these, that into Positive and Preventive, is value-neutral—though Malthus' descriptions of some of the members of these two categories are very far from being value-neutral, or even fair. In the *First Essay* they are made to be mutually exclusive but together not quite exhaustive. In the *Second Essay* Malthus improves on his first thoughts by so extending them that they come nearer to being mutually exclusive and together exhaustive. But they still need a little more tidying.

First, we need to draw the dividing line more clearly, putting it definitely either at conception or at birth. Since Malthus was presumably thinking of induced abortions when he wrote of "improper arts to conceal the consequences of irregular connections," it looks as if, if pressed to indelicate precision, he would have drawn it at birth. This spares us the paradox of counting unborn foetuses as units of population, though at the price of counting spontaneous miscarriages as preventive while pestilence counts as positive. Second, we should probably amend Malthus' second definition of "positive checks" which "include every cause . . . which in any degree contributes to shorten the natural duration of human life" (*Second Essay*, Vol. I, p. 15) to "every cause of death." The reference to "the natural duration of human life" serves no useful purpose: it raises unnecessary issues of definition; it must complicate arguments and calculations made in terms of the theory; and in any case deaths even in ripe old age are still checks on the increase of a population. The phrase "which in any degree contributes" serves only sententiously to remind that deaths may have remoter as well as immediate causes; and it does this at the cost of making virtually impossible the measurement of the force of the different checks. Malthus certainly wanted to measure: "It would be a most curious, and, to every philosophical mind a most interesting, piece of information, to know the exact share of the full power of increase which each existing check prevents; but at present I see no mode of obtaining such information" (*1806 Appendix,* Vol. II, p. 453 *n*).

When these changes are made, the concepts of positive check and of preventive check become much less fuzzy: The latter are checks on the birthrate; while the former are simply causes of death. It becomes fairly easy to make exhaustive lists of checks in both categories. If positive checks are made to be simply causes of death, then the measurement of their relative efficacy presents no theoretical difficulties. Nor should we now, with the example of the late Dr. Kinsey before us, despair of the possibility of constructing quantitative indexes of the force of different preventive checks!

(ii) The second set of categories employed to classify checks is strongly evaluative and prescriptive. The insistence that "All these [i.e., the preventive, the positive, and the rest] checks may fairly be resolved into misery and vice" (p. 100) determines the conclusion of the *First Essay:* that "any extraordinary improvement in society" is impossible, and that we must eschew vice and resign ourselves to the inescapable miseries of man's condition. The introduction in the *Second Essay* of the new third category "moral restraint" enabled Malthus "to soften some of the harshest conclusions of the first Essay" (Vol. I, p. viii) by determining the more hopeful moral that, while still, of course, eschewing vice, we may nevertheless reduce misery by promoting and, where appropriate, practicing moral restraint.

In presenting and employing these categories, Malthus is open to every sort of criticism. He was careless, hasty, and—by his own later admission—mistaken to rush to the conclusion in the *First Essay,* without listing possible checks systematically, that they could all "be resolved into misery and vice." Although he was induced before writing the *Second Essay* to admit a third possibility, he again rashly claims, while still neglecting to compile any really systematic list of checks, that his set of categories as now extended is this time certainly exhaustive. He offers no rationale for this tripartite system of classification, which is certainly awkward and unbalanced, since two very general and comprehensive categories are harnessed with a narrow and specific one, and which looks arbitrary, since there is no obvious reason for expecting it to apply exhaustively. Again, his definition of "moral restraint" is narrow and stilted; the clause "restraint *from* marriage" (italics mine) woodenly overlooks the possibility, which Mill was later to urge (*Loc. cit.*: Bk. II, Ch. XIII), of restraint *in* marriage; and, of course, he takes it for granted that contraception even within marriage is indisputably immoral.

If anyone wished to salvage something from this classification, he might divide checks into those beyond human control and those within human control, subdividing the latter into illicit and licit. But this, though it would be an improvement on Malthus, would represent a fairly radical departure from his conceptual framework.

F. The final stage is to point out that the values of the various checks are not unconnected (see Sec. II.F). Although Malthus himself made curiously little of this in his general arguments, once the notions of positive and preventive check have been tidied up it becomes clearly true. For if a population is to remain stable the totals of births and deaths must balance; if it rises it must be because there are more births than deaths, and if it is to fall it can only be by a surplus of deaths over births. If the alternative evaluative–prescriptive classification is made similarly exhaustive, the same thing will, with the appropriate alterations, apply in that case also.

IV

Our examination in the previous section of Malthus' conceptual framework has, I think, shown that he was right when he claimed, "I could have intrenched myself in an impregnable fortress . . ." (*Second Essay*, Vol. I, p. vii), but that, if he was taking his actual guiding ideas to be unassailable just as they were, he was seriously in error. We are now at last in a position to consider the nature and function of his theory taken as a whole.

A. The first thing to remark is the simplicity and familiarity of the facts and ideas involved. Malthus introduced no new concept and embodied no factual discovery in his theory. What he did was: bring together one or two familiar facts of life; make an unfortunately precise and general supposition about a limit on the expansion of food production; and deduce what he took to be the necessary consequences. All his demographic investigations were generated by these fairly immediate apparent consequences of a few obvious facts and simple ideas, and all his practical recommendations were conditioned by them.

There are in these and other respects interesting similarities between Malthus and Darwin. For the fundamental facts and ideas in Darwin's theory were also extremely simple and familiar: that all living creatures possess formidable powers of multiplication; that, in general, offspring resemble their parents, though there are variations which are often transmitted to at least some of the offspring of the offspring; that the resources of food and living room available to any species are always limited; and so on. From the conjunction of such simple and familiar facts it follows as a deductive consequence that in time there must be a struggle for existence, natural selection, and at least some evolution. This idea that Darwin's theory of evolution by natural selection has a deductive core is one which I have developed elsewhere.* This similarity between the theories of Malthus and Darwin is not, of course, a coincidence. Darwin in his *Autobiography* tells us how he "happened to read for amusement 'Malthus on Population'"; and in his Introduction to *The Origin of Species* he acknowledges that "the Struggle for Existence . . . is the doctrine of Malthus, applied to the whole animal and vegetable kingdoms."

B. The second thing to remark is that the master question

* See "The Structure of Darwinism," in *New Biology*, Vol. 28, Penguin Books, 1959, pp. 25–44.

which stimulates and guides Malthus' population studies is negative: he is asking why and how something does *not* happen. This question is generated by his fundamental law of population, which states the rate at which population increases, *when unchecked*. Malthus' theory here bears a certain resemblance to classical mechanics. For the first law of motion states, "Every body continues in its state of rest or of uniform motion in a right line *unless it is compelled to change that state by forces impressed upon it*" (*Principia*, Bk. I; italics mine). Since in actual fact most, if not all, bodies are in motion relative to some other bodies, and since this motion never continues for long in a right line, the questions arise: Why do bodies *not* continue in a state of rest or of uniform motion in a right line, what forces operate to prevent this, and how? This similarity again is certainly not altogether a coincidence, for in the *First Essay*, Malthus expresses admiration for "the grand and consistent theory" (p. 159) and "the immortal mind" (p. 363) of Newton, and argues strongly that "the causes of population and depopulation have probably been as constant as any of the laws of nature with which we are acquainted" (pp. 126–7).

This analogy, so flattering to Malthus, should not be pressed beyond the point to which we have taken it. Nevertheless, it may suggest two comments. First, it can be used to bring out the unsympathetic perversity of such a criticism as this: "Man cannot live without food. Hence the two ratios would both be arithmetical. What then becomes of the geometrical series? It is reduced to the rate of food production in each period . . . The invalidity of Malthus' ratios could never have escaped detection if he had stated the real series of increase and hence deduced all that it implied." * One might as well argue that the invalidity of the first law of motion would never have escaped detection if Galileo and Newton had stated the real motions of bodies. The same critic later complains, "Although his illustrations

* See—again—K. Smith, *The Malthusian Controversy*, Routledge and Kegan Paul, London, 1951.

and proofs have a first appearance of careful inductive work, the basis of all his ideas is the postulate of the geometrical ratio which he does not find in practice" (*Ibid.*, p. 331). The social are scarcely likely to overtake the natural sciences if in them every notion not embodying a description of directly observable fact is to be assailed as invalid and unreal. (In any case, as we have seen in Secs. II.A and III.A, the existence of this power of reproductive multiplication is supported by an appeal to evidence as strong and as direct as one could reasonably demand.)

Second, it can be used to bring out how Malthus sometimes failed himself to maintain an adequate level of theoretical sophistication. In the *1817 Appendix* he defends his talk of a natural tendency, which in fact is always to a greater or lesser extent checked by counteracting forces, by appealing to the practice "of the natural philosopher . . . observing the different velocities and ranges of projectiles passing through resisting media of different densities." He complains that he cannot "see why the moral and political philosopher should proceed upon principles so totally opposite" (Vol. II, p. 485). So far so good. Unfortunately, he is inclined to misinterpret his contention that the power of populations to multiply is inordinately greater than their capacity to produce food. He is inclined to construe it as if it were the same thing as saying, or at any rate involved, that population always does and inevitably must press hard upon the means of subsistence. (See Secs. II.C and III.C.) The crucial difference was brought out well by Archbishop Whately in 1832, when he distinguished between two senses of "tendency": that in which a tendency to produce something is a cause which, operating unimpeded, would produce it; and that in which to speak of such a tendency is to say that that result may reasonably be expected in fact to occur (*Lectures on Political Economy*, Lecture IX). Substantially the same point had been made slightly earlier by Nassau Senior in his *Two Lectures on Population* (1831). It was tacitly and rather grudgingly accepted by Malthus in the ensuing correspondence, printed as an Appendix to the lectures, although he apparently never saw its relevance to his argument from the comparison of the ratios.

C. The next main point to remark is that Malthus' conceptual framework was originally built as a practical theory, designed as a guide to political and social action or inaction. Although its fundamental principle also generated the speculative question which Malthus by his own work showed to be of great heuristic value, his theory always retained this essentially practical character. The evaluative–prescriptive method of classifying checks was always used alongside the value-neutral descriptive one. (See Secs. II.E and III.E.) Malthus also throughout retained the argument of the comparison of the ratios to support simultaneously, and without sufficient distinction, both the speculatively stimulating conclusion that some checks *are* operating everywhere and the practically crucial contention that there always *must be* checks. (See Secs. II.C and III.C.) Though Malthus made one vitally important addition, the category of moral restraint, and various minor alterations in the *Second Essay* and after, it always remained essentially the conceptual framework of the *First Essay* with which he approached all population questions.

It should therefore not surprise us that these ideas are more suited for the rough and ready understanding of broad trends, and for guiding the wide lines of general policy, than for assisting in detailed demographic analysis. It was, for instance, left to David Booth, one of Malthus' early critics, to bring out the crucial importance for such analysis of age and sex distribution and particularly of the proportions of women of child-bearing age. (See his "Mathematical Dissertation," in William Godwin, *Of Population*, London, 1820.) These are refinements neglected by Malthus in his schema (see Sec. III.A).

However, for the rough, yet practically vital, understanding of the population explosions now occurring in so many of the backward countries, Malthus' simple model of an

enormous power of increase opposed by various counteracting forces is perhaps both necessary and sufficient. For it
can bring out that in these countries the application of
modern medical knowledge is weakening the positive check,
while nothing is occurring, or being done, to produce a proportionate strengthening of the preventive check. And if,
as is surely possible, the fallacious argument of the comparison of the ratios is replaced by a soundly based and valid
argument for the slightly weaker conclusion that the power
of increase is so enormous that it must always be checked
in the fairly short run, then Malthusian ideas can be used
to support some enormously important general practical
conclusions.

Thus if Malthus' facts and arguments, so amended, are
correct, and if it is accepted that there can be no right to
the physically impossible, then it is surely preposterous to
assert or assume that every (married) couple has a right to
produce as many children as they wish, regardless of what
others may be doing or wanting to do, and that all these
children will have a right to support in childhood and as
adults to earn a living, to marry, and to have a similarly unrestricted right to produce children with similar rights in
their turn. It is preposterous, that is, unless you also make
the gigantic and even more preposterous assumption that
the sum of all these separate possible desires will always
work out providentially to a practically manageable birth
rate. This is a conclusion which Malthus always drew. Its
importance can be appreciated by considering how widely
and bitterly it was, and still is, resisted.

Again, it must surely be unsound in principle to offer as a
scheme for raising average standards of living a plan for
increasing production, unless *either* you have good independent reason to believe that any parallel increase in population will be less than proportionate, *or* your scheme itself
makes provision for securing this as an objective. This is a
conclusion which guided Malthus in all the political and
social arguments of the second part of the *Second Essay*,

although he is very much open to criticism both for his general pessimism and for the narrowness of his ideas about means of securing the necessary check. The importance of this conclusion too can best be appreciated by considering how until Malthus it had been almost entirely overlooked, and how it is still with discreet cowardice ignored by so many official reports and plans dealing with the problems of raising living standards in the backward countries. Senior, in his perhaps over-generous summing up of the agreement reached in his controversy with Malthus, puts the point judiciously: "no plan for social improvement can be complete, unless it embraces the means both of increasing production, and of preventing population making a proportionate advance" (*Loc. cit.*, p. 90).

Science and Government

Alan T. Waterman, *National Science Foundation*

The University of Delaware has performed a notable service in sponsoring a Seminar in the Philosophy of Science and making it available not only to its own students but to the community as a whole. Never has there been a time in history when there has been so urgent a need for public understanding of science and the implications of science for our lives.

A century ago, public lectures in science were widely in vogue both here and abroad, but as science has grown in complexity and the issues involving science become ever more pressing, the matter of communicating the significance of science to the public at large has become more difficult. In the National Science Foundation we have given much thought to this problem and have supported a variety of efforts designed to improve ways and means of informing the public of new discoveries in science and their significance for mankind.

My topic—"Science and Government"—would probably have sounded strange even a generation ago, for science has become a major preoccupation of government only within the last twenty years. When future historians examine the middle decades of our century, I believe they will find one of the most striking phenomena to be the development of the complex interrelationships of science and government. During World War II the Government for the first time called upon both academic and industrial research institutions to play a major role in the military research effort, and the resulting partnership has not only continued but has had a lasting impact on both.

Prior to the war, the role of government in science had

been traditional; that is, the Government had supported research related to certain of its specific functions—for example, agricultural research, meteorological research, standards and testing, and research related to the national defense. Since the war the Government has entered into new and broader relationships with the community of science.

The continuing importance of military research, the appearance of atomic energy as a major field, the rapid growth of research in the health-related sciences, and most recently the emergence of space research, have all contributed to the greatly expanded role of government in relation to research and development. This expansion is reflected in the Federal budget. Its total of $10.5 billion for research and development and research and development plant for the current fiscal year represents about 12 per cent of the total Federal budget.

In addition to supporting research, development, and engineering directly related to the achievement of specific objectives, the Government has also found it expedient to support basic research for its own sake and to take certain measures with respect to science education, including the training of scientists, the improvement of science teaching, and the provision of funds for physical facilities for research and instruction.

The scientific and technological revolution has thus become a major concern of the Federal Government and, among other effects, has produced radical changes in the relationships between the Federal Government and education.

The United States is probably unique among the great nations of the world in having practically excluded education from direct support by the national government. We have preserved the principle of local control of education and our schools have been supported from local funds and private sources. World War II made it quite clear, however, that in an atomic age the Federal Government must henceforth be concerned not only with the furtherance of science but with the education of scientists. A prophetic assessment, both as to the needs and the means of meeting them, was set forth in 1945 in Vannevar Bush's report to the President— *Science, the Endless Frontier.* Dr. Bush and the scientists who advised him in the preparation of this far-seeing report saw that unless basic science were strongly supported and able students with appropriate aptitude encouraged and assisted in acquiring an education in science, the United States would lack the elements basic to a strong science and technology.

The primary recommendation of the Bush report was the establishment of a National Science Foundation for the support and encouragement of basic research and the training of scientists and engineers. The Foundation was established in May 1950. Five years of legislative debate preceded the enactment of the National Science Foundation Act, however; and during this period the scientific activities of the Federal Government had begun to proliferate.

The Office of Naval Research, established by special legislation in 1946, began to support a broad program of basic research, much of which was related only in general terms to the interests of the Navy. The U. S. Atomic Energy Commission, also established in 1946, was engaged not only in producing atomic weapons and other materials but also in supporting research. The National Institutes of Health, research arm of the U. S. Public Health Service, grew rapidly and a whole series of specialized research institutes came into being. Research activities of the Department of Defense grew and multiplied. Thus when the Foundation began operations in 1951, it took its place in an expanding community of Federal agencies engaged in various types of research and development.

Since that time the only major new agency to enter the field is the National Aeronautics and Space Administration, established in 1958 to meet the growing needs of space research. The new space agency incorporated the National Advisory Committee for Aeronautics, which since 1915 had operated with noteworthy efficiency with respect to the scientific study of problems of flight and the conduct of research and experimentation in aeronautics.

The war produced the research contract as a convenient device whereby the Federal Government could obtain the services of scientists and engineers outside the Government. This device, initiated and used with striking success by the Office of Scientific Research and Development, was adapted after the war by many agencies to strengthen research, particularly in the universities.

The impact of science upon the foreign policy of the United States has been recognized in a number of ways—in the Department of State by the establishment of the post of Science Advisor to the Secretary of State and the assignment of science attachés to a number of important diplomatic posts around the world. The Office of Naval Research has for years maintained a scientific liaison office in London with primary emphasis on research. Although its headquarters is in London, its coverage of science extends throughout Europe. Last year the Foundation placed two representatives in the U. S. Embassy in Tokyo to work in close association with the scientific attaché. Not least among the foreign policy problems in science and technology is the provision of aid and guidance to the emerging countries to enable them to develop their own economies.

Science has also had its impact upon the Congress. In addition to the Joint Committee on Atomic Energy, there is now a Senate Committee on Aeronautical and Space Sciences and a House Committee on Science and Astronautics.

At the highest level of government, science is represented in the post of the Special Assistant to the President for Science and Technology and in the President's Science Advisory Committee, composed of outstanding scientists from outside the Government with certain Government scientists serving as consultants. In order to coordinate scientific and technological activities of all Federal Agencies and Departments, the President in 1958 created the Federal

Council for Science and Technology. Council members are high-ranking officers representing each of the agencies with major research and development programs.

During recent years there have been repeated proposals, especially by members of the Congress, to "streamline" the whole government structure in research and development by the creation of a Department of Science. A wide variety of suggestions has been made, embodying various combinations of the existing Federal science agencies that might be included in such a department. In my opinion, and in the practically unanimous view of responsible officials of the Executive Branch of government, such consolidation would cause far more difficulties than it would solve.

Although the term "Department of Science" is used to designate the proposed new agency, it is quite obvious that both science *and* technology (or research and development) are intended to be included, because the chief administrative and budgetary difficulties arise in the broader area. One should bear in mind, however, that research and development are not an end in themselves. They are a means to an end. To accomplish their missions, a number of Federal agencies—no less than modern industrial and technical organizations—must support research and development. Each agency of government must be given primary authority over the research and development required to fulfill the mission for which it is held responsible. Centralization in one organization of authority over all Federal research and development would dull the edge of agency responsibility for the completion of its own mission. Furthermore, from the administrative standpoint a research department, say in the Navy, could not tolerate supervision from a central agency along with simultaneous supervision from the Navy. The aggregate of decisions and operations relating to the research and development activities of many agencies is too large and too complex to impose upon a single administration.

There are other compelling reasons against such a drastic

reorganization, but I shall not review them here. The majority of the scientific community believes that the strength and effectiveness of the Government's role in science derive from its very diversity.

The present organization for science and technology in the Federal Government operates in this fashion:

So far as science itself is concerned, the National Science Foundation is responsible for national policy with respect to basic research. Its primary mission is the support and encouragement of basic research and education in the sciences. These and related functions are all directed towards a single purpose, namely, the progress, health, and strength of science in the United States. It is obvious, of course, why such an agency should be independent.

In the White House, the Special Assistant to the President for Science and Technology is available to the President at all times for first-hand advice. He is in a position to know the situations in which science and technology are likely to have important bearing upon national policy. The function of the President's Science Advisory Committee is to advise on important questions in science and technology that relate to national issues of all kinds.

The role of the Federal Council for Science and Technology is to provide agencies a forum for discussion of matters of common interest, to achieve coordination on scientific programs involving more than one agency, and to exercise planning and policy roles in connection with government-wide science and technology matters. On over-all budgetary problems in research and development, each of these agencies contributes its advice and counsel to the Bureau of the Budget and the President. Under present circumstances it appears that this administrative arrangement is able to deal responsibly with the issues that arise, and to do so more satisfactorily than a single cabinet department. In any event, the organization as I have described it has been in operation hardly long enough for anyone to judge its ultimate effectiveness or to determine whether further changes may be needed.

Another question that bears profoundly on the relations of science and government is the growth and nature of scientific research in the universities. For an over-view of the problem, let us consider for a moment the dollars involved. Total national expenditures for research and development now exceed $14 billion. Of this amount the Federal Government is the source of $9.5 billion. Of the Federal support for research and development, the lion's share—$5.8 billion—goes to industry, which, incidentally, performs over 70 per cent of the work. The Government accounts for $2.2 billion in its own laboratories, $1.2 billion goes to educational institutions and research centers, and the remainder goes to other nonprofit organizations. Something less than half of Federal research and development funds to colleges and universities go to them for purely basic research with no other purpose than to extend man's knowledge of nature. Other monies are available for research and development plant and for educational purposes.

In national planning for science, one may identify three factors essential to the vigor of the national research effort: (1) the progress of science itself; (2) the development of the individual—student and teacher; and (3) the strength of the institutions where research and teaching take place.

We recognize, of course, that science and science education are not separate from higher education in general and that their ability to grow in accordance with national needs is dependent upon the sustained excellence of the intellectual effort as a whole. A special and concerted effort on behalf of science may be necessary now because our national welfare and safety depend on science in a way unique to our times. But this is not bad; in my opinion, strengthening one critical area of education is a more feasible goal than attempting comprehensive improvement across the board, and may be the most expeditious means of bringing about improvement in other areas.

Let us consider the three factors as they bear upon current issues regarding science and government.

Progress of Science

Basic research cannot be self-supporting; it never has been. People have been slow to realize that the advancement of technology depends fundamentally upon the progress of basic research, both for new data acquired and discoveries made, and for the advanced training of scientists and engineers.

In *Science, the Endless Frontier*, Bush [1] observes:

> Basic research is performed without thought of practical ends. It results in general knowledge and an understanding of nature and its laws. This general knowledge provides the means of answering a large number of important practical problems, though it may not give a complete specific answer to any one of them. . . . One of the peculiarities of basic science is the variety of paths which lead to productive advance. Many of the most important discoveries have come as a result of experiments undertaken with very different purposes in mind. . . . Basic research leads to new knowledge. It provides scientific capital. It creates the fund from which the practical applications of knowledge must be drawn.

Since the war, support of basic research by the Federal Government, apart from national laboratories and research centers, has taken the form of support of particular research projects by contract or grant. In fact, this system has become so widespread that it has occasionally been sharply criticized.

The project method of research support originated in Federal agencies with practical missions. They found it a satisfactory procedure for accomplishing certain objectives through the pursuit of research by individuals and groups outside the Federal Government. Later, as developed by the National Science Foundation and the National Institutes of Health, the research project came to be used as a device for providing support to universities and nonprofit groups for research essential to scientific progress but which the institutions could not themselves finance.

A very important feature of project support is that scientists in the various disciplines have been able for the first time to play a part in determining the direction in which science should move in their fields. This has been accomplished by the increasing use of scientists to review projects and as members of advisory committees. From the standpoint of the progress of science, this procedure is about as good as could be devised, provided the word "project" is broadly interpreted to include both large and small studies—within, of course, a coherent area of science.

Development of the Individual

Development of the individual is fundamental. The process should begin with identification of able young people, and should include opportunity for them to progress as far as their talents permit and assurance of competent teachers and adequate facilities and equipment. Senior investigators should be given leaves of absence for study and research in their own fields. Although the Federal Government has contributed much to the attainment of these desirable objectives, more remains to be done.

Many Foundation programs are directed toward the development of the individual, including summer and year-round institutes for training science and mathematics teachers, and a group of fellowship programs from predoctoral through senior postdoctoral levels. Among the most important of these activities is the improvement of subject matter or course content in the fundamental subjects for secondary schools: mathematics, physics, chemistry, and biology. The course-content studies are resulting in thoroughly up-to-date and teachable materials for use in science and mathematics.

Development of the individual is the direct and deep concern of our entire educational program. The issues involved, therefore, require careful and increasing attention not only by the Federal Government but by educational institutions, by the states and local communities, and by private organizations devoted to educational and scientific matters. So far as the Government is concerned, the Office of Education in the Department of Health, Education and Welfare is responsible for matters of this general nature in all subjects, but many Federal agencies contribute in various ways, including the provision of opportunities for graduate students to work on research projects. Any way one looks at the problem, the individual is the focus of all educational planning.

The Institution

The strength and vitality of institutions engaged in scientific research and training are, of course, most important. It is fair to say that whereas the Federal Government has devoted substantial support to the progress of science and a reasonable amount of support to ways and means of developing the individual, the institutions themselves have, on the whole, suffered relative neglect. Undoubtedly, this neglect stems from our traditional reluctance to relate the Federal Government to our educational system and its institutions.

The National Defense Education Act established a precedent for direct support of education by the Federal Government. Although the word "defense" was included in the title of the Act, the realization is growing that for the foreseeable future participation by the Federal Government in research and educational matters will be essential.

So far as the institutions are concerned, it is only recently that the Government observed that as a result of the increasing amount of Federally supported research, many universities were receiving so much project-support money that they were beginning to lose flexibility and independence in planning the work of their own departments. To add to the predicament, the buildings and facilities at colleges and universities were not only deteriorating but were also in need of modernization, and these deficiencies aggravate the problem of retaining scientific and engineering faculty against the recruitment efforts of industry and government.

Within the last few years some progress has been made towards the solution of these problems, largely through efforts of the National Institutes of Health and the National Science Foundation, both of which now award funds on an uncommitted basis, as well as for laboratory construction and equipment.

The Foundation's institutional grant is a new concept, under which the head of the institution receives annually, on request, a sum equal to 5 per cent of the research grant funds received by the institutions within the previous year. This sum may be used without restriction for scientific pursuits but not for indirect costs. The intent is to provide money that can be used by the institution freely for any of its science needs. If this plan works well, it would seem to be a very good solution to the problem of providing support while safeguarding the independence of the institution in the development of its own plans for growth. In its graduate-laboratory program, the Foundation supports, on the basis of matching funds, the construction of research buildings, wings of buildings, and the renovation of research laboratories at colleges and universities.

The institutional grants program of the National Institutes of Health is similar but is directed towards medical and health-related schools. Its construction program is broadly directed towards health-related facilities.

In Summary

The needs of graduate education and of basic research are inseparable. This point was strongly emphasized in the so-called Seaborg Report [2] published in 1960 by the President's Science Advisory Committee. The Committee observed:

> It is a fundamental contention of this report that the process of graduate education and the process of basic research *belong*

together at every possible level. We believe that the two kinds of activity reinforce each other in a great variety of ways, and that each is weakened when carried on without the other. We think also that this proposition has substantial implications for the policy of both the Federal Government and the universities.

In releasing the report the President commented:

I call particular attention to the conclusion of the Science Advisory Committee that the process of basic scientific research and the process of graduate education in universities must be viewed as an integrated task if the nation is to produce the research results and the new scientists that will maintain the leadership of American science. In this great endeavor, the partnership between the Federal Government and the nation's universities will assume growing importance in the future.

The continuing need for Federal support of both education and research does not and should not, in my opinion, relieve us of the necessity of providing support from private and local sources as well. The Ford Foundation's designation of a $100 million fund for the support of liberal arts colleges represents philanthropic giving at its best. In expressing its editorial approval of the gift, *The New York Times* * commended especially the manner in which the money is to be given. Observed the *Times* in part: "By setting a demanding but realistic requirement for matching the grants, the foundation will aid the colleges' own fund raising."

Similarly, Federal funds should never be regarded as the only source of support for our colleges and universities, but rather as an essential part of total support—richer for its very diversity.

The general nature of the problem facing the country in relation to science and science education is reflected in a report of the National Science Foundation entitled "Investing in Scientific Progress," a careful attempt to analyze

* Editorial, September 26, 1961.

scientific manpower trends and needs in the country for the next decade. One of the most arresting conclusions is a quantitative estimate of the acceleration of pace. For example, the gross national product is increasing at a rate that would approximately double in 20 to 25 years; the number of baccalaureates awarded by our colleges and universities is doubling about every 18 years; the number of doctorates in science and engineering in 12 years, and the nationwide research and development effort in 6 or 7 years.

Manpower trends were analyzed with special care. The significant fact emerges that the trend in baccalaureate and doctorate degrees has been maintained for more than 40 years, in spite of aberrations such as the war. This fact appears to justify an extrapolation that a second point of doubling in the output of trained scientists and engineers will occur by about 1970, provided the international situation continues much as at present, the economy does not fluctuate too violently, *and* we are prepared to pay the costs involved. A most gratifying aspect of this projection is that the increase in numbers of scientists and engineers would involve only about one in twenty of the top 1 per cent in intellectual capacity. Thus, there seems every prospect that science and engineering will not make undue demands upon this special sector of the population at the expense of other professions.

Despite the fundamentally promising outlook, however, the evidence indicates that the United States is not providing the facilities, equipment, and teaching manpower required to support this trend and maintain the present quality of training. In fact, the report estimates that we are already $1.5 billion in arrears on the total cost of this effort and $10 billion more will be required during the next decade. The immediate problem, therefore, would seem to be one of educating citizens to an understanding of the importance of science in our national life and of the need to make adequate provision for training scientists and engineers.

The problem is not easy to resolve: first, because of its

growing complexity, science is increasingly difficult to explain in terms understandable to the layman; and second, because some people are genuinely concerned about the "bigness" of science and whether its relation to government is healthy—either for science or the state.

The close interrelationships of government and science have been viewed with misgivings on both sides. Former President Eisenhower undoubtedly voiced a common fear when he warned in his farewell address against the growth of power elites, including a scientific elite. As a people we have tended generally to distrust bigness, as witnessed by legislation designed to curb big business, and, in more recent years, to restrict the powers of organized labor.

The scientific community, for its part, has observed apprehensively its increasing dependence upon the Federal Government as the principal source of funds for research support, for the provision of needed facilities and equipment, for the improvement of science teaching, and for the training of scientists and engineers.

No one is prepared to suggest, however, how a desirable rate of scientific progress is to be maintained without significant assistance from the Federal Government. There can be no thought of returning to the *status quo ante*. All nations are now convinced that their future is closely bound up with their capabilities in science and technology. Among those with the greatest capabilities, sharp competition has developed in both the military and economic aspects of technology. Among developing nations, the conviction grows that their future progress depends upon the rate at which they can import or successfully develop their own science and technology. Science has become, in a very real sense, an instrument of both national and international policy.

For scientists who are apprehensive about the effects of massive Federal support upon genuine creativity, there is no retreat to the more leisurely days when research was supported solely by the universities, with some help from the private foundations. In addition to the mounting impact of science upon the national welfare, there is also the problem of funds. The instruments and facilities needed for much research at the frontiers of science are now of a cost and size beyond the range of private sources of funds. One cannot visualize, for example, how space research could be carried on except with government money and the massive logistics support that is thus far available primarily through the military services.

I believe, however, that there already exist within the system certain checks and balances that tend to offset the inherent dangers of "big science." I have tried to outline some of these in this paper. Most important is the present diversity, not only in the sources of government funds but in the organization of government scientific activities. The number and variety of agencies supporting research and development, and the differences in their missions and objectives, give assurance that a variety of points of view will be brought to bear on the whole question of support. The established practice of calling upon the scientific community for advice and review with respect to government scientific programs means that scientists themselves have a substantial voice in the direction of government scientific activities. The coordination and supervision exercised at the highest levels of government by the President's Science Advisory Committee and the Federal Council for Science and Technology in their recommendations are sufficiently flexible to avoid the dangers of centralization and arbitrary power.

The fact that we have managed thus far to achieve a high rate of scientific progress without falling prey to the obvious dangers that might result from a close relationship between government and science has come about through deliberate effort and a continued awareness of the problem. The scientists who have played a leading role in developing government science policy during the last 20 years have been deeply and personally aware not only of their responsibilities to government but also of their stewardship toward the progress of science. Whether the future is to be equally fruitful in terms of government–science relationships will depend on an appreciation of the pitfalls as well as the potentialities, and more especially upon the character of the men who make the decisions on both sides. At any event, this continuing close relationship is essential, in my judgment. I am confident that with intelligence and good will on both sides we can gain the support and understanding that are fundamental to the achievement of our national objectives and to the upholding of our highest traditions.

References

1. Vannevar Bush, *Science, the Endless Frontier*, U. S. Government Printing Office, Washington, D. C. (Rev. Ed., July, 1960), pp. 18 ff.
2. *Scientific Progress, the Universities, and the Federal Government.* Statement by the President's Science Advisory Committee, The White House, Washington, D. C., November 15, 1960, p. 5.

PART VI

Philosophical Aspects of Physics

PART IV

Philosophical Aspects

of Physics

Causality and Dualism on Trial

Alfred Landé, *Ohio State University*

I. How Is Mathematical Physics Possible?

In his Herbert Spencer Lecture, Albert Einstein [1] remarked:

> It is my conviction that pure mathematical construction enables us to discover the concepts and mathematical laws connecting them which give us the key to the understanding of the phenomena of nature. Experience . . . cannot possibly be the source from which [the laws and concepts] are derived. Experience of course remains the sole criterion of the serviceability of mathematical construction for physics, but the truly creative principle resides in mathematics.

Einstein himself has given us a most impressive example of the harmony between nature and mathematics by his relativistic theory of gravitation. When someone asked him, "If the deflection of starlight near the Sun according to your mathematical equations should prove wrong during the next eclipse, what would be your reaction?", his answer was, "I would be very much surprised indeed." Yet one cannot help wondering: What has Nature to do with the abstract creations of the mathematician? How can mathematical reflection disclose necessary and universal physical relations? Which is primary, and which is modelled in the other's image, Reason or Nature, the Rational or the Real, Mind or Matter? The most diverse answers have been given to this question, from Pythagoras' number mysticism to Descartes' rationalism, Locke's empiricism, Kant's categorism, Poincaré's conventionalism, Eddington's shadow symbolism, and a certain version of dialectical materialism [2] according to which "the categories of *science,* or 'things seen,' always

reflect in a class society the particular . . . functioning of
the working class, whereas the categories of *mind* . . . reflect the particular functioning of the ruling class." At any
rate, there seems to be some room for clarification.

Let us, therefore, take a great leap backward, from Einstein to a Second Grader, who is given the following concrete physical problem: A father leaves eight sheep to his
three sons equally dear to him. How many sheep will each
son receive? Our pupil will immediately carry out a logical
analysis, replace sheep by his fingers or anything else, then
via the abstract identity, $8 = 2 \cdot 3 + 2$, he will retranslate the
result to sheep again. And like Einstein he would be very
much surprised if the visible result should not agree with
his mathematics, namely, two sons obtain three and one son
obtains two sheep—supposed that a Solomonic division into
fractional sheep is not allowed.

I submit that the case of the eight sheep, including its
dependence on restrictive conditions, integral numbers or
fractions, contains the answer to the problem of conformity
between the Rational and the Real, as plain as Einstein's
achievement. First of all, mathematics is the art of developing stimulating though *tautological* implications of basic
formal propositions, as the word "equation" signifies. The
physical issue, whether it concerns sheep or gravitational
fields, is a *story problem,* the result of which may be re-
phrased in our example as a general law: *Whenever* a father
leaves eight sheep to three sons, the practical outcome is
always . . . , etc. Sometimes the physical story is given
first, and its elements (three sons equally dear, etc.) are to
be analyzed as to their logico-mathematical structure. Then
an abstract mathematical transformation is carried out.
Finally, the result is retranslated into realistic physics again.
On other occasions, a finished mathematical structure may
be ready, and a certain physical problem seems to have an
equal, or at least a similar, logical structure. In this case,
abstract mathematics may suggest new aspects to the physical problem (fractions or integers, Euclidian or non-Euclid-

ian geometry). According to the quotation above, "experience of course remains the sole criterium of the serviceability of mathematical construction for physics." But I cannot follow Einstein when he continues, "the truly creative principle rests in mathematics." For history shows that the relation is mutual, with precedence sometimes here and sometimes there. Nor is the situation correctly represented by the poetic phrase: "the Creator must be a great mathematician." Actually it is *we* who select series of observations in a way so as to fit them into one among an infinite variety of possible mathematical schemas which are tautological, i.e., logical implications of basic formal propositions, parallel to physical propositions.

Later I shall demonstrate that modern quantum mechanics runs parallel to, and could have been predicted as a logical mathematical consequence of, simple propositions, more complicated, of course, than those underlying the story of three sons and eight sheep. But first I turn to another primitive example of mathematical reasoning, the application of which leads to the conclusion that chance and random must play an intrinsic part in natural events, and that the ordering principle of "equal causes, equal effects" fails.

II. Symmetry

The story runs as follows.[3] Balls are dropped through an aiming device onto the edge of a steel blade, so that each ball has two chances, either dropping down to the right or to the left of the blade (discounting an eternal balancing act on the edge itself). The problem now is: How many balls, among a great number of them, will end up on the right or left of the blade, respectively? A stone-ager may reply: "How can I know? Just try and see!" Anyone with the least mathematical sense, however, will reason as follows: "Since the aim is at the center, giving no preference to the right or left, and since, on the other hand, each single ball has no choice but to act unsymmetrically, then at least the *average* number of balls will be distributed at a 50:50

ratio; you can bet on it!" And lo, observation confirms this *a priori theory* of agreement between physical geometrical symmetry and physical statistical symmetry, connected by the mathematical symmetry concept, with great, though never exact, precision.

Suppose now that, in spite of the best possible symmetrical adjustment of the aiming device, the statistical ratio persistently comes out 51:49 in favor of right over left. Are we to regard this as a failure of the theory? Certainly not. We rather take it as a sign that the aim is not exactly central, or that other unsymmetrical influences falsify the expected result. Thereby, however, we have taken geometrical symmetry as *equivalent* to exact statistical symmetry. Does this not turn our empirical law of agreement between the two symmetries into a mere *definition* of one symmetry in terms of the other? I do not think so. We have only introduced an *extrapolation* of the empirical law from a region where fairly accurate observations of both physical correspondents are possible, into a region where exact geometrical accuracy is hard to achieve, whereas statistical accuracy can be approached to any desired degree by ever larger numbers of tests. If only a small number of tests were admitted, the situation would be the reverse. And natural laws, being idealizations, can never be confirmed with absolute precision. At any rate, the fact that geometrical symmetry leads to statistical symmetry is an empirical law of nature, yet it can be foreseen *a priori* on the grounds of twice applying the mathematical symmetry concept, to a geometrical and a statistical situation, respectively. The result leads to a serious dilemma, however.

III. Causality versus Chance

Agreement between geometrical and statistical symmetry is very simple at face value. Yet it implies the amazing feature that a series of events, admittedly haphazard and independent, obey a law of mutual interdependence with a certain predictable average result. This *statistical cooperation* of independent events forming a regular pattern is a most startling feature of the world around us. Physicists often take it for granted, or proffer a convenient "causal explanation" of this marvel: If a ball drops to the right of the blade, this *must* be due to some right-favoring asymmetry of the setup in this individual case, e.g., a right whiff of wind. The right whiff of wind, in its turn, must be the effect of some other right-favoring cause, and so back to infinity. In short, the observed *r*-event supposedly is the final link of a deterministic chain . . . *rrrr*. The trouble with this causal explanation is that it does not explain the essential point, which is, the marvel of statistical cooperation. Assuming a 50:50 ratio of right and left whiffs of wind merely shifts the blame for today's statistical marvel to yesterday. Any appeal to hidden individual causes is begging the question, rather than answering it. For this reason I regard the often-quoted von Neumann proof not only as circular but as entirely beside the point: we do not need elaborate mathematics to "prove" that hidden variables do not help. On the other hand, simply pointing out that, due to the symmetry of aim, there is *no* cause for the statistical result to be asymmetrical is just the opposite of a causal explanation. And I must entirely take Karl Popper's side when he opposes Einstein's contention [4] that "one can derive statistical conclusions from a deterministic theory." Einstein gives the example of a particle running with constant velocity around a circle divided into a right and left half. One then can predict that N inspections taken at random instants will yield in the average $\frac{1}{2}N$ cases of the particle on the right. However, this is not a *conclusion* from deterministic theory; it rests on the *a priori* trust in the correspondence between geometrical and statistical symmetry. From the deterministic mechanical point of view, the result $\frac{1}{2}N$ is an unexplainable marvel, since there is no *physical* connection between the N random instants of inspection and the conservation of velocity of the particle.

A possible causal explanation of the random distribution

of r and l cases with a 50:50 average ratio might read as follows. A long time ago there was a *demon* who wanted to sway twentieth-century scientists away from the true deterministic faith toward the heresy of a random theory of nature. He deliberately started three causal r chains (by pushing three buttons on his right side, say), then two l chains, followed by five r chains. Then, noticing that he had given too much preference to r chains, he initiated six l chains in a row. Or better, in order to make his fraud undetectable, he used the systematic method of producing randomlike series proposed by Popper [5]—all this in order to feign the *appearance* of random, although in reality it was all caused according to plan. However, such a 'causal explanation' of random by a *deus ex machina* is not very convincing. Another opinion is that the present 'molecular disorder' has been inherited from one single 'natural mixing' of initial conditions some four billion years ago, and that only from there on the world ran off in a deterministic fashion. This soft determinism permitting one exception is a 'quagmire of evasion,' using William James' term. Therefore, I venture to say that the very existence, wherever we look, of randomlike statistical distributions is an irrefutable argument that the doctrine of continuous causal chains cannot be carried through, that we must accept *probabilistic theory as fundamental and irreducible,* without hope to return to causal theory on a more fundamental level.

Contrary to Niels Bohr,[6] I cannot discover an essential difference of statistically controlled randomlike quantum events from those observed in any game of chance and in a gas of many particles. What essential difference is there between N particles in a vessel with a hole through which fN particles escape during the next second, as against N radium atoms which emit fN electrons during the next second? Or between the probability f of one definite particle escaping per second from the vessel, and the probability f of one electron escaping per second from one intact radium atom? Only the classical *theory* made academic reservations about a possible reduction to causal chains in the gas example, whereas most, but not all, quantum *theorists* have given up strict causality as a hopeless dream. It is hopeless, indeed, not because of the quantum h, nor on the basis of von Neumann's (circular) proof, but because *no* statistical distribution can be accounted for by causal chains, unless one admits either one "natural" mixing or the deliberate act of a demon who, by the way, is the counterpart to Maxwell's demon. The latter produces order out of disorder, which is good, whereas my demon is evil and produces disorder from order, e.g., from two sets of pushbuttons.

IV. Continuity

I now come to another concept which has played an important part in mathematical construction as well as in physics, to wit, that of *continuity*. The first to make conscious use of a *general principle* of continuity was Leibniz. According to him,

> When the cases approach each other continuously and finally get lost in one another, then the events in the sequel do so also.

or, in modern terminology: "A finite change of effect requires a finite change of cause." Let us apply the principle of *cause–effect continuity* to our ball–blade game again, this time in case of asymmetry.

Suppose the aiming device is first directed toward the right, and then gradually shifted to the left. The *a priori* question now is: Will there be an *abrupt* change, from r balls to l balls, the moment the physical (not ideal) aim passes the physical (not ideal) center? On the grounds of general experience supporting continuity, one will not expect such an abrupt change of effect under a gradual change of cause. He rather will anticipate to find a small but *finite* transition range $\Delta\alpha$ of the (physical) angle of α aim inside of which a gradual change from r balls to l balls takes place. The next inference will be that in the intermediate cases some balls will end up to the right and others to the left and, further, that this partition will be a statistical one—supposing as always that regularity rather than chaos prevails in nature. The continuity postulate, applied to the gradual shift of aim as cause, first predicts gradually changing statistical ratios. But the existence of any statistical ratio shows, as we saw before, that the doctrine of uninterrupted causal chains is insufficient, demons being excluded. It may be said, therefore,[7] that the *cause–effect continuity postulate for average ratios of events supplies sufficient reason for the lack of sufficient causes of individual events.*

To the physicist it is of interest *how large* is the range of uncertainty, in our case how large is the angular range $\Delta\alpha$ of physical aim, inside of which uncertainty prevails about the ultimate fate of a ball. According to classical mechanics, the answer depends on the temperature and other details. And classical theorists also imagine that the uncertainty of prediction could be reduced to *zero* 'in principle.' The merit of the quantum theory has been the finding of definite lower limits for the uncertainty of prediction (Heisenberg's uncertainty rule, see below).

V. Duality

When speaking of wave–particle duality in modern physics, one must distinguish between two versions. First, the original and genuine idea of duality that *some* phenomena of matter (e.g., linear tracks on films and clicks in Geiger counters) display a discrete corpuscular structure, whereas *other* phenomena (e.g., reaction to crystals) indicate matter to be continuously spread out so as to support waves. And since the two classes of phenomena cannot be cast into one consistent unitary pattern, we must renounce objective reality and be content with two subjective *pictures,* one of particles and the other of waves, neither of which has a claim to physical reality in the traditional sense of the word. The only reality, if any, is the mathematical formalism which

represents the variety of observations in two opposite interpretations of the symbols. Dualism was originally accepted
as a necessary evil. It is now praised as deep philosophical
insight, as progress from naive ontological materialism to
dialectical positivism of two contrary though *complementary*
aspects. Yet, as will be seen presently, dualism has become
ideological ballast; it has long been superseded by a unitary
theory for matter particles and systems of particles, known
as quantum mechanics. When confronted with these developments, theorists often take refuge in a second version, a
kind of neo-dualism described below. But let us first discuss
the original, honest, and genuine wave–particle dualism.

Its empirical showpiece has been the famous diffraction
experiment of matter. When a stream of individual and
countable electrons hits a crystal, the latter deflects them
according to the usual reflection law, but only when the
angle of incidence, which equals that of reflection, has certain selected magnitudes. It turns out that the discrete
angles of reflection can be *calculated* by hypothetically assuming that each electronic particle of momentum p is transformed near the crystal into a broad wave covering the
whole crystal. The waves of length $\lambda = h/p$, when reflected
from the parallel lattice planes, now interfere with one another and yield strong reflection only in discrete directions
belonging to path differences of one, two, etc., wavelengths
λ. After having done their duty, the waves reform into
particles again, as manifest in the corpuscular statistical
buildup of the diffraction pattern.

This metamorphic behavior may be admitted as a first
probing hypothesis; it also may be used for heuristic purposes. But it hardly becomes a respectable theory by changing the term 'forth-and-back transmutation' to 'double
manifestation,' embellished by the words 'as if,' first as-if-
particles, then as-if-waves, finally as-if-particles again. All
this may be an exciting message, but it will not satisfy the
scientist who aims at a consistent theory based on clear and

unitary realistic concepts, either with particles as the real basic constituents of matter occasionally displaying wave-like appearances, or the other way around.

Attempts by de Broglie, Schrödinger, and others to construct a unitary wave theory of matter which would not only account for diffraction but also for discrete tracks on films and clicks in Geiger counters, did meet with success only with the admission of very complicated ingredients. A pure and *simple* particle theory including the wavelike diffraction phenomena, however, was established in 1923 by W. Duane [8] (who at his time thought of diffraction of photonic particles). According to Duane, one does *not* have to introduce the odd idea that particles near the crystal spread out in space like waves. Rather, it is the crystal which *is* already spread out in space and acts as a rigid mechanical unit according to the conservation laws of energy and momentum. There is the added restriction, however, that its periodic structure in space permits the crystal to change its momentum only in certain selected amounts * so as to drive the particles into selected directions. The whole process has nothing to do with wave interference! Duane not only introduced the general idea of a *statistical particle interpretation of wavelike atomic phenomena* three years earlier than Max Born; he also was the first to give us a valid quantitative account of the selectiveness of crystal reflection, later incorporated into the general quantum mechanics of 1926. After the question of diffraction was answered satisfactorily, everything else fell into place without dualistic miracles. In particular, the difficulty of understanding, from the particle point of view, the diffraction of matter through one or two holes was seen to rest on the wrong notion that "a hole is Nothing," whereas in fact "a hole is Nothing with Some-

---

* If L indicates a periodic length component of the space structure of the diffracting body, the latter can change its momentum only in amounts $p = h/L$, where h is Planck's action constant. The reason will be seen in Section VII.

thing around." And this something around is as important in the case of a doughnut as it is in case of diffraction through holes in a solid screen.[9] But there is no mention in the current literature of Duane's pioneer work, nor any realization that his *unitary particle theory of diffraction disposed forever of the fantastic idea of double manifestation.* If people had grasped in time the significance of Duane's well-neglected work, the extravagant and unnecessary hypothesis of duality would never have taken root as a serious theory, let alone made the basis of a new 'world view of physics.'

The weakness of dualistic thinking becomes obvious in a case where quantum mechanics happens to yield the same result as classical theory, namely, when a stream of particles is reflected from an ordinary rigid wall. Quantum mechanics here does not lead to selective reflection angles, since an ordinary wall, having an unperiodic structure, contains *all* space periodities L from the smallest to the largest ones, hence gives out any momentum amount $p = h/L$ whatsoever. A devout dualist, however, would have to interpret the equality of the angles of incidence and reflection as an interim transformation, or manifestation as if transformed into waves, reflection of the latter according to the Huygens principle, and final reformation into particles again. If the assumption of a wave interlude is absurd here, it is absurd also in case of a crystal. Here, as always, it is much more economical, i.e., scientific, to account for the whole process in a unitary fashion, with particles always remaining particles, and never misbehaving as waves. A student of quantum theory may be instructed that he often can obtain correct results from *pretending* that particles act *as though* they were temporarily transformed into waves. It is quite another thing telling him that matter *has* a dual nature, a rather daring assertion indeed.

In the strife between Newton and Huygens, modern quantum theory has given the verdict that, for matter, Newton was right (particles, quantized), whereas for light,

Huygens was right (continuous wave field,* quantized). But here I seem to differ from my dualist colleagues who want to have it both ways—also in a more sociological respect: In practice as adherents of quantum mechanics, they accept the *scientific* outlook of the working class that matter always consists of particles, even near a crystal. In their idle hours they adhere to the sophisticated ruling class doctrine of the *mind* that we must be content with two mental pictures of equal rank, with the word "real" pronounced only with derision and written in quotation marks. People ingrained with the archetype of two subjective pictures replacing one physical reality react to all this with the conditioned reflex question: What do you mean by a particle being "real"? What I mean is, as real as the planet Neptune to Leverrier, and as real as any table here. You can kick a particle, but you cannot kick the wavelike function of probability. This ought to satisfy even those quantum physicists who have memories of a compulsory course in humanities with a glimpse at Berkeley's idealism.—The next stereotyped question is: How about the epistemological lesson (a favorite word) of the uncertainty principle? Does this not show that the concept of a particle breaks down, and even that the concept of an object breaks down? This question I must answer in greater detail.

VI. Uncertainty versus Indeterminacy

Let us first study the empirical background of Heisenberg's rule (not 'principle'). When the location, i.e., the space coordinate q, of a particle is confined within a range of magnitude Δq, e.g., within a shutter of width Δq, the very act of confinement involves a mechanical action whereby

---

* In his standard work, *The Quantum Theory of Radiation*, W. Heitler often *speaks* about the duality of light quanta versus the continuous wave field. But he makes the significant remark: "Light quanta occur in the theory only as quantum numbers attached to the radiation oscillators" which are harmonic components of the field, each of them being spread out continuously in space.

the particle receives an impulse p from the confining body (just as when interacting with a crystal). Although the magnitude of the momentum given out by the shutter and received by a particle in a single instance cannot be predicted, it can be ascertained afterwards with any desired accuracy from the angle of deflection of the particle. It is found now that the various p values received by the particles, accurately measured, are spread statistically over a range of magnitude $\Delta p \sim h/\Delta q$. The empirical meaning of Heisenberg's Δp is that of a statistical scattering range of many exactly observed, though unpredictable, momentum values, in agreement with quantum mechanics. These are the facts.

Niels Bohr, however, amplifies the facts by the assertion that there never *is* an exact p value of a particle within Δq, that we must not even *think* or conceive of, let alone imagine, an exact p value to exist—similar to Zeno's arrow which cannot be thought of having position and velocity at the same time. What is the source of this strange Denkverbot? Duality, of course! Bohr starts from the well-known fact that a wave aggregate confined to a space range Δq never *has* a definite wavelength λ but is composed of many different λ's. Hence one must not even *think* of associating a definite wavelength with a wave aggregate of width Δq, its λ is *indeterminate* in principle. This legitimate wave feature of indeterminacy is now literally translated by Bohr, unwittingly but arbitrarily, into particle terms (*via* the relation $p = h/\lambda$) and is supposed to show that a particle, too, when confined to Δq, does not really *have* a definite momentum p, that p is not only unknown but unknowable, that we must not even *think* of a definite p value of a particle within Δq as existing 'in reality,' that there is an indeterminacy of p being, rather than an uncertainty of what p will be. This peculiar statement takes it for granted that wave indeterminacy must necessarily mean particle indeterminacy, too. According to quantum mechanics, however, an indeterminacy range of λ becomes a statistical distribution range of p values, each with individual real and observable existence, though with an uncertainty range of prediction. Although it is true that one cannot always determine simultaneous values of "incompatible observables" (a technical term indicating lack of simultaneous predictability), one can determine simultaneous values of q and p in Heisenberg's example. The latter thus shows just the opposite of what it is supposed to show according to Bohr.

The objection that an individual p value existing within Δq can be determined only *indirectly* from the point of impact on a distant film is self-defeating. For the range Δp, too, can be determined only from many 'indirect' p values, and Δp would lose its empirical significance if 'indirect evidence' were excluded. The same holds for the corresponding argument that an exact time instant t of a radioactive emission does not really exist for a particle leaving with uncertain energy E, according to the relation $\Delta E \cdot \Delta t \sim h$, the time instant t can be measured 'indirectly.'

I am entirely on Einstein's [10] side in his dispute between uncertainty of prediction as an empirical fact as against indeterminacy of existence as pseudo-scientific *talk* about facts. Therefore, I feel helpless to understand why Heisenberg's uncertainty relation should demonstrate that the concept of a particle breaks down in favor of a hybrid between particle and wave, sometimes named 'wavicle.' It is the other way around: The preconceived idea of dualistic wavicles has led afterwards to the reinterpretation of uncertainty as an indeterminacy of being. It is true that Heisenberg himself was guided to his statistical relation by a wave *analogy*. But on the basis of the statistical interpretation of wavelike phenomena, it has become *illogical* to construe an antithesis between a thing, a bundle of qualities called a particle, as against *one* of its qualities, namely, its disposition or probability of being found here or there under specified conditions, even when this disposition can be symbolically depicted by a periodic curve or 'wave function.' According to the same quantum logic, automobile

drivers are dualistic since they manifest themselves sometimes as the picture of individuals, and sometimes as the
picture of an up-and-down accident curve with peaks on
Sundays.

There is a big *gap* between the wave and particle concepts. Which of them is real and which is apparent is on
the same level as the question of whether a cloud really
is, or only looks like, continuous white stuff. Here as there
one only has to take a close look to see the discrete structure of clouds and of atomic matter. Also, scientific analysis
shows the reason why clouds of water droplets sometimes
display periodic strata, and why atomic particles are controlled by statistical wave equations. Evading the issue of
the 'real' versus the 'apparent' by accepting two equivalent
'pictures' depending on the relative standpoint of the observer is but a poor imitation of Einstein's relativity. The
latter has taught us a most important 'epistemological lesson' (borrowing Bohr's expression), whereas the scruples
concerning the real constitution of matter have long been
dissolved by Duane and Born and by quantum *mechanics*
in general, so that dualism belongs to history.

The claim, therefore, that Heisenberg's relation leads to
a breakdown of the concept 'particle' and its replacement
by a 'wavicle' rests on the change of *one* among many
qualities of a *thing*. If particles obey statistical laws, so do
dice, without becoming new things. Only the special form
of the probability law, that of interference, is new. But even
this law can be explained on elementary particle grounds
(see Duane). Therefore, I cannot find sufficient reason for
abandoning the particle concept which everybody accepts
anyway in his deeds and even in his language, all protes-
tations of faith in the dualistic doctrine to the contrary.

If it were true that there is a dilemma, an antinomy between sometimes wavelike, at other times corpuscular,
manifestations of matter, then it would be an achievement
in dialectics to bridge the impasse by the concept of *complementarity*. But in physics this is misleading because a

particle cannot be complementary to its own probability (amplitude) function, even if the latter is wavelike. And outside physics I fear that it is bound to degenerate into a drawing room game: "What is complementary to what?" Authoritative examples such as emotions versus conscious reflection, justice versus charity, the individual versus the community, one human culture versus another, etc., may be useful illustrations of what is meant by complementarity in general. But assurances that "complementarity, in one sense, is the most revolutionary conception of our day" are premature. If during the creative period of the 1920's analogy and intuition had been the mysterious forces of insight, it is time now to restore consistency and economy of thought to the quantum ideology.

VII. Neo-Dualism

When the peaceful coexistence of dualistic talk and unitary theory became all too precarious, theorists began to endow the term "duality" with an entirely different meaning. Starting from the symmetry between particle position and particle momentum in classical as well as in quantum mechanics, they associate particle position with 'particle' and particle momentum with 'wave.' Ergo, there is a symmetry between particle and wave. I wonder how this conclusion can be expressed in symbolic logic. Others, not satisfied with semantic tricks, defend a kind of *Neo-* or *Ersatz-dualism*, as distinguished from the genuine but bankrupt dualism of two alternate manifestations. Neo-dualists acknowledge that quantum mechanics is a unitary theory according to which matter always acts 'as if' composed of particles, even near a crystal. However, they point out that the mathematical presentation of the theory may be converted into another form which, though very much more complicated than the usual particle formalism, suggests quantum processes in a continuous medium supporting waves. Naturally, this wavelike 'second quantization' yields the same data as the usual 'first quantization,' since the two are observationally equivalent—just as Ptolemy, Tycho, and Copernicus describe the same data obtained from looking at the sky. Therefore, it is asked, why should we regard one form of the theory as more true than the other? The answer is: for the same scientific reasons that let us prefer Copernicus over Ptolemy and Tycho, namely, under the criteria of formal simplicity, with a minimum of *ad hoc* ingredients, and last, but not least, *explainability* under simple and general ground postulates. For example, instead of regarding an atom as a system of N electrons dominated by the linear Schrödinger equation in $3N$ dimensions, the second quantization introduces a medium controlled by a complicated *nonlinear* three-dimensional differential equation which does not show those N particles any more and, from the wave point of view, is very artificial. Furthermore, in quantum theory, as in astronomy, there are not only two but many possible coordinate transformations. But it would run counter to scientific exigencies to apply the term 'duality' or 'triality' to planetary or atomic phenomena because of two or three equivalent mathematical representations. There may be no harm if physicists busy with research are not interested in such 'pedantic subtleties' concerning the foundations of quantum theory and prefer to let many flowers bloom. It is quite another thing if authorities pontificating about "the world view of modern physics" seem to think that a somewhat shopworn genuine duality, erroneously supported by the matter diffraction experiment, is good enough for The Masses, yet when challenged, transfer the once respected trademark to an entirely different Ersatz article. No wonder, then, if the *teaching* of quantum mechanics often resorts to the method of convincing the student that he must forego consistency and conceptual clarity in favor of acquiring a certain instinct for obtaining correct results from formulas and rules which are below his dignity as a hardboiled empirical scientist to try understanding, instead he asks:

"What do you mean by 'understanding' anyway?" The answer will be found in the following reduction of quantum mechanics to nonquantal principles.

VIII. Derivation of the Quantum Rules from Nonquantal Postulates

Explaining the wavelike quantum rules, $E = h\nu$ and $p = h/\lambda$ as well as the formal rules of modern quantum mechanics, means deriving them from a nonquantal, nonwavelike background.[11] In order to show the parallelism of mathematical construction and physical reality, the physical story will be given first, and its mathematical counterpart will be added in parentheses.

1. We begin with the ordering of microphysical experience. There are various *observables*, A and B and C, etc. (A may stand for energy, B for momentum, C for position, and so forth). Observables are defined operationally by various instruments of observation, an A-meter, B-meter, etc. A given object (atom), when subjected to an A-meter, will display one out of a series of *possible* values, A_1, A_2, $A_3 \cdots A_M$. When tested with a B-meter, the same object may display one among the values B_1, B_2, $B_3 \cdots B_N$. These "eigenvalues," whether they are discrete or form a continuity of values, are characteristic of the meter as well as of the tested object.

[Imagine a series of meaningless entities, A_1, $A_2 \cdots A_M$, and another series B_1, $B_2 \cdots B_N$, and so forth.]

2. In order that A and B, etc. qualify as "observables," their values are to be in a *statistical* (probability) *relation*. That is, when a first test of our atom with an A-meter has shown the value A_m, or the atom to be in the "state" A_m, and now a B-meter is applied, then it is unpredictable which B-value will turn up. For each possible value B_n, however, there is a probability (relative statistical frequency), $P(A_m, B_n)$, representing the *transition probability* from the state A_m to B_n, and determinable by a great number of ex-

periments subjecting the atom to subsequent A-meter and
B-meter tests. The transition probabilities from the various
states A to B may be tabulated in a "matrix":

$$\begin{bmatrix} P(A_1, B_1) & P(A_1, B_2) & P(A_1, B_3) & \cdots \\ P(A_2, B_1) & P(A_2, B_2) & P(A_2, B_3) & \cdots \\ \cdots & \cdots & \cdots & \cdots \end{bmatrix} = \{P(A, B)\}$$

Other matrices, $\{P(A, C)\}$ and $\{P(B, C)\}$ and so forth, may
also be obtained from statistical series of experiments. The
probability character of the P's implies that every *row* of a
P-matrix sums up to *unity*, and that P-values connecting two
values of the same observable, such as $P(A_m, A_k)$ are *zero*
when $k \neq m$, and *unity* when $k = m$.

[Each entity, such as A_m, is connected with every other
entity, such as B_n, by a positive quantity, $P(A_m, B_n)$ between
0 and 1. When arranged in matrices, the P's satisfy the sum
rule for the *rows*

$$\Sigma_n P(A_m, B_n) = 1$$

in particular $P(A_m, A_k) = \delta_{mk}.$]

3. Corresponding to the reversibility of classical mechanical processes, we now introduce the *symmetry postulate* that
the probability of the transition from A_m to B_n equals the
probability of the reverse transition:

$$P(A_m, B_n) = P(B_n, A_m) \qquad \text{(Symmetry)}$$

[A mathematical consequence of the symmetry of the P's
is that not only the rows but also the columns of every P-matrix
sum up to unity, from which follows further that the various
series of eigenvalues A and B and C, etc., all have the same
number of members, the same *multiplicity*, $M = N$. Hence
all P-matrices are quadratic with N rows and N columns, each
of them summing up to unity. The P-matrices thus are *unit
magic squares*.]

4. Next, we introduce the very general and noncommittal
assumption that the transition probabilities listed in the
various P-matrices are not independent of one another but

are interrelated by some still unknown general *connection law* so that the members of the matrix $\{P(A, C)\}$ are either determined or at least somehow restricted when the members of the matrices $\{P(A, B)\}$ and $\{P(B, C)\}$ are given. The interconnection law is to be so general, however, that the same formal relation connecting the three matrices just mentioned shall also hold when the letters A, B, C are replaced by the same letters in any other order, or by any other three letters. That is, the connection law is to be *general* (symmetric with respect to all observables), transitive, and shall, of course, preserve (= keep *invariant*) the unit magic square quality of the P-matrices. What could be a possible form of such a general connection law between the probabilities?

[Find a general law connecting unit magic squares.]

A mathematical discussion of this problem leads to the result [12] that there can be only one general triangular connection law between unit magic squares; it is known as *unitary transformation* and runs as follows:

Associate with every quantity $P(A_m, B_n) = P(B_n, A_m)$ two mutually complex conjugate quantities, $\psi(A_m, B_n) = \psi^*(B_n, A_m)$, of value $\psi = \sqrt{P}$ and determine the phases of the ψ so that the resulting ψ-matrices are connected by the matrix *multiplication law:*

$$\{\psi(A, B)\} \times \{\psi(B, C)\} = \{\psi(A, C)\}$$

A complex quantity ψ can be represented by a *vector* in a plane. The unitary transformation law connecting the quantities P *via* associated complex quantities ψ thus ordains that the probabilities P (or rather their square roots, laid out as vectors), constitute a kind of structural framework in two dimensions.

The mathematical law of unitary transformation, which solves our problem of finding a general coordination law between unit magic squares, turns out to be identical with the *interference law of probabilities,* which the physicists have found by speculative ingenuity after a long period of trial and error. The quantum law of probability interference is thus revealed as a necessity, rather than an oddity, under the quite noncommittal, nonquantal assumption that the probabilities P are connected by *some* general coordination law at all, rather than representing a chaotic array. The reason for the wavelike interference character of quantum mechanics can thus be understood.

5. There is another wavelike law of quantum mechanics. It concerns the *periodic* connection between coordinates q and momenta p, and also between energy E and time t, known from Planck's $E = h\nu$ and de Broglie's $p = h/\lambda$. These wavelike rules, together with those of modern quantum mechanics (the p operator and the pq commutation rules) can be shown [13] to be necessary consequences of the nonquantal postulate that mechanics be unaffected by linear displacements of the zero points of q, p, E, and t; that is, that quantum mechanics, like classical mechanics, ought to be *invariant* with respect to Galileo and/or Lorentz transformations.

The possibility of deriving the principal quantum rules of probability interference and of qp and Et periodicity from simple and plausible nonquantal postulates of *symmetry* and *invariance* puts atomic theory on a new basis. Instead of accepting the perplexing quantum rules merely because they work so well, they can now be understood on the grounds of nonquantal propositions. In short, when one abandons the effort of restoring strict causal chains in favor of statistics, and avoids the ideological pitfalls of the duality doctrine, the rest is almost self-evident, at least to those schooled in mathematical tautology.

References

1. A. Einstein, "On the Method of Theoretical Physics," Oxford, 1933.
2. Chr. Caudwell, *The Crisis in Physics*, London, 1939 and 1950.
3. A. Landé, *Scientific Papers presented to Max Born*, Edinburgh, 1953.

4. Einstein's letter to Karl Popper, see quotation 5, p. 459.
5. K. R. Popper, *The Logic of Scientific Discovery*, New York, 1959, Section 55.
6. N. Bohr, "Discussion with Einstein," in D. Schilpp, Ed., *Albert Einstein, Philosopher–Scientist*, New York, 1949.
7. A. Landé, *Philosophy of Science*, **20**, 101 (1953).
8. W. Duane, *Proceedings of the National Academy of Sciences of the United States of America*, **9**, 158 (1923).
9. P. Ehrenfest and P. Epstein, *Proc. Natl. Acad. Sci., U. S.*, **10**, 133 (1924) and **13**, 400 (1927).
10. A. Einstein, "Reply to Criticism," see reference 6.
11. A. Landé, *From Dualism to Unity in Quantum Physics*, Cambridge, 1960.
12. A. Landé, *Physikalische Zeitschrift*, **164**, 558 (1961).
13. A. Landé, *Ibid.*, **162**, 410 (1961).

Discussion

W. L. Gore: It is generally believed that the speed of light is constant. Do you feel that this is a constancy of speed of all the particles that make up light or is the speed of light an average of different speeds of different particles?

A. Landé: First, there *are* no localized particles of light as identifiable things. The case of light is just opposite to that of matter. Matter consists of real, i.e., identifiable, particles with definite masses, charges, etc. Diffraction effects only *appear* as though produced by matter waves; in reality, they are produced by matter particles in a statistical fashion, as the experiment shows, and theoretically according to Born in general, and Duane in particular. In the case of light, there is a *real* electromagnetic field obeying the Maxwell field equations. But the periodic field components are subjected to quantum rules producing the superficial *appearance* as though there were photons chasing around. In his standard book on the *Theory of Radiation*, Heitler often talks about the duality of light quanta *vs.* the continuous wave field. But Heitler makes the significant remark: "Light quanta occur in the theory only as *quantum numbers* attached to the radiation oscillators," that is, to the continuous oscillating field components, dealt with and quantized already by Planck in his theory of blackbody radiation. But a quantum number is not a particle, and it does not travel with the velocity c nor with any other velocity.

F. E. Williams (*University of Delaware*): On the subject of light, according to the ideas you have just expressed, light is discrete or corpuscular. One of the beauties of quantum mechanics is that it treats both photons and electrons or any particles as being particles governed by certain wave functions. According to your ideas, light is not discrete; there are no photons. Then how do you account for the gross photoelectric effect; that is, the light releases electrons, which you recognize as real particles, independent of how low the radiation density is. My second question is: How do you account for the blackbody spectrum that Planck was forced after a great deal of suffering to appeal to quantized electromagnetic radiation to explain?

Professor Landé: My reply is almost the same as that given to the first question. According to the modern theory of radiation, which began already with Planck's original paper, a monochromatic field component of frequency v can give off and receive energy only in the amount hv. This can be misinterpreted as showing that individual 'photonic particles' are dashing around—just the opposite of the misinterpretation of diffraction being produced by matter waves, when only the probabilities have wavelike features. The idea of photons, although of great heuristic value, belongs to the age of innocence, before a consistent quantum theory of radiation and its interaction with matter particles was developed.

Dr. Williams: I think that this may be just a difference in speaking; that is, if you arbitrarily cut the intensity of a light source down and down and still the light is absorbed in it with a discrete chunk, then you might speak of this as having a photon-like character?

Professor Landé: If you merely say, "this has a photon-like character," then I do not object. Yet there is a great difference between what a thing *is* and what it *is like*.

Dr. Williams: Then would you agree that if we were to take your unitary theory, would it affect any of the facts as we know them or are you presenting this, shall we say, as having heuristic merit only?

Professor Landé: If a theory disagrees with the facts, it would have to be discarded right away. We are discussing here only the *interpretation* of the facts. In my mind, a unitary interpretation is preferable to a dualistic one. If we can explain the facts of matter diffraction without a mysterious double manifestation but simply by the quantum mechanics of particles, then this represents a better 'understanding' of the facts. If we can explain radiation effects in terms of quantized waves alone, without using 'photons,' this again is preferable. And all dualistic talk to the contrary, since 1926–27 we *have* a set of unitary quantum rules applicable to *all* systems, to matter particles as well as to continuous fields. So why say "your unitary theory" when it is everybody's unitary theory?

Dr. Williams: I think we are all talking about quantum theory. There is a difference in the language of interpretation and I think that the point just made is a very good one; namely, that if you've got a mechanics, a mechanics that deals with all systems, whether they are electromagnetic or real matter, this is much more satisfying and, as you have pointed out, quantum mechanics does this; but in the usual interpretation, one doesn't make this strong distinction between photons and electrons that one is particle and the other only radiation. Rather, that both have particle-like character but are governed by wavelike equations, but let me be more specific and ask a question about a recent experiment. It was on particles in the sense that we agree on by "particles," namely, on electrons. You have two slits, so that the particle has two alternate paths, and then a field is applied (actually a magnetic field was used; however, the effect of an electrostatic field is easier to describe). The field changes the interference pattern. There is no crystal with which the electron is interacting and yet the interference pattern changes. This is completely understandable with quantum mechanics using the wavelike features that have been discussed. This is discussed in the Furry and Ramsey article in *Physical Review*, 118, 623 (1960). Now, if you go to this interesting other idea, based on Duane's work, where the electrons are strictly particles—no waves— how do you account for the change in the interference pattern in this system as a consequence of a field alone and not involving matter?

Professor Landé: I do not know of Furry and Ramsey. But it is even easier to grasp that charged particles are deflected by a field than that waves are deflected by a field. Remember also that the waves only symbolize particle distributions.

Dr. Williams: Bohm had some interesting ideas on modifying quantum mechanics with hidden variables and things of that sort, and he proposed this experiment. It was all understandable, as was made clear in the Ramsey and Furry article by conventional quantum mechanics, not by the ideas of Duane, but straight quantum mechanics in which you use the wavelike equations to describe these particles and the uncertainty principle comes in quantitatively. On a strictly particle picture, it isn't evident to me that you can account for these results. Whereas, if you put in the wave mechanics with the wavelike character, then it is predictable quantitatively.

Professor Landé: The idea of Duane of quantized momentum transfer is straight and conventional quantum mechanics, whereas double manifestation was a conventional escape mechanism thirty-five years ago. Since Born, even wave mechanics uses a strict particle picture. You see a difference where there is none.

General Bibliography

Ackermann, Wilhelm. "Begründung einer strengen Implikation." *Journal of Symbolic Logic,* **21** (June, 1956), 113–128.

Anderson, Alan Ross. "Church on Ontological Commitment." *Journal of Philosophy,* **56** (May 7, 1959), 448–452.

Anderson, Alan Ross, and Nuel D. Belnap, Jr. "First Degree Entailments." Technical Report No. 10, Office of Naval Research Contract SAR/Nonr-609 (16), New Haven, 1961.

Anderson, Alan Ross, and Omar K. Moore. "Culture." *Synthese,* forthcoming.

Aristotle. *Posterior Analytics.*

Asimov, Isaac. *The Intelligent Man's Guide to Science.* 2 volumes. New York: Basic Books, 1960. (The Biological Sciences)

Ayer, Alfred Jules. *Language, Truth and Logic.* London: Gollancz, 1946.

Barker, Stephen F. "The Role of Simplicity in Explanation" (with the comments on this paper by W. Salmon, P. Feyerabend, and R. Rudner and Barker's rejoinders). Herbert Feigl and Grover Maxwell, eds. *Current Issues in the Philosophy of Science.* New York: Holt, Rinehart and Winston, 1961, pp. 265–286.

Bartley, W. W., III. "Achilles, the Tortoise, and Explanation in Science and History." *The British Journal for the Philosophy of Science,* **13** (1962), pp. 15–33.

Barzun, Jacques Martin. *The House of Intellect.* New York: Harper & Brothers, 1959.

Berg, Leo S. *Nomogenesis; or, Evolution Determined by Law*. Translated from the Russian by J. N. Rostovtsow. London: Oxford University Press, 1926.

Bergson, Henri Louis. *Creative Evolution*. Trans. by Arthur Mitchell. New York: Henry Holt & Co., 1911.

Bohr, Niels. "Discussion with Einstein on Epistemological Problems in Atomic Physics." Paul Arthur Schilpp, ed. *Albert Einstein: Philosopher-Scientist*. 2 volumes. New York: Harper & Brothers, 1959, pp. 199–241.

Booth, David. "Mathematical Dissertation." William Godwin, ed. *Of Population*. London, 1820.

Braithwaite, Richard B. *Scientific Explanation*. New York: Cambridge University Press, 1953.

Brodbeck, May. "Explanation, Prediction and 'Imperfect' Knowledge." Herbert Feigl and Grover Maxwell, eds. *Minnesota Studies in the Philosophy of Science*. Vol. III (*Scientific Explanation, Space, and Time*). Minneapolis: University of Minnesota Press, 1962, pp. 231–272.

Bromberger, Sylvain. "The Concept of Explanation." Ph.D. thesis, Harvard University, 1961.

Bunge, Mario. "Causality, Chance, and Law." *American Scientist*, 49 (1961), 432–448.

———. *Causality*. Cambridge, Mass.: Harvard University Press, 1959.

Bush, Vannevar. *Science, the Endless Frontier*. Revised ed. Washington: U. S. Government Printing Office, July, 1960.

Campbell, Norman. *What Is Science?* New York: Dover Publications, 1952.

Cantor, Georg. *Contributions to the Founding of the Theory of Transfinite Numbers*. Trans. by Philip E. B. Jourdain. London: The Open Court Publishing Co., 1915.

Carnap, Rudolf. "Empiricism, Semantics, and Ontology." *Revue internationale de Philosophie*, 11 (1950), 20–40. Reprinted in Leonard Linsky, ed. *Semantics and the Philosophy of Language*. Urbana, Ill.: University of Illinois Press, 1952, pp. 208–228.

————. "Statistical and Inductive Probability." Reprinted from a pamphlet published in 1955 in Edward H. Madden, ed. *The Structure of Scientific Thought*. Boston: Houghton Mifflin Co., 1960, pp. 269–279.

Caudwell, Christopher. *The Crisis in Physics*. New York: Dodd, Mead and Co., 1951.

Chambers, Robert. *Vestiges of the Natural History of Creation*. London: John Churchill, 1844.

Collingwood, Robert George. *The Idea of History*. Oxford: Clarendon Press, 1946.

————. *The New Leviathan*. Oxford: Clarendon Press, 1942.

Commoner, Barry. "In Defense of Biology." *Science*, 133 (June 2, 1961), 1745–1748.

Copernicus, Nicolaus. *De monetae cudendae ratione*, 1526.

Danto, Arthur C. "A Note on Expressions of the Referring Sort." *Mind*, n.s. 67 (July, 1958), 404–407.

Darwin, Charles Robert. *Autobiography*. London: Collins, 1958.

————. *The Origin of Species*. Philadelphia: University of Pennsylvania Press, 1959.

Descartes, René. *Rules for the Direction of the Mind*.

Dickens, Charles. *David Copperfield*. London, 1850.

Dobzhansky, Theodosius G. *Evolution, Genetics, and Man*. New York: Wiley, 1955.

————. "Evolution of Genes and Genes in Evolution." *Cold Spring Harbor Symposia on Quantitative Biology*, 24 (1959), 15–30.

Dobzhansky, Theodosius G. "Variation and Evolution." *Proceedings of the American Philosophical Society,* 103 (April, 1959), 252–263.

Dray, William Herbert. *Laws and Explanation in History.* London: Oxford University Press, 1957.

Duane, William. "The Transfer of Quanta of Radiation Momentum to Matter." *Proceedings of the National Academy of Sciences of the United States of America,* 9 (May 5, 1923), 158–164.

Dubos, René Jules. *The Dreams of Reason.* New York: Columbia University Press, 1961.

Dyson, Freeman J. "Innovation in Physics." *Scientific American,* 199 (Sept., 1958), 74–82.

Eberle, Rolf, David Kaplan, and Richard Montague. "Hempel and Oppenheim on Explanation." *Philosophy of Science,* 28 (October, 1961), 418–428.

Ehrenfest, P., and P. Epstein. "Remarks on the Quantum Theory of Diffraction." *Proceedings of the National Academy of Sciences of the United States of America,* 13 (June, 1927), 400–408.

Einstein, Albert. *On the Method of Theoretical Physics.* New York: Oxford University Press, 1933.

————. "Remarks Concerning the Essays Brought Together in This Co-Operative Volume (Reply to Criticisms)." Paul Arthur Schilpp, ed. *Albert Einstein: Philosopher-Scientist.* 2 volumes. New York: Harper & Brothers, 1959, pp. 663–688.

————. A letter to Karl Popper, 1935. Trans. by Karl Popper. In Karl Popper. *Logic of Scientific Discovery.* London: Hutchinson and Co., 1959, pp. 457–460.

Epstein, P. S., and P. Ehrenfest. "The Quantum Theory of the Fraunhofer Diffraction." *Proceedings of the National Academy of Sciences of the United States of America,* 10 (April, 1924), 133–139.

Feigl, Herbert, and Grover Maxwell, eds. *Minnesota Studies in the Philosophy of Science.* Vol. III (*Scientific Explanation, Space and Time*). Minneapolis: University of Minnesota Press, 1962.

Feyerabend, Paul K. "Explanation, Reduction, and Empiricism." Herbert Feigl and Grover Maxwell, eds. *Minnesota Studies in the Philosophy of Science.* Vol. III (*Scientific Explanation, Space and Time*). Minneapolis: University of Minnesota Press, 1962, pp. 28–97.

Fitch, Frederick B. "Actuality, Possibility, and Being." *Review of Metaphysics,* 3 (March, 1950), 367–384.

Flew, A. G. N. "The Structure of Darwinism." *New Biology* (published irregularly by Penguin Books, Ltd., West Drayton, Middlesex, England), 28 (1959), 25–44.

Frank, Philipp G. *Philosophy of Science.* Englewood Cliffs, N. J.: Prentice-Hall, 1957.

Fürth, R. "Prinzipien der Statistik." S. Flügge, ed. *Handbuch der Physik.* Vol. IV. Berlin: Springer-Verlag, 1929.

Gasking, Douglas A. T. "Mathematics and the World." *Australasian Journal of Psychology and Philosophy,* 18 (September, 1940), 97–116.

Geach, Peter T. *Mental Acts, Their Content and Their Objects.* New York: Humanities Press, 1960.

Goddard, L. "Proof-Making." *Mind,* 71 (January, 1962), 74–80.

Goodman, Nelson. "The Revision of Philosophy." Sidney Hook, ed. *American Philosophers at Work.* New York: Criterion Books, 1956, pp. 75–92.

————. *The Structure of Appearance.* Cambridge, Mass.: Harvard University Press, 1951.

————. "A World of Individuals." I. M. Bochenski, Alonzo Church, and Nelson Goodman, eds. *The Problem of Universals.* Notre Dame, Ind.: University of Notre Dame Press, 1956, pp. 13–31.

Goodman, Nelson and W. V. Quine. "Steps Toward a Constructive Nominalism." *Journal of Symbolic Logic,* 12 (December, 1947), 105–122.

"Gresham's Law." *Encyclopaedia Britannica,* 1910, XII, 583.

Grünbaum, Adolf. "Carnap's Views on the Foundations of Geometry." Paul Arthur Schilpp, ed. *The Philosophy of Rudolf Carnap.* LaSalle, Ill.: Open Court Publishing Co., 1962.

————. *Philosophical Problems of Space and Time.* New York: Alfred A. Knopf, forthcoming.

————. "Temporally-Asymmetric Principles, Parity between Explanation and Prediction, and Mechanism Versus Teleology." *Philosophy of Science,* 29 (April, 1962), 146–170.

————. "Das Zeitproblem." *Archiv für Philosophie,* 7 (1957), 184–185.

Haldane, J. B. S. "The Origin of Life." *Rationalist Annual* (1928), 148–153.

Hanson, Norwood Russell. "On the Symmetry between Explanation and Prediction." *The Philosophical Review,* 68 (July, 1959), 349–358.

Heitler, W. *The Quantum Theory of Radiation,* 2nd ed. London: Oxford, 1944.

"Help for the Small Colleges," editorial. *New York Times,* Tuesday, September 26, 1961, p. 38.

Hempel, Carl G. "Deductive-Nomological vs. Statistical Explanation." Herbert Feigl and Grover Maxwell, eds. *Minnesota Studies in the Philosophy of Science.* Vol. III (*Scientific Explanation, Space and Time*). Minneapolis: University of Minnesota Press, 1962, pp. 98–169.

————. "Explanation in Science and in History." R. G. Colodny, ed. *Frontiers of Science and Philosophy.* Pittsburgh: University of Pittsburgh Press, 1962.

Hempel, Carl G. "The Function of General Laws in History." *The Journal of Philosophy*, 39 (January 15, 1942), 35–48.

————. "The Logic of Functional Analysis." Llewellyn Gross, ed. *Symposium on Sociological Theory*. Evanston, Ill.: Row, Peterson and Co., 1959, pp. 271–307.

————. "Rational Action." *Proceedings and Addresses of the American Philosophical Association*. Yellow Springs, Ohio: The Antioch Press, 1962.

————. "The Theoretician's Dilemma." Herbert Feigl, Michael Scriven, and Grover Maxwell, eds. *Minnesota Studies in the Philosophy of Science*. Vol. II (*Concepts, Theories, and the Mind-Body Problem*). Minneapolis: University of Minnesota Press, 1958, pp. 37–98.

———— and Paul Oppenheim. "Studies in the Logic of Explanation." *Philosophy of Science*, 15 (April, 1948), 135–175.

Hilbert, David. "Mathematical Problems." *Bulletin of the American Mathematical Society*, 8 (1901–02), 437–479.

Hill, E. L., and A. Grünbaum. "Popper on Irreversibility." M. Bunge, ed. *The Critical Approach, Essays in Honor of Karl Popper*. Glencoe, Ill.: The Free Press, forthcoming.

Hoebel, Edward Adamson. *The Law of Primitive Man*. Cambridge, Mass.: Harvard University Press, 1954.

Hook, Sidney, ed. *American Philosophers at Work*. New York: Criterion Books, 1956.

Hume, David. *A Treatise of Human Nature*.

Huxley, Aldous L. *Brave New World*. New York: Modern Library, 1956.

Kant, Immanuel. *Critique of Practical Reason*.

————. *Critique of Pure Reason*.

Kaplan, David. "Explanation Revisited." *Philosophy of Science*, 28 (October, 1961), 429–436.

Kemeny, John G. "A Philosopher Looks at Political Science." *Journal of Conflict Resolution,* 4 (September, 1960), 292–302.

Kim, J. "Explanation, Prediction, and Retrodiction: Some Logical and Pragmatic Considerations." Ph.D. thesis, Princeton University, 1962.

Kleene, Stephen C. *Introduction to Metamathematics.* New York: Van Nostrand, 1952.

Kornberg, Arthur. "Pathways of Enzymatic Synthesis of Nucleotides and Polynucleotides." W. D. McElroy and B. Glass, eds. *The Chemical Basis of Heredity.* Baltimore: Johns Hopkins Press, 1957, pp. 579–608.

Landé, Alfred. "Continuity, a Key to Quantum Mechanics." *Philosophy of Science,* 20 (April, 1953), 101–109.

———. *From Dualism to Unity in Quantum Physics.* New York: Cambridge University Press, 1960.

———. "Ableitung der Quantenregeln auf nicht-quantenmässiger Grundlage." *Zeitschrift für Physik,* 162 (April, 1961), 410–412.

———. "Warum interferieren die wahrscheinlichkeiten?" *Zeitschrift für Physik,* 164 (October, 1961), 558–562.

———. "Probability in Classical and Quantum Theory." *Scientific Papers Presented to Max Born on His Retirement from the Tait Chair of Natural Philosophy in the University of Edinburgh.* New York: Hafner Publishing Co., 1953, pp. 59–64.

Lewis, W. Arthur. "Some Economic and Social Problems of Transition to an Industrial Economy." *Duke of Edinburgh's Study Conference on the Human Problems of Industrial Communities within the Commonwealth and Empire: Background Papers.* Vol. II. London: Oxford University Press, 1957.

Macaulay, Lord. *The History of England from the Accession of James II.* Philadelphia: E. H. Butler & Co., 1861.

Malthus, T. R.   *An Essay on the Principle of Population; or, a View of Its Past and Present Effects on Human Happiness; with an Inquiry into our Prospects Respecting the Future Removal or Mitigation of the Evils Which It Occasions*, 6th ed. 2 volumes. London: John Murray, 1826.

————. *An Essay on the Principle of Population as it Effects the Future Improvement of Society, with Remarks on the Speculations of Mr. Godwin, M. Condorcet, and other Writers*. London: J. Johnson, 1798.

————. "Population," for the 1824 *Supplement* of the *Encyclopaedia Britannica*.

————. *A Summary View of the Principle of Population*. Reprinted in D. V. Glass, ed. *Introduction to Malthus*. London: C. A. Watts, 1953, pp. 116–181.

Mayr, Ernst.   "Cause and Effect in Biology." *Science*, **134** (November 10, 1961), 1501–1506.

Mehlberg, Henryk.   "Physical Laws and Time's Arrow." Herbert Feigl and Grover Maxwell, eds. *Current Issues in the Philosophy of Science*. New York: Holt, Rinehart and Winston, 1961, pp. 105–138.

Mill, John Stuart.   *Principles of Political Economy*, 1909 edition. New York: Longmans, Green and Co., 1909.

Myhill, John R.   "Some Remarks on the Notion of Proof." *Journal of Philosophy*, **57** (July 7, 1960), 461–471.

Nagel, Ernest.   *The Structure of Science*. New York: Harcourt, Brace and World, Inc., 1961.

Neale, John Ernest.   *Elizabeth I and Her Parliaments, 1559–1581*. London: Cape, 1953.

Newton, Isaac.   *Philosophiae Naturalis Principia Mathematica*.

Northrop, F. S. C.   *The Complexity of Legal and Ethical Experience*. Boston: Little Brown & Co., 1959.

Northrop, F. S. C. *The Logic of the Sciences and the Humanities*. New York: Macmillan, 1947.

——. *Man, Nature and God*. Forthcoming.

——. *Philosophical Anthropology and Practical Politics*. New York: Macmillan, 1960.

Oparin, Aleksandr Ivanovich. *The Origin of Life on the Earth*, 3rd ed. Trans. from the Russian by Ann Synge. New York: Academic Press, 1957.

Pirie, N. W. "The Meaninglessness of the Terms 'Life' and 'Living'." J. Needham and D. E. Green, eds. *Perspectives in Biochemistry*. New York: Cambridge University Press, 1939, pp. 11–22.

Pitt, Jack. "Generalizations in Historical Explanation." *The Journal of Philosophy*, **56** (June 18, 1959), 578–586.

Plato. *Republic*.

Popper, Karl R. "The Arrow of Time." *Nature*, **177** (March 17, 1956), 538.

——. A reply to Richard Schlegel's "Irreversibility and Mechanics." *Nature*, **178** (August, 1956), 381–382.

——. *The Logic of Scientific Discovery*. London: Hutchinson and Co., 1959.

Quine, Willard Van Orman. *From a Logical Point of View*. Cambridge: Harvard University Press, 1953.

——. "On What There Is." *Review of Metaphysics*, **2** (September, 1948), 21–38.

Reichenbach, Hans. *The Direction of Time*. Berkeley: University of California Press, 1956.

——. *Philosophic Foundations of Quantum Mechanics*. Berkeley: University of California Press, 1948.

Report, of The (British) Royal Commission on Population. London: Her Majesty's Stationery Office, June, 1949.

Rescher, Nicholas. "On Prediction and Explanation." *British Journal for the Philosophy of Science,* 8 (1958), 281 ff.

Rogers, Hartley, Jr. *Theory of Recursive Functions and Effective Computability,* Vol. I. Mimeographed 1956–57.

Ross, Alf. *Towards a Realistic Jurisprudence.* Trans. by Annie I. Fausböll. Copenhagen: Ejnar Munksgaard Forlay, 1946.

Rudner, Richard. "An Introduction to Simplicity." *Philosophy of Science,* 28 (April, 1961), 109–119.

————. "The Ontological Status of the Esthetic Object." *Philosophy and Phenomenological Research,* 10 (March, 1950), 380–388.

Russell, Bertrand. *Introduction to Mathematical Philosophy.* London: George Allen & Unwin, 1919.

————. "Logical Atomism." Robert C. Marsh, ed. *Logic and Knowledge.* London: George Allen & Unwin, 1956, pp. 321–345.

Russell, Edward Stuart. *The Interpretation of Development and Heredity.* New York: Oxford University Press, 1930.

Ryle, Gilbert. *The Concept of Mind.* New York: Hutchinson's University Library, 1949.

Saccheri, G. *Euclides ab omni naevo vindicatus.* Milan, 1733.

Scheffler, Israel. "Explanation, Prediction and Abstraction." *British Journal for the Philosophy of Science,* 7 (1957), 293–309.

————. "Prospects of a Modest Empiricism; I." *Review of Metaphysics,* 10 (March, 1957), 383–400.

————. "Prospects of a Modest Empiricism; II." *Review of Metaphysics,* 10 (June, 1957), 602–625.

Schmalhausen, I. I. "Evolution and Cybernetics." *Evolution,* 14 (December, 1960), 509–524.

Scientific Progress, the Universities, and the Federal Government. Washington: President's Science Advisory Committee, November 15, 1960.

Scriven, Michael. "Discussion: Comment on Professor Grünbaum's Remarks at the Wesleyan Meeting." *Philosophy of Science,* 29 (April, 1962), 171–174.

—————. "Explanation and Prediction in Evolutionary Theory." *Science,* 130 (August 28, 1959), 477–482.

—————. "Explanations, Predictions, and Laws." Herbert Feigl and Grover Maxwell, eds. *Minnesota Studies in the Philosophy of Science.* Vol. III (*Scientific Explanation, Space and Time*). Minneapolis: University of Minnesota Press, 1962, pp. 170–230.

—————. "Truisms as the Grounds for Historical Explanations." Patrick Gardiner, ed. *Theories of History.* Glencoe, Ill.: The Free Press, 1959, pp. 443–475.

Senior, Nassau. *Two Lectures on Population.* London: Saunders and Otley, 1829.

Smith, Kenneth. *The Malthusian Controversy.* London: Routledge and Kegan Paul, 1951.

Stevenson, Charles L. *Ethics and Language.* New Haven: Yale University Press, 1944.

Tolman, Richard Chace. *The Principles of Statistical Mechanics.* New York: Oxford University Press, 1938.

Tylor, Edward B. *Primitive Culture.* 2 volumes. New York: Henry Holt & Co., 1889.

Watanabe, M. S. "Symmetry of Physical Laws. Part III. Prediction and Retrodiction." *Reviews of Modern Physics,* 27 (1955), 179–186.

Whately, Archbishop Richard. *Introductory Lectures on Political Economy,* Lecture IX, 2nd ed. London, 1832.

Winch, Peter. *The Idea of a Social Science and Its Relation to Philosophy*. London: Routledge and Kegan Paul, 1958.

Windelband, Wilhelm. *Geschichte und Naturwissenschaft*. Rectorial address at Strasbourg, 1894.

Wittgenstein, Ludwig. *Philosophical Investigations*. Trans. by G. E. M. Anscombe. New York: Macmillan, 1953.

Index

367